LINEAR AND MATRIX ALGEBRA

Linear and Matrix Algebra

BERNARD VINOGRADE
Iowa State University

D. C. HEATH AND COMPANY, BOSTON

LIBRARY OF CONGRESS CATALOG NUMBER: 67-16911

PRINTED MAY 1967

PREFACE

THE PURPOSE OF THIS BOOK is to present the elements of linear and matrix algebra to readers who have a modest knowledge of analytic geometry. We first appeal to intuitively plausible geometric situations for definitions and concepts such as coordinates, mappings, vectors, dimension, linear transformations, invariance, and similarity; and then we proceed somewhat more formally to the classical results on linear transformations and canonical matrices. As soon as possible, the ideas of invariant subspace and restricted mapping are complemented by the ideas of factor space and factor mapping, thus making these ideas available for the later discussions of rank and canonical matrices. In the treatment of canonical matrices, the algebraically closed case is completed before the general case.

The overall approach favors the attitude that matrix algebra is best understood and is most interesting when considered as an aspect of the theory of linear transformations. However, a good deal of emphasis is given to matrix algebra because it is exceptionally adaptable to the needs of the physical and social sciences.

CONTENTS

CHAPTER 3 Similarity

CHAPTER 4 Vector Spaces

CHAPTER 5 Invertibility

CHAPTER 6 Linear Transformations from **V** into **W**

CHAPTER 7 Invariant Subspaces and Canonical Matrices

LINEAR AND MATRIX ALGEBRA

1

Coordinates and Vectors In the Plane

1.1 COORDINATES

We begin by discussing informally the familiar plane of real analytic geometry. We recall that configurations in this plane are studied with the help of a *reference frame*. The latter is usually a *Cartesian coordinate system* whose mutually perpendicular coordinate axes carry the same uniform scale. In terms of this scale each point in the plane is assigned a unique 2-*tuple* (*ordered pair*) of real numbers, called the *Cartesian coordinates of the point*. Reciprocally, every 2-tuple of real numbers displays the Cartesian coordinates of a single point. At the intersection of the axes is the point whose coordinates are (0, 0), called the *origin* and labeled $\boldsymbol{O}$.

However, any two distinct lines which intersect at a point $\boldsymbol{O}$ can be chosen for coordinate axes, even with a different scale on each. With these so-called *oblique axes*, we still achieve a correspondence between points and 2-tuples of numbers. To find the *oblique coordinates of a point*, we measure parallel to the oblique axes, using the respective scales. Therefore, a Cartesian frame is a special choice of oblique frame, as is the more flexible rectangular frame (which allows different scales on perpendicular axes). The use of oblique frames is in the spirit of linear algebra. So, unless otherwise indicated, we shall regard a 2-tuple of coordinates, say (a, b), as oblique coordinates.

EXAMPLE 1. Consider the line in Fig. 1, p. 2, where the 2-tuples are Cartesian coordinates with respect to axes not shown. Let (a, b) be the Cartesian coordinates of a particular point other than $\boldsymbol{O}$. For any real number k, we see that (ka, kb) are the Cartesian coordinates of a point which is $|k|$ times as far from $\boldsymbol{O}$ as (a, b) and on the same line. The sign of k determines on which side of $\boldsymbol{O}$ the point (ka, kb) lies: when $k > 0$ it is on the same side as (a, b), when $k < 0$ it is on the opposite side. Every point on the line corresponds to a unique value of k, and vice versa. Thus we have a scale on the line, with *unit point* at (a, b). This line is typical of an oblique axis. The oblique coordinate k locates (ka, kb) relative to (a, b).

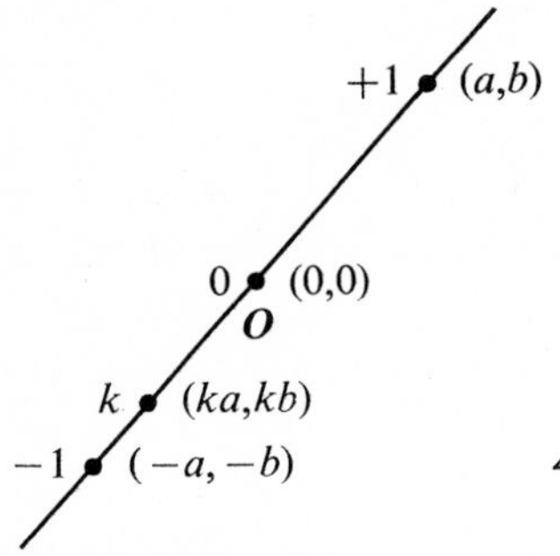

FIGURE 1

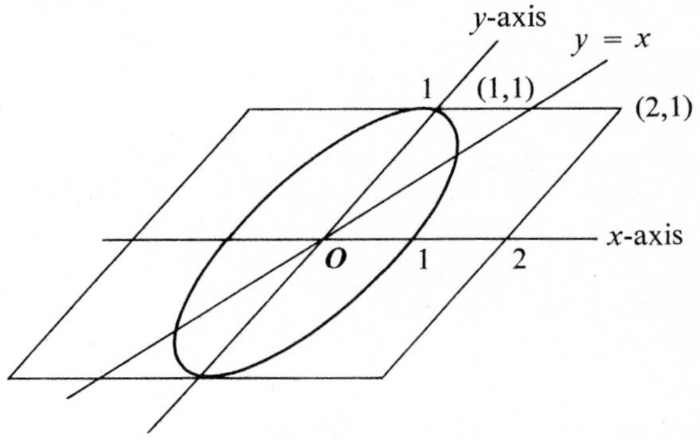

FIGURE 2

EXAMPLE 2. The geometric locus of a coordinate equation, say of $x^2 + y^2 = 1$, will generally be different when plotted with respect to different frames. Thus, with respect to the frame in Figure 2 we show the locus of $x^2 + y^2 = 1$ as an ellipse, and the four points $(\pm 2, \pm 1)$ as the vertices of a parallelogram. These loci are relatively mild distortions of the familiar unit circle and rectangle which one obtains with respect to a Cartesian frame. In fact, we shall sometimes regard this effect as the result of a special *mapping of the plane* (to be defined in Section 1.2), rather than the effect of a choice of oblique frame. By using the equations of Problem 6 below, we can try to identify the locus of an equation expressed with respect to some oblique frame by re-expressing it with respect to the more familiar Cartesian frame. In particular, lines correspond to linear equations in every oblique frame.

PROBLEMS

1. With respect to an oblique frame like the one in Figure 2, sketch the loci of the following equations: (a) $x + y = 1$, (b) $x^2 - 4y^2 = 1$, (c) $y = e^x$.
2. In Figure 2 assume that the positive halves of the oblique axes are at an angle of 45°, and that the unit on the x-axis is the standard unit of distance while the unit on the y-axis is twice the standard unit. Find the formula for the distance of a point (x, y) from the origin, and write a coordinate equation whose locus plotted with respect to this frame is the standard unit circle with center at $\boldsymbol{O}$.
3. Introduce a Cartesian x', y' frame with its horizontal coordinate axis the same as the one in the oblique x, y frame of Problem 2, and with its other axis positive end up. If the oblique coordinates of a point are (x, y), then denote the Cartesian coordinates of the *same point* by (x', y'). Show that $x = x' - y'$ and $y = y'/\sqrt{2}$, and hence $x^2 + y^2 = 1$ has the same locus as $2x'^2 - 4x'y' + 3y'^2 = 2$. Compare also the loci of $y = x$ and $y' = x'$.

4. In Figure 2 assume an angle of θ radians and that the units on the axes are, respectively, k and l times the standard unit (k and l positive). Generalize the distance formula of Problem 2 and apply the result to the case: $\theta = \pi/4$ radians, $k = l = 1$.

5. Show that the facts concerning (ka, kb) stated in Example 1 are true even if (a, b) are oblique coordinates. If (a, b) and (c, d) are points (other than $\boldsymbol{O}$) on two different lines through $\boldsymbol{O}$, show that $ad - bc \neq 0$.

6. Suppose that, with respect to some Cartesian x', y' frame at $\boldsymbol{O}$, the unit points of a given oblique x, y frame at $\boldsymbol{O}$ have the Cartesian coordinates (a, b) and (c, d), respectively. Show that $x' = ax + cy$ and $y' = bx + dy$. Show that this is still true if (a, b), (c, d), and (x', y') are oblique coordinates with respect to a second frame which is not necessarily Cartesian.

7. Derive necessary and sufficient conditions on the constants a, b, c, d of the equations in Problem 6 in order that $x^2 + y^2 = x'^2 + y'^2$ hold identically.

1.2 MAPPINGS OF THE PLANE

*A **mapping of the plane** into itself is a rule which assigns to each point a single point, called the **image point**.* We may describe particular mappings geometrically or in terms of coordinates, as illustrated below, just so each point has a *uniquely* determined image. The coordinate description is given, of course, with respect to some reference frame. This description is preferred because the plane is often abstracted as a set of 2-tuples among which certain operations are performed (Section 1.5, Equations (1)). A *fixed* point is one that is its own image.

EXAMPLE 1. *Similitude of positive magnitude k.* This is a *mapping* under which there is a fixed point, say $\boldsymbol{O}$, and every other point has an image which is located k times as far from $\boldsymbol{O}$ on the same radius out from $\boldsymbol{O}$. In terms of a coordinate system, the image of (x, y) is (kx, ky), as shown in Figure 3. A related mapping is the *reflection of the plane through a point* $\boldsymbol{O}$. We can describe this mapping best with respect to a coordinate system at $\boldsymbol{O}$. The image of (x, y) is $(-x, -y)$. Note that if we allow the number k in the above similitude mapping to be negative, then a reflection through $\boldsymbol{O}$ is the

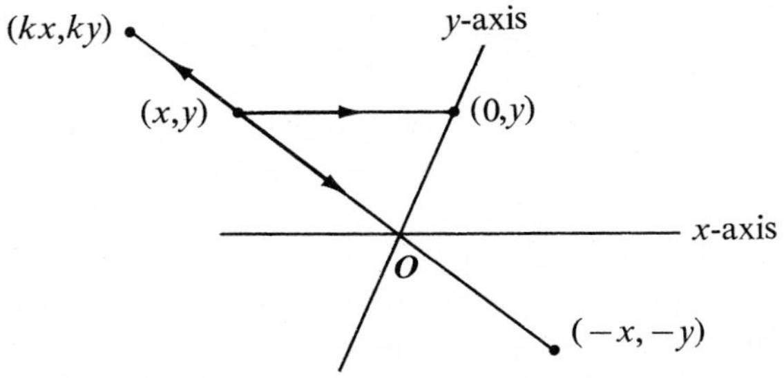

FIGURE 3

case $k = -1$. Geometrically, this reflection mapping is characterized by the fact that the fixed point $\boldsymbol{O}$ is the midpoint of the line segment joining any point to its image.

EXAMPLE 2. *Projection of the plane onto the y-axis.* The name of this mapping implies that some coordinate system is given. The image of (x, y) is $(0, y)$. In particular, each point on the y-axis is its own image. Note that the projection need not be perpendicular. Rather, the emphasis is on the fact that it is parallel to the x-axis, as shown in Figure 3. Any line can be the y-axis, with the x-axis chosen in the "direction" of the desired projection onto the y-axis.

In another common terminology, a ***mapping*** *is a function, so a mapping of the plane is a function whose domain is the set of all points in the plane and whose range is a subset of these points.* What we have already called an image point is, therefore, a point in the range. *Any point that is mapped onto a given image point is called a* ***counterimage*** *of the image point.* Two mappings are equal if and only if they agree everywhere on the domain. The domains and ranges of our mappings will gradually be allowed to consist of other than just subsets of the plane.

In a reflection through $\boldsymbol{O}$, the range consists of all the points in the plane. In a projection onto the y-axis, the range consists of all the points on the y-axis. Note that in the latter case, a point $(0, y)$ is the image of (x, y) for every x; hence each point in the range has an infinite number of counterimages.

Suppose both f and g are real-valued functions of two real variables x, y and are defined for all real values of x and y. Then, with a reference frame in mind, a pair of equations $x' = f(x, y)$, $y' = g(x, y)$ can be interpreted as a mapping of the plane. The 2-tuple (x, y) is regarded as the coordinate description of a point (in the domain of the mapping) whose image point has coordinates $(x,' y')$, and the two equations are called ***coordinate equations of the mapping.*** A point (x, y) is *fixed under the mapping* if and only if $x = f(x, y)$, $y = g(x, y)$. Under a mapping, a point with coordinates (x, y) and its image point with coordinates (x', y') are generally different points, whereas in Section 1.1 the same point had two descriptions because it was referred to two reference frames. (*Under* means *as a consequence of.*)

The similitude and projection mappings of Examples 1 and 2 have coordinate equations: $x' = kx$, $y' = ky$ $(k > 0)$; and $x' = 0$, $y' = y$; respectively. Now, *by the image of a given set of points, or of a given locus, we mean the set of image points of the points in the given set, or on the given locus.* Thus, under the similitude of magnitude k, the image of the locus of $y = kx^2$ is the locus of $y = x^2$. (We suppress the primes after making the substitution for x and y.) Under the projection onto the y-axis, the image of the locus of $y = kx^2$ is the locus of $y \geq 0$, $x = 0$; but here we do not get the image by direct substitution, because the coordinate equations of the mapping do not have a single-valued solution for x, y in terms of x', y'.

PROBLEMS

1. Write coordinate equations for the following mappings: (a) projection onto the x-axis (in the direction of the y-axis), (b) projection onto a point $\boldsymbol{O}$, that is, every point has the same image point, $\boldsymbol{O}$.
2. Give a geometric description of the mapping whose coordinate equations are $x' = y, y' = x$. Do the same for $x' = x \cos y, y' = x \sin y$. In the latter mapping, what is the counterimage of $(0, 0)$?
3. With respect to a Cartesian frame, describe the ranges of mappings defined by: (a) $x' = \sin x, y' = \cos y$, (b) $x' = x + c, y' = y + d$, where c and d are constants, (c) $x' = y, y' = x^2$. What points of the plane are fixed under these mappings?
4. Describe the image of the locus of $x^2 + y^2 = 1$ and of $x + y = 1$ under each of the mappings of Examples 1 and 2.
5. Regard the equations in Section 1.1, Problem 6 as coordinate equations of a mapping. If three points lie on a line, show that so do their images. If one of these points is half-way between the other two, show that the same is true for the images.
6. Regard the equations $x = x' - y', y = y'/\sqrt{2}$ in Section 1.1, Problem 3 as the coordinate equations of a mapping in which (x', y') is the image point of (x, y). Find the equation of the image of the locus of $x^2 + y^2 = 1$, and of the counterimage of $x = 1$.

1.3 TRANSLATIONS AND THE VECTORS AT O

A very simple kind of mapping of the plane is the one called *translation*. It is abstracted from the displacement that occurs when a rigid body is moved without rotation, that is, the motion in which every point of the body goes the same distance in the same direction. For us a ***translation*** *is a mapping of the plane which assigns to each point an image point whose distance and direction from the counterimage is the same for every point. Hence a translation can be specified geometrically by a directed line segment drawn anywhere in the plane, like the one labeled* **u** *in Figure* 4. (*The reader may wish to write* **u** *as* $\vec{u}$ *or* $\vec{u}$, *to distinguish it from written scalars.*)

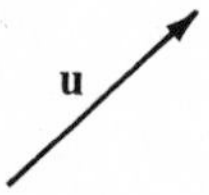

FIGURE 4

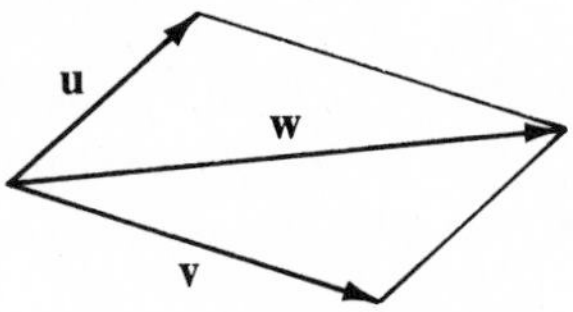

FIGURE 5

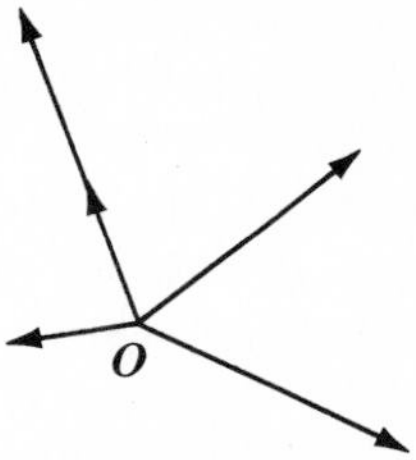

FIGURE 6

Suppose we classify such segments by putting into a common class all those that specify the same translation. Each class is determined by any one of its constituent segments. We shall say that a directed line segment **u** *represents* the class to which it belongs; and, as the symbol of a class *and* a translation, we call $\mathbf{u}$ a ***translation vector.*** Representatives of distinct classes can be manipulated to reflect the *characteristic properties of translations.* When these properties are finally abstracted, in Section 1.6, then a *translation vector* will appear as a very special and intuitive geometric illustration of what is meant in linear algebra by the term *vector.*

EXAMPLE 1. To illustrate the use of directed line segments as *translation vectors*, let the directed line segments $\mathbf{u}$ and $\mathbf{v}$ (Fig. 5, p. 5) specify two translations and represent two classes of segments; hence they are *translation vectors.* The successive application of these translations is equivalent to a third (*resultant*) translation which is specified by a directed line segment $\mathbf{w}$ uniquely constructed from $\mathbf{u}$ and $\mathbf{v}$ according to what is commonly called the *parallelogram law*, using an obvious limiting construction of the parallelogram when $\mathbf{u}$ and $\mathbf{v}$ are parallel. Thus we may speak of a resultant *translation vector* $\mathbf{w}$.

To tie translation vectors in with a coordinate system, we note that distinct translations and hence, distinct translation vectors, can be put in correspondence with distinct directed line segments radiating from an arbitrarily selected point, say $\boldsymbol{O}$, *as in Fig.* 6, *p.* 5. Whether or not it is used to specify a translation, *each directed radial segment at* $\boldsymbol{O}$ *is called a* **vector at** $\boldsymbol{O}$. *The* vectors at $\boldsymbol{O}$ *are also called* **position vectors** *at* $\boldsymbol{O}$, *because they reach out to all points in the plane in a one-to-one correspondence: every point is reached, and distinct vectors reach distinct points.* The vectors at $\boldsymbol{O}$ will be our basic illustration for ideas developed in Chapters 1–3.

Now, if we make $\boldsymbol{O}$ the origin of a coordinate system, *every vector at* $\boldsymbol{O}$ *is specified by a 2-tuple of coordinates.* A vector at $\boldsymbol{O}$ which extends to a point whose coordinates are (x, y) is sometimes conveniently referred to as the *position vector to* (x, y).

EXAMPLE 2. Suppose (a, b) specifies a vector $\mathbf{u}$ at $\boldsymbol{O}$ with respect to a Cartesian frame at $\boldsymbol{O}$, so $\mathbf{u}$ is the position vector to (a, b). Then we can compute the length $|\mathbf{u}|$ and the direction cosines $\cos\alpha$ and $\cos\beta$ as usual from $|\mathbf{u}|^2 = a^2 + b^2$, $\cos\alpha = a/|\mathbf{u}|$, $\cos\beta = b/|\mathbf{u}| = \sin\alpha$, where α and β are the angles shown in Figure 7. When $|\mathbf{u}| = 1$, we can use the convenient coordinate description $(\cos\alpha, \sin\alpha)$ for the end-point of a *unit vector* at $\boldsymbol{O}$ making an angle α with the positive half of the x-axis.

EXAMPLE 3. Suppose with respect to some coordinate system we specify a translation by the position vector $\mathbf{u}$ to $(1, 1)$. Then the image of the locus of $y + x^3 = 0$ is the locus of $(y - 1) + (x - 1)^3 = 0$, as in Figure 8. The axes are fixed, but the coordinates of the image of any point (x, y) are $(x + 1, y + 1)$; that is, $x' = x + 1$, $y' = y + 1$ are the coordinate equations of this mapping.

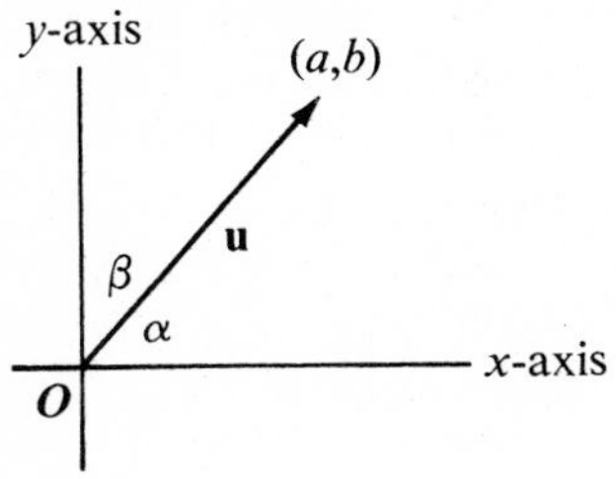

FIGURE 7

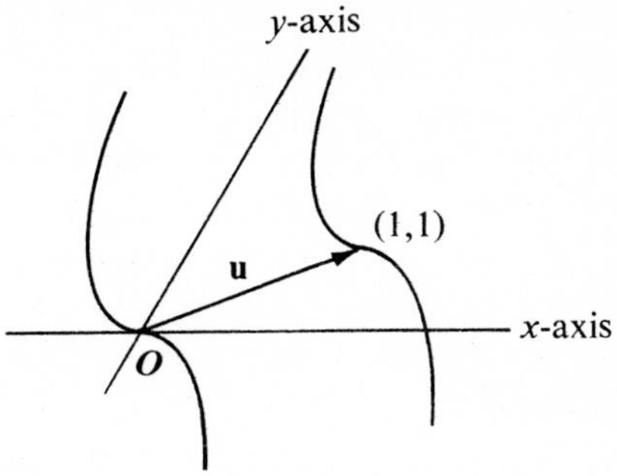

FIGURE 8

A vector at O is determined by its end-point. Let O be the origin of a coordinate system. Suppose a mapping of the plane is given. Then it maps the particular point O onto some point O' and, in general, maps each point (x, y) onto its image point (x', y'). Let $\mathbf{u}$ be the position vector at O to (x, y), and let $\mathbf{u}'$ be the position vector at O' to (x', y'). Using the given mapping of the plane, we can induce *a mapping from the set of vectors at* O (which is the domain) *into the set of vectors at* O' (which *contains* the range) by assigning to each vector $\mathbf{u}$ at O the image vector $\mathbf{u}'$ at O'. We say "into" because not every vector at O' need be an image vector; that is, the range of the induced mapping need not be the whole set of vectors at O'. To give an extreme example, the given mapping may happen to map every point onto the same point O'.

The case where O is fixed under the given mapping is of initial concern to us; its effect is to swivel each vector at O about the point O while possibly changing its length. Since O equals O' in this case, we speak simply of *a mapping of the set of vectors at* O. Whether or not O is fixed, our induced mapping maps the zero-length vector at O onto the zero-length vector at O'.

PROBLEMS

1. If a translation is specified by the position vector to (a, b), show that the image of a point whose coordinates are (x, y) is a point whose coordinates are $(x + a, y + b)$. Hence show that the image of the locus of $f(x, y) = 0$ is the locus of $f(x - a, y - b) = 0$. Show that the image of a line is a parallel line.
2. Show geometrically that the successive application of three translations is equivalent to the application of a suitable single translation.
3. Define vectors at a point O in solid (3-dimensional) space and work the analogue of Problem 2.
4. Suppose a mapping of the plane has coordinate equations $x' = |x|$, $y' = |y| + 1$. Describe geometrically the effect of this mapping on the set of vectors at O, where O is the origin of a coordinate system.

1.4 VECTOR ADDITION AND SCALAR MULTIPLE

Let us use the symbols **u**, **v**, **w**, . . . for vectors at *O*. To express the characteristic properties of translations, we introduce among the vectors at *O* two operations, one called *vector addition* (or *vector sum*) and one called *scalar multiple*. In this section we consider these geometrically.

a. *Vector addition*. Let **u** and **v** specify two translations. The successive application of these translations, in either order, is equivalent to a single translation (the resultant) which is specified by some vector, say **w**. *We define the **vector sum*** **u** + **v** *by*

$$\mathbf{w} = \mathbf{u} + \mathbf{v}.$$

An economy in symbols is afforded by the use of the familiar plus sign for this vector sum. This usage also reflects the fact that addition of vectors shares the basic properties of ordinary addition. This vector sum can be constructed geometrically by the parallelogram law, again illustrated in Figure 9. We see that $\mathbf{u} + \mathbf{v} = \mathbf{v} + \mathbf{u}$, which expresses the *commutativity* of vector addition.

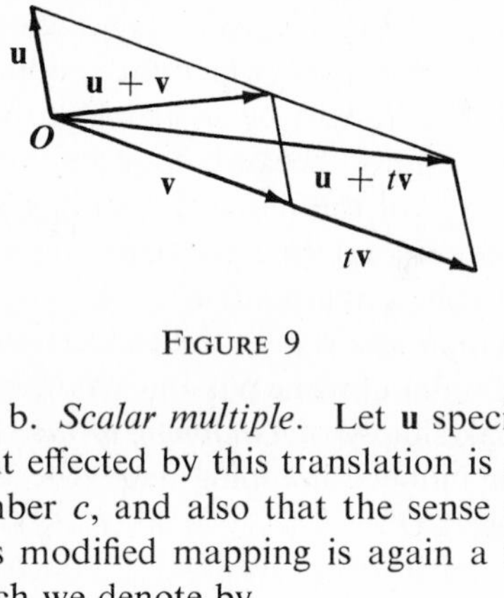

FIGURE 9

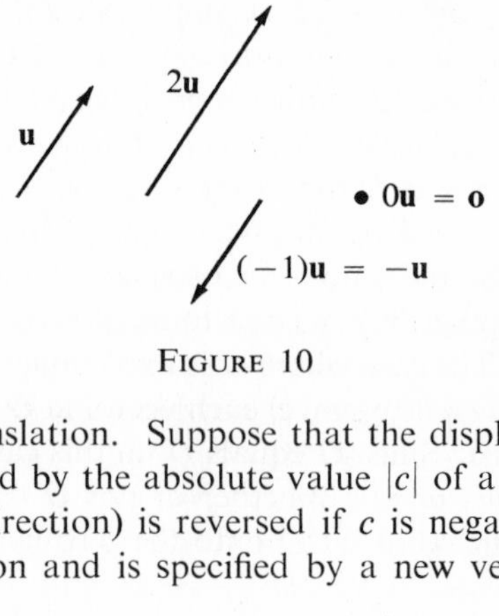

FIGURE 10

b. *Scalar multiple*. Let **u** specify a translation. Suppose that the displacement effected by this translation is multiplied by the absolute value $|c|$ of a real number c, and also that the sense (of its direction) is reversed if c is negative. This modified mapping is again a translation and is specified by a new vector which we denote by

$$c\mathbf{u}.$$

The vector $c\mathbf{u}$ is called the ***scalar multiple*** *of* **u**, *by the **scalar*** c. Thus,

$$|c\mathbf{u}| = |c||\mathbf{u}|.$$

If $c < 0$, then $c\mathbf{u}$ has sense opposite to that of **u**, as illustrated in Figure 10.

As in arithmetic, one writes $-\mathbf{u}$ for $(-1)\mathbf{u}$, and $\mathbf{u} - \mathbf{v}$ for $\mathbf{u} + (-\mathbf{v})$. The scalar multiple $0\mathbf{u}$ has length zero and is written **o**.

*Any sum of scalar multiples of a finite set of vectors is called a **linear combination** of these vectors*. For two vectors **u** and **v**, a linear combination has the form $c\mathbf{u} + d\mathbf{v}$ or $d\mathbf{v} + c\mathbf{u}$. In a linear combination of given vectors, summands which are zero multiples are often omitted. Thus $\mathbf{u} - \mathbf{v}$ is a particular linear combination of **u**, **v**, and **w**.

EXAMPLE 1. Two particular linear combinations, $2\mathbf{u} - \mathbf{v}$ and $2\mathbf{u} - \mathbf{v} + \mathbf{w}$ of three vectors $\mathbf{u}$, $\mathbf{v}$, $\mathbf{w}$ at O are constructed in Figure 11. To get $2\mathbf{u} - \mathbf{v} + \mathbf{w}$, we assume the associative law for addition (see Problem 1 below).

EXAMPLE 2. In Figure 9, consider the scalar multiple, $t\mathbf{v}$, of $\mathbf{v}$ by t. As t varies, the end-point of the variable linear combination $\mathbf{u} + t\mathbf{v}$ traces a line parallel to $\mathbf{v}$ and passing through the end-point of $\mathbf{u}$. If $\mathbf{w}$ is a position vector to a point on this line, then for some value of t we have $\mathbf{w} = \mathbf{u} + t\mathbf{v}$, and vice versa. Thus we have found a *vector equation of the line*.

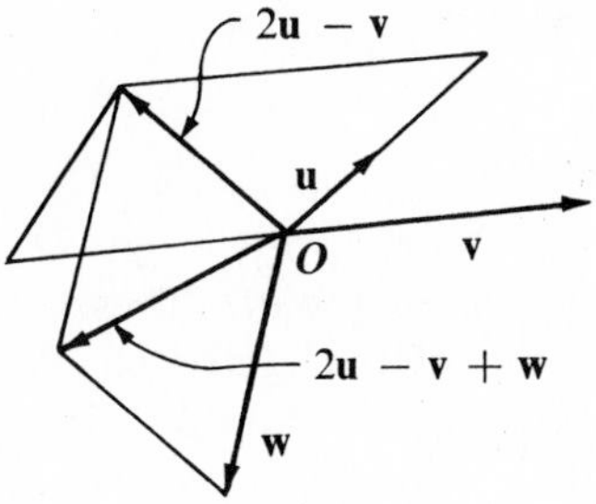

FIGURE 11

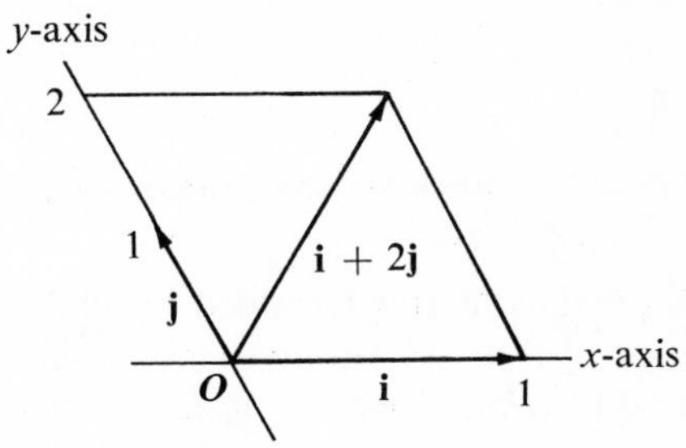

FIGURE 12

EXAMPLE 3. In any coordinate system, denote the position vector to $(1, 0)$ by $\mathbf{i}$, and the position vector to $(0, 1)$ by $\mathbf{j}$. Suppose $\mathbf{u}$ is the position vector to (x, y). We can construct $\mathbf{u}$ in *exactly one way* as a linear combination of $\mathbf{i}$ and $\mathbf{j}$, namely $\mathbf{u} = x\mathbf{i} + y\mathbf{j}$. This is illustrated in Figure 12. For applications, the common choice of coordinate system is Cartesian, wherein $\mathbf{i}$ and $\mathbf{j}$ (or $\mathbf{i}, \mathbf{j}, \mathbf{k}$ in solid space) are mutually perpendicular unit vectors. The line $x + y/2 = 1$ has a vector equation $\mathbf{u} = \mathbf{i} + t(2\mathbf{j} - \mathbf{i})$, where $\mathbf{u}$ is the position vector to the general point (x, y) on the line. The line $y = 1$ has a vector equation $\mathbf{u} = \mathbf{j} + t'\mathbf{i}$, where $\mathbf{u}$ is the position vector to the general point (x, y) on the line. A pair of values for t and t' such that $\mathbf{i} + t(2\mathbf{j} - \mathbf{i}) = \mathbf{j} + t'\mathbf{i}$, determines the position vector to the intersection of the two lines. Thus, using the uniqueness of the expression $x\mathbf{i} + y\mathbf{j}$, we deduce that the intersection occurs when $t = t' = \frac{1}{2}$, hence $\mathbf{u} = \mathbf{i}/2 + \mathbf{j}$. (In general, t and t' will not be equal at the intersection of lines in whose equations they are the *parameters*.)

PROBLEMS

1. Verify the associative law

$$(\mathbf{u} + \mathbf{v}) + \mathbf{w} = \mathbf{u} + (\mathbf{v} + \mathbf{w})$$

geometrically by application of the parallelogram law.

2. Compare $|(cd)\mathbf{u}|$ and $|c(d\mathbf{u})|$, as well as the directions of $(cd)\mathbf{u}$ and $c(d\mathbf{u})$, and thus show the mixed associative law: $(cd)\mathbf{u} = c(d\mathbf{u})$. Show the mixed distributive law: $(c + d)\mathbf{u} = c\mathbf{u} + d\mathbf{u}$.
3. Express $(c - d)(\mathbf{u} - \mathbf{w})$ and $c(d(\mathbf{u} - e\mathbf{v}) + \mathbf{w})$ as linear combinations of $\mathbf{u}$, $\mathbf{v}$, and $\mathbf{w}$.
4. Referring to Figure 12, find a vector equation of the line through $\boldsymbol{O}$ in the direction of $\mathbf{i} + 2\mathbf{j}$, and find the position vectors to its intersections with the two lines discussed in Example 3, and also with the line $\mathbf{u} = \mathbf{j} + t(2\mathbf{i} - \mathbf{j})$.
5. If $\boldsymbol{O}$ is the center of an n-sided regular polygon, show geometrically that the position vectors at $\boldsymbol{O}$ to the vertices add up to $\mathbf{o}$.

1.5 COORDINATE ROWS AND 2-TUPLE VECTORS

We have noted that upon choice of a coordinate system with origin $\boldsymbol{O}$, each vector $\mathbf{u}$ at $\boldsymbol{O}$ is determined by the coordinates of its end-point. These coordinates, say (a, b), supply a numerical representation of the vector $\mathbf{u}$. We call (a, b) the ***coordinate row*** *of* $\mathbf{u}$. Among coordinate rows it is natural to introduce counterparts of vector addition and scalar multiple. Thus, *if a vector* $\mathbf{u}$ *has the coordinate row* (a, b) *and a vector* $\mathbf{v}$ *has the coordinate row* (d, e), *then the expressions* $(a, b) + (d, e)$ *and* $c(a, b)$ *are defined as follows:*

$(a, b) + (d, e) = (a + d, b + e)$, corresponding to computation of the coordinate row of $\mathbf{u} + \mathbf{v}$ from the coordinate rows of $\mathbf{u}$ and $\mathbf{v}$. (1)
$c(a, b) = (ca, cb)$, corresponding to computation of the coordinate row of $c\mathbf{u}$ from the coordinate row of $\mathbf{u}$.

The computations of the coordinate rows of $\mathbf{u} + \mathbf{v}$ and $c\mathbf{u}$ follow from the parallelogram law and comparison of similar triangles, as shown in Figure 13.

EXAMPLE 1. A *linear combination of two coordinate rows* has the form $x(a, b) + y(d, e)$. In particular, every coordinate row (x, y) can be expressed as $(x, y) = x(1, 0) + y(0, 1)$. This is the *only* way it can be expressed as a linear combination of $(1, 0)$ and $(0, 1)$.

Coordinate rows are equal if and only if the vectors they represent are equal, hence if and only if corresponding entries are equal. Note the two different uses of the plus sign, as well as the two kinds of multiplication, in Equations (1). When a coordinate system is fixed at a point $\boldsymbol{O}$, then calculations with the vectors at $\boldsymbol{O}$ can be duplicated by calculations with their coordinate rows. *Let us denote the correspondence between a vector* $\mathbf{u}$ *and its coordinate row by the notation*

$$\mathbf{u} \leftrightarrow (x, y). \tag{2}$$

EXAMPLE 2. The diagonals of the large parallelogram in Figure 13 lie on lines whose vector equations, when written in *coordinate row form*, are the parametric equations

$$(x, y) = t(a + d, b + e)$$

and

$$(x, y) = (a, b) + t'(d - a, e - b).$$

The first of these describes the line through $\boldsymbol{O}$ and $(a + d, b + e)$, while the second passes through (a, b) and (d, e). They intersect for those values of t, t' which give the same coordinate row (x, y), namely $t = t' = \frac{1}{2}$. So the intersection is, as expected, at the common midpoint of the diagonals.

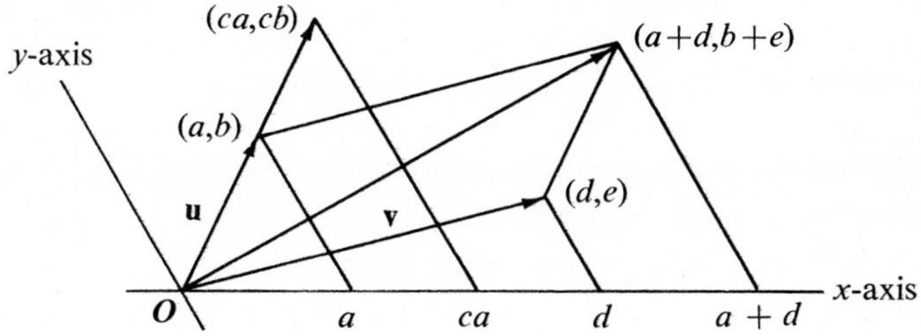

FIGURE 13

Equations (1) infuse the coordinate rows with a life of their own, because *the operations have meaning whether or not the numbers in the rows are coordinates. When the coordinate rows are thus divorced from their geometric origin and then subjected to Equations* (1), *they are called* ***row vectors.*** Once a coordinate system is chosen at $\boldsymbol{O}$, each row vector can be identified with a coordinate row, and vice versa. Now, suppose the entries in a coordinate row are listed in a column, say $\begin{pmatrix} a \\ b \end{pmatrix}$, instead of in a row (a, b). Equations (1) can be adapted to these ***coordinate columns,*** which are then called ***column vectors.***

This apparently fussy and unnecessary distinction between rows and columns is actually a useful device in *matrix algebra*, but is not of importance to us in this chapter. Hence let us refer to a row vector or a column vector indifferently as a 2-***tuple vector.*** Now, we see that Equation (2) *is a one-to-one correspondence between vectors at* $\boldsymbol{O}$ *and* 2-*tuple vectors, established with respect to a fixed coordinate system at* $\boldsymbol{O}$.

EXAMPLE 3. In solid space the coordinate rows of vectors at $\boldsymbol{O}$ have the form (x, y, z). Equations (1) extend in a natural way to 3-***tuple vectors.*** Thus:

$$(a, b, c) + (d, e, f) = (a + d, b + e, c + f),$$
$$g(a, b, c) = (ga, gb, gc).$$

The set of all 2-tuple vectors and the set of all vectors at $\boldsymbol{O}$ are but two instances of a more generally conceived structure called a ***vector space***, which we shall soon introduce formally. It is convenient, now, to anticipate by referring to our two sets of vectors as the *vector space of* 2-*tuples* and the *vector space at* $\boldsymbol{O}$, *respectively*.

When a mapping of the plane has a fixed point $\boldsymbol{O}$, then this mapping induces a *mapping of the vector space at* $\boldsymbol{O}$ *into itself*, as explained at the end of Section 1.3. Furthermore, if a coordinate system is introduced at $\boldsymbol{O}$, then a mapping of the coordinate rows of the vectors at $\boldsymbol{O}$ is induced simultaneously with that of the points and of the vectors. This applies at every fixed point.

EXAMPLE 4. In Example 2, Section 1.2, the point coordinate 2-tuples (x, y) are also coordinate rows of vectors at the fixed point $\boldsymbol{O}$. The mapping of (x, y) onto $(0, y)$ also maps the position vector to (x, y) onto the position vector to $(0, y)$.

Now consider the correspondence of Equation (2) again, regarding (x, y) as a 2-tuple vector. Suppose we have

$$\mathbf{u} \leftrightarrow (x, y) \quad \text{and} \quad \mathbf{u}' \leftrightarrow (x', y').$$

Then from Equations (1) we infer that

$$\mathbf{u} + \mathbf{u}' \leftrightarrow (x + x', y + y') \qquad \text{and} \qquad c\mathbf{u} \leftrightarrow (cx, cy). \tag{3}$$

Because sums and scalar multiples are thus matched, the correspondence between vectors at $\boldsymbol{O}$ and 2-tuple vectors is called an *isomorphism of the two vector spaces.* The correspondence is based on a choice of coordinate system at $\boldsymbol{O}$.

More generally, a one-to-one correspondence between any two vector spaces for which (a) *the sum of two vectors corresponds to the sum of their images, and* (b) *the scalar multiple of a vector corresponds to the same scalar times the image of the vector, is called an* ***isomorphism of the two vector spaces.*** We again anticipate a bit in order to note that our row vectors and our column vectors each constitute a vector space and that each of these two vector spaces is isomorphic to the 2-tuple vector space and hence to the vector space at $\boldsymbol{O}$. When two isomorphic vector spaces coincide, then the isomorphism is called an ***automorphism.*** *Automorphisms and isomorphisms of vector spaces* are particular types of *linear transformations*, the idea of which we introduce in Chapter 2.

PROBLEMS

1. For 2-tuple vectors, verify the commutative and associative laws, using Equations (1).
2. Write parametric equations of a line and of a plane in solid space, using coordinate rows.
3. Do Section 1.4, Problem 4 in terms of coordinate rows.

4. Show that the fact that the vector space at $\boldsymbol{O}$ and the vector space of 2-tuples are isomorphic can be expressed by the single correspondence:

$$c\mathbf{u} + c'\mathbf{u}' \leftrightarrow c(x, y) + c'(x', y').$$

5. Show that the correspondence $\mathbf{u} \leftrightarrow -\mathbf{u}$, for every vector $\mathbf{u}$ at $\boldsymbol{O}$, defines an automorphism of the vector space at $\boldsymbol{O}$. Does the mapping in Section 1.2, Example 2 induce an automorphism?

6. Consider a 2-tuple vector as a real-valued function with domain equal to the set of two integers $\{1, 2\}$. Describe Equations (1) in functional notation. Extend this idea to n-tuples, where n is a positive integer.

1.6 VECTOR PROPERTIES ABSTRACTED

In the vector space at $\boldsymbol{O}$ and in the vector space of 2-tuples, the operations called addition and scalar multiple obey common rules. To isolate these rules from their special contexts, we regard the symbols $\mathbf{u}, \mathbf{v}, \mathbf{w}, \ldots$ below, without commitment, as either position vectors or 2-tuple vectors all the way through, calling them just ***vectors.*** And although the scalars continue to be real numbers, it is clear that in the following list we use only a few of the basic properties of the real numbers.

For all choices of *vectors* $\mathbf{u}, \mathbf{v}, \mathbf{w}, \ldots$ and all choices of *scalars* $c, d, \ldots$ we have observed the rules:

I $\mathbf{u} + \mathbf{v}$ and $c\mathbf{u}$ are uniquely determined vectors.

II $\mathbf{u} + \mathbf{v} = \mathbf{v} + \mathbf{u}$ and $(\mathbf{u} + \mathbf{v}) + \mathbf{w} = \mathbf{u} + (\mathbf{v} + \mathbf{w})$, which express the commutativity and associativity of addition.

III $c(\mathbf{u} + \mathbf{v}) = c\mathbf{u} + c\mathbf{v}$, $(c + d)\mathbf{u} = c\mathbf{u} + d\mathbf{u}$, and $(cd)\mathbf{u} = c(d\mathbf{u})$, which express the mixed distributive and associative laws.

IV $1\mathbf{u} = \mathbf{u}$ for every vector $\mathbf{u}$. $0\mathbf{u}$ is the *same* vector for every $\mathbf{u}$ and is called the ***zero vector,*** and is denoted by $\mathbf{o}$.

V There exists a *finite* subset of vectors such that each vector in the vector space is a *unique* linear combination of the vectors in this subset. Such a special subset is called a ***basis*** (strictly speaking, a *finite basis*, but the implicit assumption of finiteness will suffice for the present).

When it is desirable to distinguish the *order in which the basis vectors are considered*, the term ***coordinate basis*** is used and the scalar coefficients that occur in the unique linear combinations (including understood zeros) are called ***coordinates.*** When the latter are arranged according to a given ordering of the basis vectors, they constitute a ***coordinate row.*** Thus each coordinate basis determines a unique coordinate row for each vector.

EXAMPLE 1. As in Section 1.4, we write $(-1)\mathbf{u} = -\mathbf{u}$. So $-(-\mathbf{u}) = (-1)((-1)\mathbf{u}) = 1\mathbf{u}$, hence $-(-\mathbf{u})$ is equal to $\mathbf{u}$ solely from the Rules (I)–(IV) above.

EXAMPLE 2. In the vector space of 2-tuples, the 2-tuple vector $(0, 0)$ is the zero vector, and the convenient set $\{(1, 0), (0, 1)\}$ is a basis. For the vector space at $\boldsymbol{O}$, a particular basis is the set $\{\mathbf{i}, \mathbf{j}\}$ of Section 1.4, Example 2. In fact, there it served, in the indicated order, as a coordinate basis.

PROBLEMS

1. In Example 2, take each of the bases in turn as a coordinate basis and find the coordinate row of a general vector. What happens to the coordinate rows when the vectors in a given coordinate basis are permuted?

2. Instead of (IV), consider:

(IV′). There is a special vector denoted by $\mathbf{o}$ such that $\mathbf{u} + \mathbf{o} = \mathbf{u}$ for every $\mathbf{u}$; also, $\mathbf{u} + (-1)\mathbf{u} = \mathbf{o}$ for every $\mathbf{u}$.

Show that (IV) and (IV′) are equivalent in the presence of (I)–(III).

3. If a, b, c are non-zero scalars, solve the equation $a\mathbf{u} = b(\mathbf{v} + c\mathbf{w})$ for $\mathbf{w}$ and express it as a linear combination of $\mathbf{u}$ and $\mathbf{v}$.

4. Using Rules (I)–(IV), show that:
(a) $(-c)\mathbf{u} = c(-\mathbf{u}) = -c\mathbf{u}$, (b) $c(d\mathbf{u}) = d(c\mathbf{u})$,
(c) $(c - d)\mathbf{u} = c\mathbf{u} - d\mathbf{u}$, (d) $c(\mathbf{u} - \mathbf{v}) = c\mathbf{u} - c\mathbf{v}$,
(e) $m\mathbf{u} = \mathbf{u} + \cdots + \mathbf{u}$ (m summands, m a positive integer),
(f) No basis contains $\mathbf{o}$.

1.7 COORDINATE BASES

The parallelogram law shows geometrically that *any two vectors at $\boldsymbol{O}$, neither of which is a scalar multiple of the other, constitute a basis*. This justifies the use of oblique frames. We can redefine an oblique coordinate system at $\boldsymbol{O}$ as a coordinate basis $\{\mathbf{u}, \mathbf{v}\}$ of the vector space at $\boldsymbol{O}$ with the line $\mathbf{w} = x\mathbf{u}$ as one axis and the line $\mathbf{w} = y\mathbf{v}$ as the other axis. So the coordinates of a point are those scalar multipliers of $\mathbf{u}$ and $\mathbf{v}$, in the given order, which yield the unique linear combination adding up to the position vector to the point (see Figure 14). The points $\boldsymbol{P}$ and $\boldsymbol{Q}$ are the *unit points* of the axes, and (x, y) is the coordinate row of $x\mathbf{u} + y\mathbf{v}$.

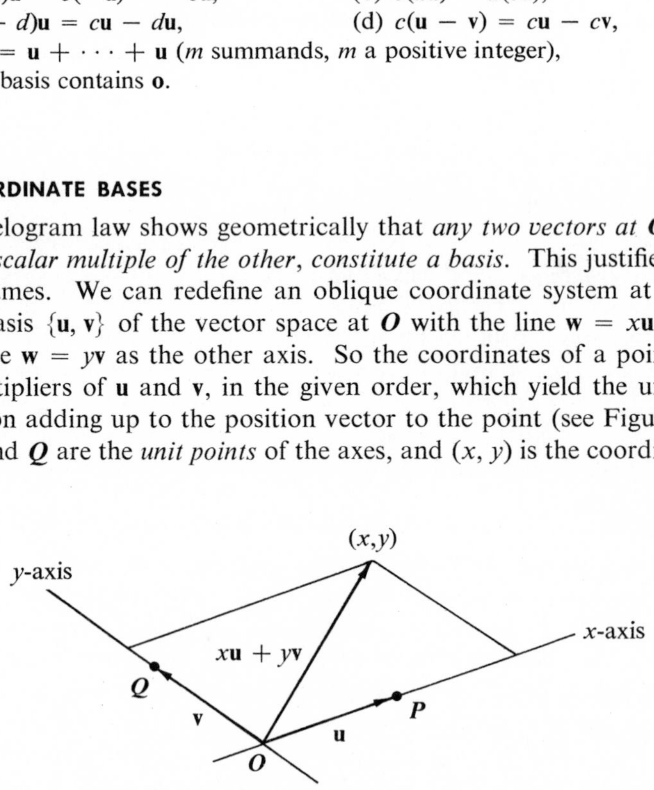

FIGURE 14

EXAMPLE 1. If (a, c), (b, d) are coordinate rows of the vectors in a basis $\{\mathbf{u}, \mathbf{v}\}$ of the vector space at $\boldsymbol{O}$, then the isomorphism between the vector space at $\boldsymbol{O}$ and the vector space of 2-tuple vectors implies that $\{(a, c), (b, d)\}$ is a basis of the latter vector space, and vice versa. Hence the intuitive fact that $\{\mathbf{u}, \mathbf{v}\}$ is a basis if and only if neither vector at $\boldsymbol{O}$ is a scalar multiple of the other, means that $\{(a, c), (b, d)\}$ is a basis if and only if neither 2-tuple vector is a scalar multiple of the other. (The choice of notation for the coordinates of the unit points is a little different here from that used in Section 1.1, Problem 6, and leads to a more natural looking pair of equations in Example 2 below.)

EXAMPLE 2. We can review a few facts about second-order ***determinants*** while we find several *direct* characterizations of a basis of 2-tuple vector space. By the definition given in Section 1.6, Rule (V), a pair of 2-tuple vectors (a, c) and (b, d) constitutes a basis if and only if *every* 2-tuple vector is a *unique* linear combination of the given pair, that is, if and only if every 2-tuple vector (e, f) determines unique scalars x, y such that $(e, f) = x(a, c) + y(b, d)$. But this is equivalent to the existence of a unique solution for the following simultaneous equations, whatever the choice of (e, f):

$$\begin{aligned} ax + by &= e, \\ cx + dy &= f. \end{aligned}$$

By the definition of a second-order determinant, we have

$$\begin{vmatrix} a & b \\ c & d \end{vmatrix} = ad - bc.$$

By *Cramer's Rule* (easily verified in this simple case by elimination), we know that when $\begin{vmatrix} a & b \\ c & d \end{vmatrix} \neq 0$, then a solution of the above equations always does exist, is unique, and can be expressed as

$$x = \begin{vmatrix} e & b \\ f & d \end{vmatrix} \Big/ \begin{vmatrix} a & b \\ c & d \end{vmatrix}, \qquad y = \begin{vmatrix} a & e \\ c & f \end{vmatrix} \Big/ \begin{vmatrix} a & b \\ c & d \end{vmatrix}.$$

But suppose $\begin{vmatrix} a & b \\ c & d \end{vmatrix} = 0$. This is equivalent to one of the 2-tuple vectors in our pair $\{(a, c), (b, d)\}$ being a scalar multiple of the other, say $(b, d) = k(a, c)$. Then

$$(0, 0) = k(a, c) - (b, d) = 0(a, c) + 0(b, d).$$

If $k \neq 0$ this expresses $(0, 0)$ in two different ways as a linear combination of the pair of 2-tuple vectors; while if $k = 0$, we have $(b, d) = (0, 0)$, so $(0, 0) = 0(a, c) + l(b, d)$ for every l. Hence, in neither case do we have a basis, and in neither case can the two linear equations always be solved, let alone uniquely (see Problem 3).

Therefore $\{(a, c), (b, d)\}$ is a basis if and only if $\begin{vmatrix} a & b \\ c & d \end{vmatrix} \neq 0$, or, equivalently, if and only if neither 2-tuple vector is a scalar multiple of the other. Neither a single 2-tuple vector nor a set of more than two 2-tuple vectors can constitute a basis (see Problems 4, 5).

When $\{(a, c), (b, d)\}$ is a *coordinate basis* of 2-tuple vector space, then the coordinate row (x, y) of a 2-tuple vector (e, f) is given by the solution of the equation

$$(e, f) = x(a, c) + y(b, d),$$

hence by

$$x = (de - bf)/(ad - bc), \qquad y = (af - ce)/(ad - bc),$$

as we have seen above.

PROBLEMS

1. (a) Show that $\{(1, 1), (1, -1)\}$ is a basis of 2-tuple vector space. (b) Show that $\{(1, 0, 1), (1, 1, 0), (0, 1, 1)\}$ is a basis of 3-tuple vector space. (c) Find the coordinate row of (a, b) in case (a), and of (a, b, c) in case (b), using the given lists as *coordinate* bases.
2. Show that (a, c) and (b, d) constitute a basis if and only if (a, b) and (c, d) do.
3. Suppose a system $ax + by = e$, $cx + dy = f$ has a solution x, y. Show that this implies $(ad - bc)x = de - bf$, $(ad - bc)y = af - ce$. Use this to show that when $\begin{vmatrix} a & b \\ c & d \end{vmatrix} = 0$, a solution exists if and only if $\begin{vmatrix} e & b \\ f & d \end{vmatrix} = \begin{vmatrix} a & e \\ c & f \end{vmatrix} = 0$, and then it is not unique because the equations are proportional.
4. Show that one 2-tuple vector can not constitute a basis of 2-tuple vector space.
5. In 2-tuple vector space, consider *any* three vectors, say (a, a'), (b, b'), and (c, c'). Show that $x(a, a') + y(b, b') + z(c, c') = (0, 0)$ has the solution

$$x = \begin{vmatrix} b & c \\ b' & c' \end{vmatrix}, \quad y = -\begin{vmatrix} a & c \\ a' & c' \end{vmatrix}, \quad z = \begin{vmatrix} a & b \\ a' & b' \end{vmatrix},$$

not all zero. Hence, for the three vectors there are two different linear combinations equal to $(0, 0)$, so they could not be part of a basis.
6. Allow the entries in the 2-tuple vector (a, b) to be any *complex numbers*. Verify that Rules (I)–(V) are obeyed by such vectors, if addition and scalar multiple are defined as in the case of real 2-tuples. Express $(1, 1)$ as a linear combination of the vectors $(1, i)$ and $(1, -i)$. Do the latter constitute a basis?
7. Construct a vector space which has a basis consisting of n vectors, where n is a prescribed positive integer.

1.8 RECOGNIZING VECTOR SPACES

A process of addition and a process of scalar multiple, simultaneously obeying Rules (I)–(IV), Section 1.6, can be discovered in or imposed on many sets besides directed line segments and 2-tuples. When we use the term *vector space* without a particular case in mind, we mean that we are considering a set among whose elements such a vector addition and scalar multiple is assumed to exist.

Suppose that in a particular set we exhibit a vector addition and scalar multiple. Then, with respect to these operations, we call this set a *vector space* and its elements *vectors*. If Rule (V) also holds, the vector space is called ***finite-dimensional,*** because the number of vectors in a basis turns out to coincide with the common notion of dimension in geometry. Although this is intuitively obvious in familiar spaces, it has to be proved in the general case. With the vector space at $\boldsymbol{O}$ in mind, we shall refer to the usual plane as *real* 2-*dimensional space* and to the usual solid space as *real* 3-*dimensional space*. And if we say that a vector space is *n-dimensional,* we merely mean that it has *at least* one basis consisting of n vectors, but we do not yet claim that *every* basis consists of n vectors.

EXAMPLE 1. We shall say that an ordinary real polynomial

$$a_0 + a_1x + \cdots + a_nx^n$$

in a "variable" x has degree n if $n > 0$ and $a_n \neq 0$. If all the coefficients in a polynomial equal zero, we have the special constant polynomial called the *zero polynomial.* Two polynomials are equal if and only if they have the same non-zero coefficients of like powers of x ($a_0 = a_0x^0$) when both are expressed in ascending powers of x. Hence we use the convenient symbol

$$\sum_{i=0}^{n} a_ix^i,$$

omitting the indication of the range of i when the context clearly conveys or does not require this information. Now consider the set of all these polynomials. We make a vector space out of it by the definitions:

$$\sum a_ix^i + \sum b_ix^i = \sum (a_i + b_i)x^i$$

(where additional zero coefficients are supplied when needed for meaning),

$$c\sum a_ix^i = \sum (ca_i)x^i.$$

These define a vector addition and scalar multiple, respectively. With respect to these operations, each polynomial is a vector.

EXAMPLE 2. Suppose k is a fixed positive integer. Then the set of real polynomials whose degrees do not exceed $k - 1$, taken together with the constant polynomials, can be regarded as a finite-dimensional vector space. A particular basis is $\{1, x, \ldots, x^{k-1}\}$ (see Problem 2 below). For instance, as a vector space, the set of polynomials of the form $a_0 + a_1x$ has the basis $\{1, x\}$.

The set $\{\mathbf{o}\}$ consisting of just the zero vector is itself a vector space (contained in the given vector space). It is called the ***zero vector space*** and for convenience is included among the finite-dimensional vector spaces. *We call it* *zero-dimensional and assign the empty set as its basis.* In proofs, cases involving the zero vector spaces are often taken for granted.

After a certain set is recognized as a vector space, then any logical consequences of Rules (I)–(IV) [or of (I)–(V)] are applicable, since these consequences will have been proved independently of any special realization of a vector space. In our various geometric examples, we assumed the validity of (V), as reflected in the use of a coordinate system.

PROBLEMS

1. If t vectors $\{\mathbf{u}_1, \ldots, \mathbf{u}_t\}$ constitute a basis of some finite-dimensional vector space, show that $a_1\mathbf{u}_1 + \cdots + a_t\mathbf{u}_t = \mathbf{o}$ if and only if $a_1 = a_2 = \cdots = a_t = 0$.
2. Show that a real polynomial $\sum a_i x^i$ equals zero for every value of x if and only if it is the zero polynomial. Show that $\{1, x, \ldots, x^{k-1}\}$ is a basis of the vector space in Example 2.
3. (a) Show how the set of complex numbers can be regarded as a 2-dimensional vector space. (b) Show how the set of 2-tuple vectors with complex entries can be regarded as a 4-dimensional vector space.
4. Show that the set of 3-tuple vectors whose third entries equal zero constitute a 2-dimensional vector space, and show that it is isomorphic to the vector space of 2-tuples.
5. For the vector space in Example 2, express the coordinate rows with respect to the given basis. Do the same for each part of Problem 3 with respect to some basis.
6. Show that any two 1-dimensional or any two 2-dimensional vector spaces (with the same scalars) are isomorphic.
7. Suppose we were to assign degree $-\infty$ to the zero polynomial and degree 0 to the other constant polynomials. Show that the degree of a product of two polynomials equals the sum of their degrees.

1.9 UNIQUENESS IN THE 2-DIMENSIONAL CASE

Suppose that a finite-dimensional vector space has a basis consisting of two vectors, say $\mathbf{u}_1$ and $\mathbf{u}_2$. Let us use the Rules (I)–(V) to prove that every basis of this vector space has two vectors. Example 2 in Section 1.7 appears as a special case of this result. We also illustrate some subscript usage.

Consider any three vectors $\mathbf{v}_1$, $\mathbf{v}_2$, $\mathbf{v}_3$ in the given vector space. Each is a unique linear combination of the basis vectors $\mathbf{u}_1$, $\mathbf{u}_2$:

$$\mathbf{v}_1 = c_{11}\mathbf{u}_1 + c_{12}\mathbf{u}_2,$$
$$\mathbf{v}_2 = c_{21}\mathbf{u}_1 + c_{22}\mathbf{u}_2,$$
$$\mathbf{v}_3 = c_{31}\mathbf{u}_1 + c_{32}\mathbf{u}_2,$$

or more concisely,

$$\mathbf{v}_i = \sum_{j=1}^{2} c_{ij}\mathbf{u}_j \ (i = 1, 2, 3).$$

We shall show that there exist three scalars a_1, a_2, a_3 not all zero such that

$$\mathbf{o} = a_1\mathbf{v}_1 + a_2\mathbf{v}_2 + a_3\mathbf{v}_3.$$

If we substitute for the $\mathbf{v}_i$'s, this equation takes the equivalent form

$$\mathbf{o} = (a_1c_{11} + a_2c_{21} + a_3c_{31})\mathbf{u}_1 + (a_1c_{12} + a_2c_{22} + a_3c_{32})\mathbf{u}_2.$$

But by uniqueness of the representation of any vector in terms of a basis, we must have

$$a_1c_{11} + a_2c_{21} + a_3c_{31} = 0,$$
$$a_1c_{12} + a_2c_{22} + a_3c_{32} = 0.$$

We could now apply the determinant theory of Section 1.7, Problem 5. Instead, assume $c_{11} \neq 0$, because the case $\mathbf{v}_1 = \mathbf{v}_2 = \mathbf{v}_3 = \mathbf{o}$ is trivial, and if $\mathbf{v}_1 = \mathbf{o}$ some other $\mathbf{v}_i \neq \mathbf{o}$. Furthermore, the case $c_{11} = 0$ and $c_{12} \neq 0$ will work out like the case $c_{11} \neq 0$ and $c_{12} = 0$.

We first eliminate a_1 from the second equation, and for new scalars c'_{22}, c'_{32} we get

$$a_1c_{11} + a_2c_{21} + a_3c_{31} = 0,$$
$$a_2c'_{22} + a_3c'_{32} = 0.$$

The second equation always has a *non-trivial* solution for a_2 and a_3 (that is, not both zero), which after substitution in the first equation yields a non-trivial solution for a_1, a_2, a_3. Hence if some basis contains at least three vectors, say $\mathbf{v}_1, \mathbf{v}_2, \mathbf{v}_3$, then $\mathbf{o} = a_1\mathbf{v}_1 + a_2\mathbf{v}_2 + a_3\mathbf{v}_3 = 0\mathbf{v}_1 + 0\mathbf{v}_2 + 0\mathbf{v}_3$ for scalars a_1, a_2, a_3 not all zero. This is impossible, so a basis of our vector space must contain *less* than three vectors. If some basis has one vector, say $\mathbf{v}$, then $\mathbf{u}_1 = a_1\mathbf{v}$ and $\mathbf{u}_2 = a_2\mathbf{v}$ for scalars a_1, a_2 such that $a_1a_2 \neq 0$. But then $\mathbf{o} = a_2\mathbf{u}_1 - a_1\mathbf{u}_2$, which is a contradiction again.

This result is itself a special case of the general theorem we shall prove later, which states that in a finite-dimensional vector space every basis has the same number of vectors.

EXAMPLE. If a non-zero vector space has a basis consisting of *one* vector, say $\mathbf{v}$, then every basis consists of one vector. For, if $\mathbf{u}_1$ and $\mathbf{u}_2$ are vectors in some other basis, then a contradiction arises just as at the end of the above proof.

PROBLEMS

1. Let $\{\mathbf{u}, \mathbf{v}\}$ be a basis of a vector space, and let a, b, c, d be scalars. Show that $\{a\mathbf{u} + c\mathbf{v}, b\mathbf{u} + d\mathbf{v}\}$ is a basis if and only if $\begin{vmatrix} a & b \\ c & d \end{vmatrix} \neq 0$, using the definition of basis in Rule (V).
2. Show that $\{\mathbf{u}, \mathbf{v}\}$ is a basis (of a 2-dimensional vector space) if and only if $c\mathbf{u} + d\mathbf{v} = \mathbf{o}$ implies $c = d = 0$.

3. In a 2-dimensional vector space, suppose $\mathbf{u}$ is a non-zero vector and that $\mathbf{v}$ is not a scalar multiple of $\mathbf{u}$. Show that $\{\mathbf{u}, \mathbf{v}\}$ is a basis of this vector space, by using the fact that for any three vectors there is a non-trivial combination equal to $\mathbf{o}$.
4. Suppose that in a given vector space there exists a set $\{\mathbf{u}, \mathbf{v}, \mathbf{w}\}$ of three vectors such that every vector in the space is a linear combination of these three. Show that $\{\mathbf{u}, \mathbf{v}, \mathbf{w}\}$ is a basis if and only if $c\mathbf{u} + d\mathbf{v} + e\mathbf{w} = \mathbf{o}$ implies $c = d = e = 0$.

2

Linear Transformations and Matrices in the Plane

2.1 MAPPINGS WITH LINEAR COORDINATE EQUATIONS

Asking whether the system of two linear equations

$$\begin{aligned} ax + by &= e, \\ cx + dy &= f, \end{aligned} \tag{1}$$

has a solution f[illegible] and y can be regarded as asking a question about a *mapping of the plane*, or [illegible]t a *mapping of the vector space at* $\boldsymbol{O}$. The explanation of this point of view [illegible]erve as an introduction to the idea of a *linear transformation* of any vector space.

Select a coordinate system with origin at $\boldsymbol{O}$. Keep the coefficients a, b, c, d fixed. Regard the 2-tuple (x, y) either as the coordinates of a point, or as the coordinate row of a vector $\mathbf{u}$ at $\boldsymbol{O}$. The substitution of a pair of numbers for x and y in the left-hand sides of Equations (1) yields a corresponding pair of numbers which we denote by x' and y', namely:

$$\begin{aligned} x' &= ax + by, \\ y' &= cx + dy. \end{aligned} \tag{2}$$

By Equations (2), a 2-tuple (x', y') is uniquely associated with the 2-tuple (x, y). We regard (x', y') as the coordinates of a point, *or* as the coordinate row of a vector $\mathbf{u}'$ at $\boldsymbol{O}$. Hence *to every point* (x, y) *we can assign the image point* (x', y'), *and thus define a mapping of the plane with* $\boldsymbol{O}$ *as a fixed point*. Finally, *this mapping induces a mapping of the vector space at* $\boldsymbol{O}$ (as in Section 1.3), *in which the vector* $\mathbf{u}'$, *whose coordinate row is* (x', y'), *is the image of the vector* $\mathbf{u}$ *whose coordinate row is* (x, y), Fig. 15, p. 22. The original question about Equations (1) may now be rephrased as follows: Does the point (e, f), or the position vector to (e, f), lie in the range of the relevant mapping?

To define the above mapping of the plane, we introduced a coordinate system, hence *Equations* (2) *are called the* ***coordinate equations of the mapping*** (as in Section 1.2). In the following examples of such *linear* coordinate equations, we also illustrate the idea of *invariance* under a mapping.

EXAMPLE 1. We have previously encountered (Section 1.2, Example 1) the case $a = d = -1$, $b = c = 0$, of Equations (2). The coordinate equations of this mapping are then simply, $x' = -x, y' = -y$, and the mapping is a *reflection in the origin of whatever coordinate system is used.* Under this mapping, each line through the origin is mapped onto itself because each point on such a line has its image and a counterimage on the same line, or, in terms of a mapping of the vectors at $\boldsymbol{O}$, because the image of each vector $\mathbf{v}$ is $-\mathbf{v}$. We express this behavior of the lines through the origin by calling them *invariant lines.* Note however, that the origin is the only point which is fixed. Of course, there are infinitely many centrally symmetric configurations which are invariant. For instance, any ellipse with its center at the origin is invariant, as illustrated in Figure 16. Under this mapping, every point in the plane is an image point, hence the corresponding Equations (1) are always solvable (that is, regardless of the choice of (e, f)).

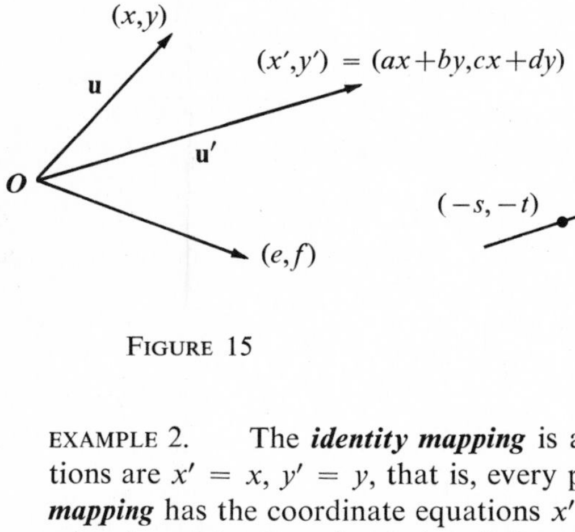

FIGURE 15

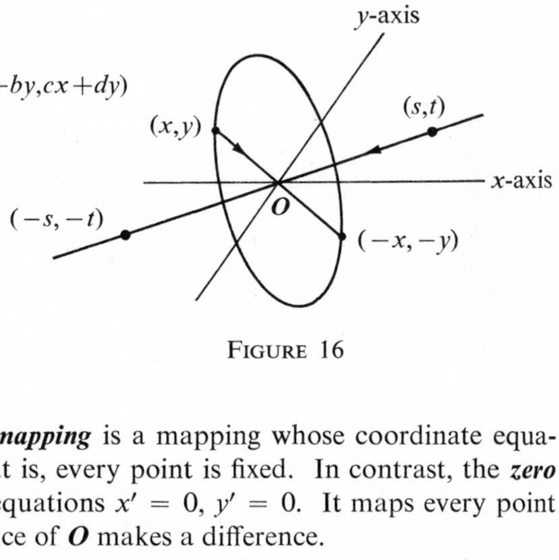

FIGURE 16

EXAMPLE 2. The ***identity mapping*** is a mapping whose coordinate equations are $x' = x$, $y' = y$, that is, every point is fixed. In contrast, the ***zero mapping*** has the coordinate equations $x' = 0$, $y' = 0$. It maps every point onto the origin $\boldsymbol{O}$, so the choice of $\boldsymbol{O}$ makes a difference.

EXAMPLE 3. When $a = d = 0$, $b = c = 1$, the coordinate equations are $x' = y$, $y' = x$, which yields a *reflection across the line* $y = x$ *parallel to the line connecting the unit points on the axes.* Under this reflection, the locus of $y = x$ and the locus of $y = -x$ are each invariant. Note that the geometric location of the line $y = x$, and also the "direction" of the reflection, depend on the choice of reference frame used to define the mapping. With respect to a Cartesian coordinate system, Figure 17 shows the image

of the familiar locus of $y = e^x$ as the familiar locus of $y = \log_e x$, and vice versa. Under this mapping, every point is an image point, hence the corresponding Equations (1) are always solvable.

EXAMPLE 4. If $a = k$, $b = c = 0$, $d = l$, where k and l are non-zero constants, then the coordinate equations are $x' = kx$, $y' = ly$, which is called a ***strain.*** Let us consider a few special strains. When $k = -1$, $l = \frac{1}{2}$, then, as Figure 18 shows, the image of the locus of $x + y = 1$ is the locus of $-x + 2y = 1$. When $k = l = 1$, we have the identity. When $k = l > 0$, we have a ***similitude.*** When $k \neq l$, then the x-axis and y-axis are the only invariant lines. Equations (1) are always solvable when $kl \neq 0$, but when $k = 0$ and $l \neq 0$, or when $k \neq 0$ and $l = 0$, the range is a line, hence Equations (1) are not always solvable.

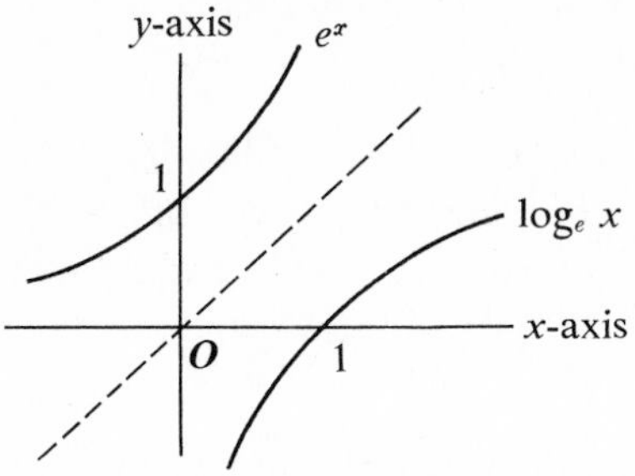

FIGURE 17

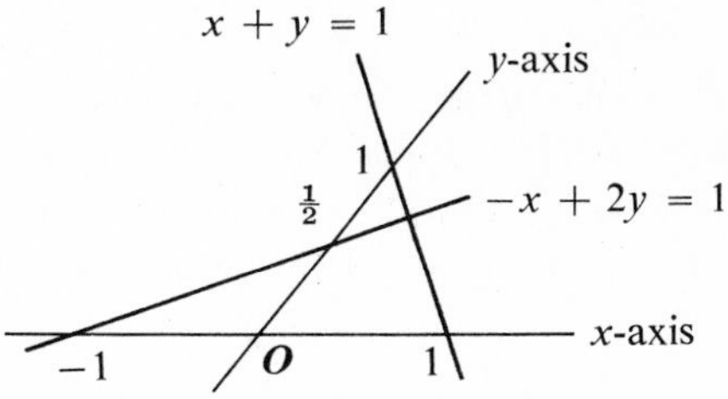

FIGURE 18

EXAMPLE 5. A somewhat more complicated mapping of the plane occurs when $a = d = 1$, $b = k \neq 0$, $c = 0$. Then the coordinate equations are $x' = x + ky$, $y' = y$, which is called a ***shear*** *parallel to the x-axis.* If we consider it with respect to a Cartesian coordinate system, then Figure 19 shows (in case $k > 0$) the locus of the circle $x^2 + y^2 = 1$ mapped onto the ellipse $x^2 - 2kxy + (1 + k^2)y^2 = 1$. Note that the x-axis is invariant, as is every horizontal line. Every point is an image.

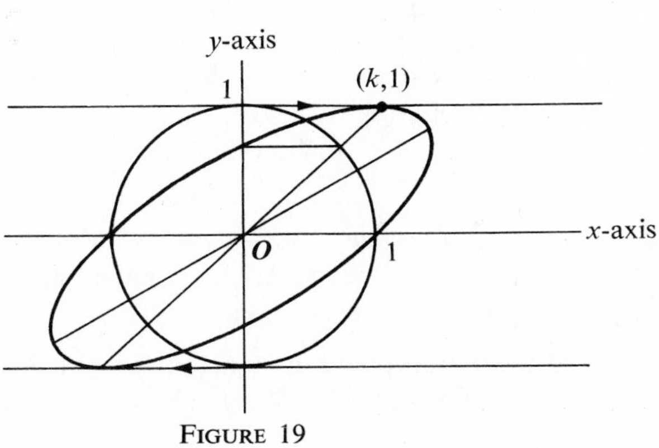

FIGURE 19

In most of these examples, *every point in the plane is an image point*. In other words, for any given point we can find at least one point which maps onto the given point. This property is expressed by saying that these mappings are ***onto*** the plane, rather than the noncommittal "into" the plane. In fact, they are *one-to-one onto*. We recall that ***one-to-one*** *means that distinct points (vectors) have distinct image points (vectors)*. But in Example 4, where we set k (or l) equal to zero (a combination of a projection with a strain), the mapping is not onto the plane. The zero mapping is an extreme case of a mapping which is not onto the plane. Only in the case when a mapping of the plane is onto the plane, can we assert that the corresponding Equations (1) have a solution for *every* choice of (e, f).

As an alternative to our coordinate interpretation of Equations (2), we may read into them a straightforward *mapping of the vector space of 2-tuple vectors*. For, first of all, the Equations (2) are a version of the equation

$$(x', y') = x(a, c) + y(b, d) \tag{3}$$

among 2-tuple vectors. Then, we naturally *assign* (x', y') *as the image of* (x, y), and we can apply our previous results concerning 2-tuple vectors, as in the following example, where "onto" means "onto the vector space of 2-tuple vectors." We shall use the same abbreviation with all vector spaces.

EXAMPLE 6. When is a given point (e, f), or the position vector to (e, f), in the range of a mapping defined by Equations (2)? This is the same as asking when the 2-tuple vector (e, f) is in the range of the mapping of 2-tuple vector space defined by Equation (3). If we refer back to Section 1.7, Example 2, we see that:

(a) The mapping defined by Equation (3) is *onto* if $ad - bc \neq 0$, and in this case, a unique solution of Equations (1) is given by Cramer's Rule for every choice of (e, f).

(b) The mapping is *not onto* if $ad - bc = 0$, for this means that (a, c) and (b, d) are proportional, or, equivalently, (a, b) and (c, d) are proportional. Let us suppose $(c, d) = k(a, b)$. When $(a, b) \neq (0, 0)$, a solution exists if and only if $f = ke$ (see Problem 3, Section 1.7), and then every 2-tuple vector (x, y), such that $ax + by = e$, is a solution. When $a = b = 0$, a solution exists if and only if $f = e = 0$, in which case the solution again is not unique.

(c) Thus, (e, f) *is in the range if* $ad - bc \neq 0$, *or if the Equations* (1) *are proportional* (in the first case the solution is unique, in the second case it is not). *Otherwise*, (e, f) *is not in the range*.

(d) Because of the isomorphism $\mathbf{u} \leftrightarrow (x, y)$, we can make corresponding claims for points, for the vectors at $\boldsymbol{O}$, as well as for row vectors and column vectors.

PROBLEMS

1. Describe, geometrically and in terms of coordinates, mappings of real 3-dimensional space which are analogous to the mappings in Examples 1–5. What mappings of the line are analogous?
2. In Example 5, find the counterimage of the line $x = c$, for any constant c.
3. Give examples of onto mappings of the type defined by Equations (2) under which no line is invariant.
4. Find a mapping whose coordinate equations are like those of Equations (2) and which has as its entire range the line $y = kx$.
5. Show that a mapping defined by the Equations (2) or (3) is one-to-one if and only if the system $ax + by = 0$, $cx + dy = 0$ has *only* $(0, 0)$ as a solution. Show that the latter system (of *homogeneous* equations) has a non-zero solution if and only if $ad - bc = 0$.
6. Show that a mapping defined by the Equations (2) or (3) is one-to-one if and only if it is onto.
7. For what values of a, b, c, d does the mapping defined by Equation (3) send $(1, 0)$ and $(0, 1)$ onto $(1, 1)$ and $(1, 2)$, respectively? Show that Equation (3) will define a unique mapping which sends (x_1, y_1) and (x_2, y_2) onto (x_1', y_1') and (x_2', y_2'), respectively, if $x_1y_2 - x_2y_1 \neq 0$. What is the geometric meaning of this determinant condition when applied to a mapping of the plane?

2.2 THE FIELD OF SCALARS

In the spirit of gradual disengagement from the restrictions of familiar analytic geometry, let us consider the subset of those vectors at $\boldsymbol{O}$ whose coordinate row representations in some fixed frame of reference involve only *rational numbers*. If we also restrict scalar multiples of such vectors to *rational multiples*, then we have a subset of the vectors at $\boldsymbol{O}$ whose elements satisfy all the Rules (I)–(V) in Section 1.6, with the scalars understood to be rational numbers. So this subset of the vector space at $\boldsymbol{O}$ is itself a vector space, with rational scalars. Furthermore, if a, b, c, d in Equations (2) are rational numbers, then, taken as coordinate equations, Equations (2) define a mapping of this vector space into itself.

A similar consideration can be made with respect to integers rather than rationals, but because only ± 1 have integral reciprocals (inverses) one does not apply the term vector space in this case. That is, the integers do not qualify as a complete set of scalars. The requirement we ultimately place on a set of numbers in order that they qualify as scalars for a vector space is that they constitute a ***field.*** A set of numbers is called a field if its elements can be added, multiplied, and otherwise manipulated according to the same well-known laws of arithmetic which govern these operations among the rational numbers, among the real numbers, and among the complex numbers; these are the most familiar fields. If $a, b, c, \ldots$ are any elements of a field, the following properties are characteristic:

(1) The sum $a + b$ and product ab are always defined and are in the same field as a and b.

(2) $a + b = b + a$, $ab = ba$, $(a + b) + c = a + (b + c)$, $(ab)c = a(bc)$, $a(b + c) = ab + ac$.

(3) There is an element 0 and an element 1 such that $a + 0 = a$ and $1a = a$ for every a in the field, $0 \neq 1$.

(4) For every a in the field there is an element $-a$ such that $a + (-a) = 0$; and if $a \neq 0$ there is an element a^{-1} such that $aa^{-1} = 1$.

The basic results of linear algebra do not depend on which *field of scalars* is involved. In Chapter 4 we shall finally transcend our present temporary restriction to real scalars; but already our notation and many of our results generalize readily. The latter remark applies to our succeeding discussions of the vector space at $\boldsymbol{O}$ which, in the 1-, 2-, or 3-dimensional case, serves as a simple realization of the corresponding abstract vector space.

EXAMPLE 1. Consider the set of polynomials in the transcendental number π with *rational* coefficients. Taking the rationals numbers as the field of scalars and the usual addition of real numbers as the vector addition, this subset of the field of real numbers can be regarded as a vector space. If we use $\sqrt{2}$ instead of π, then the corresponding set of polynomials is a 2-dimensional vector space with a rational field of scalars.

EXAMPLE 2. In most applications, the scalar fields contain the rational numbers as a subset. The simplest contrary cases are those called "integers modulo a prime p," in which addition among the familiar integer symbols $\{0, 1, \ldots, p - 1\}$ is subjected to the singular rule (see Problem 5 below):

$$\underbrace{1 + \cdots + 1}_{p \text{ summands}} = 0.$$

If x is one of these symbols and $x \neq 0$, then it can be shown that $x^{p-1} = 1$; hence $x^{-1} = x^{p-2}$.

EXAMPLE 3. For any positive integer n and any field of scalars, we can construct n-tuple vectors whose entries are in the given field. This allows us to match the generalization of Equations (2) with a generalization of Equation (3), and thus *always have a vector space interpretation of the generalized Equations* (2).

PROBLEMS

1. Consider a pair of integral 2-tuple vectors (integral entries) such that neither is an integral multiple of the other. Show by example that you may not be able to express every integral 2-tuple vector as a linear combination of the given pair, using integral coefficients.
2. Consider the set of polynomials in $2^{1/3}$, with rational coefficients. Show that it is a finite-dimensional vector space (see Section 1.9, Problem 4).
3. Show that if Equations (1) have a solution in some field which contains all the coefficients (and constants e, f), then they have a solution in any field which contains these numbers.

4. How many n-tuple vectors are there with entries in the field of integers modulo p?

5. With respect to a fixed prime p, classify the integers as follows: Put into a common class all those integers, and only those, which differ pairwise by an integral multiple of p. This means that two integers m and n are in the same class if and only if $m - n = kp$ for some integer k. Denote by $\bar{l}$ the class to which an integer l belongs. Define a sum and a product of classes by $\bar{m} + \bar{n} = \overline{m + n}$, $\bar{m}\bar{n} = \overline{mn}$. Show that a complete list of classes is given by $\{\bar{0}, \bar{1}, \bar{2}, \dots, \overline{p - 1}\}$, and that this set is a field with respect to the defined operations.

2.3 LINEAR TRANSFORMATIONS

We have seen that for each choice of coordinate system at a point $\boldsymbol{O}$ of the plane, Equations (2) define a mapping of the plane. *Among all possible mappings of the plane, this particular type is called a* ***linear transformation of the plane.*** We have commented on the definition of a mapping of the plane in functional terms (Section 1.2). To adapt this to the induced mapping of the vector space at $\boldsymbol{O}$, let $\mathbf{u}$ be the position vector to (x, y), let $\mathbf{u}'$ be the position vector to (x', y'), and *let* $\boldsymbol{a}$ *be the functional symbol for the mapping which Equations* (2) *induce in the vector space at* $\boldsymbol{O}$. Then the equation

$$\mathbf{u}' = \boldsymbol{a}(\mathbf{u}) \tag{4}$$

expresses the fact that $\mathbf{u}'$ is the image of $\mathbf{u}$ upon application of the mapping whose functional symbol is $\boldsymbol{a}$. (*The reader may wish to write* $\boldsymbol{a}$ *as* $\underline{a}$ *to distinguish it from written scalars and vectors.*)

Equation (4) avoids the details of the coordinate equations. It allows easy expression in vector terms of the following properties which, as we shall verify in Section 2.6, characterize those mappings of the plane or of the vector space at $\boldsymbol{O}$ that have *linear coordinate equations*, that is, as in Equations (2). The properties are:

$$\begin{aligned} \boldsymbol{a}(\mathbf{u}_1 + \mathbf{u}_2) &= \boldsymbol{a}(\mathbf{u}_1) + \boldsymbol{a}(\mathbf{u}_2) \text{ for every pair of vectors } \mathbf{u}_1, \mathbf{u}_2, \\ \boldsymbol{a}(s\mathbf{u}) &= s\boldsymbol{a}(\mathbf{u}) \text{ for every vector } \mathbf{u} \text{ and every scalar } s. \end{aligned} \tag{5}$$

In Figures 20, 21 the meaning of Equations (5) is illustrated geometrically, and in Example 1 below we check Equations (2) for the equivalent coordinate row expression of these properties.

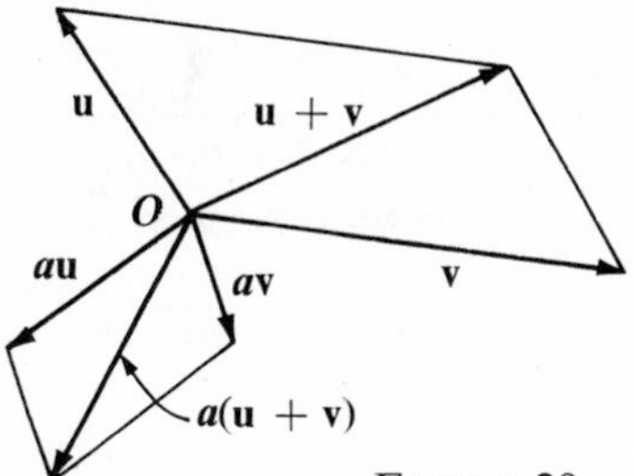

FIGURE 20

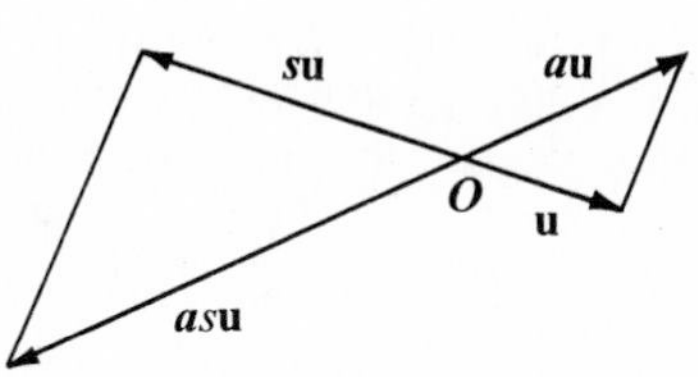

FIGURE 21

EXAMPLE 1. Let $\boldsymbol{a}$ be the mapping induced in the vector space at $\boldsymbol{O}$ by Equations (2), and denote by (m, n), (p, q), (x, y), and (x', y'), the coordinate rows of vectors $\mathbf{u}$, $\mathbf{v}$, $\mathbf{w}$, and the image vector $\boldsymbol{a}(\mathbf{w})$ at $\boldsymbol{O}$, respectively. Suppose that $\mathbf{w}$ is a linear combination of $\mathbf{u}$ and $\mathbf{v}$, given by $\mathbf{w} = h\mathbf{u} + k\mathbf{v}$ for some scalars h and k. In Equations (2), we replace x and y by their expressions in terms of the coordinates of $\mathbf{u}$ and $\mathbf{v}$, as computed from $\mathbf{w} = h\mathbf{u} + k\mathbf{v}$. We get

$$x' = a(hm + kp) + b(hn + kq) = h(am + bn) + k(ap + bq),$$
$$y' = c(hm + kp) + d(hn + kq) = h(cm + dn) + k(cp + dq),$$

which is equivalent to the following equation in coordinate rows treated as row vectors:

$$(x', y') = h(am + bn, cm + dn) + k(ap + bq, cp + dq). \tag{6}$$

But this is exactly the coordinate row expression of the vector equation

$$\boldsymbol{a}(\mathbf{w}) = h\boldsymbol{a}(\mathbf{u}) + k\boldsymbol{a}(\mathbf{v}). \tag{7}$$

Equation (7) is true for every choice of $\mathbf{u}$, $\mathbf{v}$, h, k, hence it is equivalent to Equations (5).

Equations (5) convey nothing explicit about a coordinate system at $\boldsymbol{O}$. *We therefore define a* ***linear transformation of the vector space at a point O*** *to be a mapping of this vector space into itself which satisfies Equations* (5). In anticipation of the proof which will show that, with respect to a coordinate basis, a mapping of the vector space at $\boldsymbol{O}$ satisfying Equations (5) is in fact *uniquely* determined by coordinate equations like Equations (2), we see that a linear transformation of *the plane* is a mapping of the plane whose coordinate equations are those of a linear transformation of *the vector space at some point* $\boldsymbol{O}$. In the former, we talk of points, and compute with their coordinate 2-tuples; in the latter, we talk of vectors and compute with their coordinate rows.

If we write *vector space* instead of *vector space at* $\boldsymbol{O}$, the above discussion leads us out of the special geometric context, because Equations (5) have meaning in, and therefore can be adopted as the definition of a linear transformation of, *any* vector space.

EXAMPLE 2. Equation (3) in Section 2.1 defines a mapping $\boldsymbol{a}$ of *the vector space of 2-tuple vectors*. The mapping satisfies Equations (5). For, if in Example 1 above we regard the coordinate rows as 2-tuple vectors, then all the computations apply and we find that Equation (6) reads

$$(x', y') = h\boldsymbol{a}(m, n) + k\boldsymbol{a}(p, q),$$

where

$$\boldsymbol{a}(m, n) = m(a, c) + n(b, d),$$
$$\boldsymbol{a}(p, q) = p(a, c) + q(b, d).$$

EXAMPLE 3. Directly from Equations (5) we see that $\boldsymbol{a}(\mathbf{o}) = \boldsymbol{a}(0\cdot\mathbf{o}) = 0\boldsymbol{a}(\mathbf{o}) = \mathbf{o}$. That is, a linear transformation maps the zero vector onto itself. Note that a translation is therefore not a linear transformation unless it is the identity mapping.

If $\{\mathbf{u}, \mathbf{v}\}$ *is a basis of the vector space at* O*, then a linear transformation* $\boldsymbol{a}$ *is completely determined by the images* $\boldsymbol{a}(\mathbf{u})$ *and* $\boldsymbol{a}(\mathbf{v})$. For, every vector $\mathbf{w}$ is a linear combination $\mathbf{w} = s\mathbf{u} + t\mathbf{v}$, and from Equations (5) we have

$$\boldsymbol{a}(\mathbf{w}) = s\boldsymbol{a}(\mathbf{u}) + t\boldsymbol{a}(\mathbf{v}).$$

EXAMPLE 4. Suppose in the plane we reflect every point across a fixed line (see Figure 22). Then this mapping is a linear transformation of the vector space at O by the following geometric argument. Pick a point O on the given line, a non-zero vector $\mathbf{u}$ at O not on this line, but parallel to the direction of the reflection, and a non-zero vector $\mathbf{v}$ at O on the line. Then, in particular, $\{\mathbf{u}, \mathbf{v}\}$ is a basis of the vector space at O. If $\mathbf{w}$ is any vector, then $\mathbf{w} = s\mathbf{u} + t\mathbf{v}$, uniquely, and the reflection of the end-point of $\mathbf{w}$ is the end-point of $\mathbf{w}'$, where $\mathbf{w}' = -s\mathbf{u} + t\mathbf{v}$. So we *assign* $\mathbf{w}'$ *as the image of* $\mathbf{w}$. In particular, $-\mathbf{u}$ is the image of $\mathbf{u}$, $\mathbf{v}$ of $\mathbf{v}$, $-(s\mathbf{u}) = s(-\mathbf{u})$ of $s\mathbf{u}$, and $t\mathbf{v}$ of $t\mathbf{v}$. Using the functional symbol $\boldsymbol{a}$ for this mapping, we have $\boldsymbol{a}(\mathbf{w}) = \mathbf{w}'$, and we see that

$$\boldsymbol{a}(s\mathbf{u} + t\mathbf{v}) = -s\mathbf{u} + t\mathbf{v} = s(-\mathbf{u}) + t\mathbf{v} = s\boldsymbol{a}(\mathbf{u}) + t\boldsymbol{a}(\mathbf{v}).$$

Although $\{\mathbf{u}, \mathbf{v}\}$ is a particular pair of vectors, the latter equation is readily verified in general by expressing an arbitrary pair of vectors as linear combinations of $\{\mathbf{u}, \mathbf{v}\}$. (See Problem 7 below.) Hence $\boldsymbol{a}$ is a linear transformation of the vector space at O.

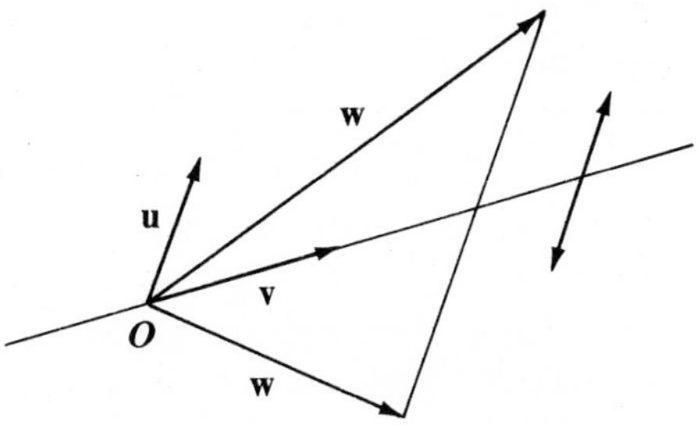

FIGURE 22

When we use the functional symbols $\boldsymbol{a}, \boldsymbol{b}, \ldots$, they do not necessarily represent linear transformations unless so specified.

PROBLEMS

1. In Example 4, show that every line whose vector equation has the form $\mathbf{w} = \mathbf{w}_0 + t\mathbf{u}$, where $\mathbf{w}_0$ is a constant vector and t is a parameter, is an invariant line.
2. Show that under a linear transformation of the plane *onto* itself, the image of a line is a line, parallel lines remain parallel, and intersecting lines have intersecting images.
3. If under a linear transformation of the plane there are three non-collinear points which are fixed, then show that this linear transformation is the identity mapping.
4. Show that a mapping of the plane *onto* itself is a linear transformation if and only if the image of every parallelogram with one vertex at a fixed point $\boldsymbol{O}$ is again a parallelogram. Show that a linear transformation maps parallel segments of equal length onto parallel segments of equal length.
5. If $\{\mathbf{u}, \mathbf{v}\}$ is a basis of the vector space at $\boldsymbol{O}$, show that the linear transformation corresponding to the coordinate equations $x' = y, y' = x$, reflects every point across the line $y = x$ and parallel to the line connecting the unit points (end-points of $\mathbf{u}$ and $\mathbf{v}$).
6. In Example 4 show that for suitable choice of coordinate axes, a point with coordinates (x, y) will have an image $(x, -y)$, hence $\boldsymbol{a}$ will have coordinate equations $x' = x, y' = -y$, which implies that $\boldsymbol{a}$ is a linear transformation.
7. Suppose $\{\mathbf{u}, \mathbf{v}, \mathbf{w}\}$ is a basis of a 3-dimensional vector space and that $\boldsymbol{a}$ is a mapping of this space such that
$$\boldsymbol{a}(r\mathbf{u} + s\mathbf{v} + t\mathbf{w}) = r\boldsymbol{a}\mathbf{u} + s\boldsymbol{a}\mathbf{v} + t\boldsymbol{a}\mathbf{w}$$
for all scalars r, s, t. Show this implies that $\boldsymbol{a}$ is a linear transformation.

2.4 MATRIX DESCRIPTION

Equations (2) are completely specified by a fixed table of scalars, namely, the table
$$\begin{pmatrix} a & b \\ c & d \end{pmatrix}.$$
To symbolize this table without a display of the specific entries, we use a capital letter, say A. We indicate this choice by writing
$$A = \begin{pmatrix} a & b \\ c & d \end{pmatrix}. \tag{8}$$
More generally, capital letters are used to denote a variety of tables, including coordinate rows and columns. We shall often find it more convenient to work with coordinate columns rather than with coordinate rows. If we symbolize the coordinate column of a vector $\mathbf{u}$ by the capital letter U, then we indicate this choice by writing
$$U = \begin{pmatrix} x \\ y \end{pmatrix}. \tag{9}$$

A table like A or U, and in fact any rectangular array, is called a ***matrix.*** The matrix A in (8) is an example of a *square matrix;* more specifically, A is a 2×2 matrix (read 2 by 2 matrix). The matrix U in (9) is an example of a *column matrix;* more specifically, U is a 2×1 matrix. When it is desirable to emphasize that the entries in a column matrix happen to be coordinates, we shall call it a *coordinate column*. We have already worked with *row matrices* in the role of *coordinate rows*.

Two matrices are considered *equal* if and only if they have the same entries in corresponding positions.

EXAMPLE 1. *The matrix that we formed from the right-hand sides of Equations* (2) *is called the* ***matrix of coefficients*** *of that system.* Among our examples of linear transformations, we find the following matrices of coefficients of their coordinate equations:

$$\begin{pmatrix} -1 & 0 \\ 0 & -1 \end{pmatrix} \text{ for a } \textit{reflection in } \boldsymbol{O},$$

$$\begin{pmatrix} 0 & 1 \\ 1 & 0 \end{pmatrix} \text{ for a } \textit{reflection across } y = x,$$

$$\begin{pmatrix} k & 0 \\ 0 & 1 \end{pmatrix} \text{ for a } \textit{strain parallel to the x-axis}, k \neq 0,$$

$$\begin{pmatrix} 1 & k \\ 0 & 1 \end{pmatrix} \text{ for a } \textit{shear parallel to the x-axis}.$$

We say that *each of these matrices* ***represents*** *a linear transformation* defined by the corresponding coordinate equations. Note that the same matrix can represent many different linear transformations of the plane, corresponding to interpretations of Equations (2) in different coordinate systems.

EXAMPLE 2. (a) If $\boldsymbol{a}(\mathbf{u}) = \mathbf{o}$ for every vector $\mathbf{u}$, then $\boldsymbol{a}$ is certainly a linear transformation. It is denoted by $\boldsymbol{o}$ and is called the ***zero linear transformation.*** The matrix which represents $\boldsymbol{o}$ consists of zero entries entirely, no matter what the coordinate basis; it is called the ***zero matrix*** and is denoted by O. (b) If $\boldsymbol{a}(\mathbf{u}) = \mathbf{u}$ for every vector $\mathbf{u}$, then $\boldsymbol{a}$ is certainly a linear transformation. It is denoted by $\boldsymbol{i}$ and is called the ***identity linear transformation*** (it is same as the identity mapping). The matrix which represents $\boldsymbol{i}$ has 1's on its diagonal and zero entries elsewhere, no matter what the coordinate basis; it is called the ***identity matrix*** and is denoted by I.

Now, referring to Equation 4, Section 2.3, wherein $\boldsymbol{a}$ is a linear transformation of the vector space at $\boldsymbol{O}$ induced by Equations (2), let

$$U = \begin{pmatrix} x \\ y \end{pmatrix} \quad \text{and} \quad U' = \begin{pmatrix} x' \\ y' \end{pmatrix}$$

denote the coordinate columns of $\mathbf{u}$ and $\mathbf{u}'$, respectively. *The matrix A in* (8) *is the matrix of coefficients of the coordinate equations of* $\boldsymbol{a}$. *In matrix notation, these coordinate equations of the linear transformation* $\boldsymbol{a}$ *are compactly expressed as a single* ***matrix equation***

$$U' = AU, \tag{10}$$

where by definition, the symbol AU means that we combine A and U according to the following rule:

$$AU = \begin{pmatrix} a & b \\ c & d \end{pmatrix} \begin{pmatrix} x \\ y \end{pmatrix} = \begin{pmatrix} ax + by \\ cx + dy \end{pmatrix}. \tag{11}$$

In general, *we take the second equality in* (11) *as the definition of the* ***product of a square matrix and a column matrix*** *in the given order*, regardless of the interpretations put on the entries in A and U, just so the entries can be computed.

*†In terms of vectors at $\boldsymbol{O}$, Equation (10) is the useful rule: *The coordinate column of the image of a vector equals the coordinate column of the counterimage multiplied by the matrix which represents the linear transformation.* Like most of our results concerning the vector space at $\boldsymbol{O}$, this one is correct for any finite-dimensional vector space.

EXMPLAE 3. In Section 2.3, Example 2, we considered the linear transformation of the vector space of 2-tuple vectors defined by Equation (3), Section 2.1, namely,

$$(x', y') = x(a, c) + y(b, d).$$

We see now that (10) gives the same information, if the column matrix U is taken as a column vector identified with the 2-tuple vector (x, y). There is no question of coordinates, since no coordinate system is involved in this interpretation.

EXAMPLE 4. All our definitions can be extended readily to larger size tables. Thus, for 3-dimensional space, a linear transformation is represented by some 3×3 matrix:

$$A = \begin{pmatrix} a & b & c \\ d & e & f \\ g & h & i \end{pmatrix}.$$

The coordinate equations in matrix form (10) are again $U' = AU$, but the coordinate columns of $\mathbf{u}$ and $\mathbf{u}'$ are the 3×1 matrices

$$U = \begin{pmatrix} x \\ y \\ z \end{pmatrix} \quad \text{and} \quad U' = \begin{pmatrix} x' \\ y' \\ z' \end{pmatrix}.$$

For instance, A may represent a particular shear,

$$A = \begin{pmatrix} 1 & k & 0 \\ 0 & 1 & 0 \\ 0 & 0 & 1 \end{pmatrix}.$$

The coordinate equations, of which this A is the matrix of coefficients, are $x' = x + ky$, $y' = y$, $z' = z$.

† An asterisk (*) will be used to designate certain facts of particular importance in Chapters 2 and 3.

EXAMPLE 5. Consider a ***rotation*** of angle ϕ radians about a point $\boldsymbol{O}$, in the plane. Let us analyze it geometrically with respect to a Cartesian coordinate system (see Figure 23). We find that a point whose Cartesian coordinates are (x, y) and whose polar coordinates are (r, θ), in the familiar relation $x = r\cos\theta$, $y = r\sin\theta$, has as its image a point whose Cartesian coordinates are given by:

$$x' = r\cos(\theta + \phi) = x\cos\phi - y\sin\phi,$$
$$y' = r\sin(\theta + \phi) = x\sin\phi + y\cos\phi.$$

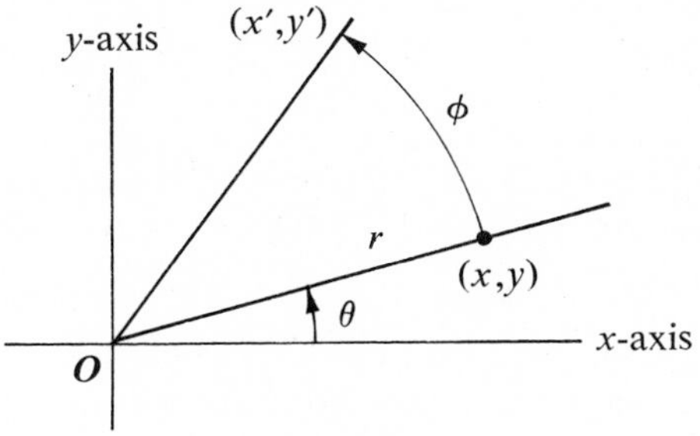

FIGURE 23

Therefore, the mapping is a linear transformation of the plane (see also Section 2.6, Example 2) and is represented in this coordinate system by the matrix

$$R = \begin{pmatrix} \cos\phi & -\sin\phi \\ \sin\phi & \cos\phi \end{pmatrix}.$$

The matrix equation $U' = RU$ is, in more detail,

$$\begin{pmatrix} x' \\ y' \end{pmatrix} = \begin{pmatrix} \cos\phi & -\sin\phi \\ \sin\phi & \cos\phi \end{pmatrix} \begin{pmatrix} x \\ y \end{pmatrix},$$

with which we may make computations, since it is equivalent to the coordinate equations. The image of the point $(1, 0)$ is $(\cos\phi, \sin\phi)$, and the image of $(0, 1)$ is $(-\sin\phi, \cos\phi)$.

EXAMPLE 6. Consider a modification of the linear transformation in Example 5, namely, one represented with respect to a Cartesian coordinate system by the matrix

$$C = \begin{pmatrix} k\cos\phi & -l\sin\phi \\ k\sin\phi & l\cos\phi \end{pmatrix}, \quad kl \neq 0.$$

Here the image of $(1, 0)$ is $(k\cos\phi, k\sin\phi)$, and the image of $(0, 1)$ is $(-l\sin\phi, l\cos\phi)$. Thus if $0 < \phi < \frac{\pi}{2}$, then the locus of the unit circle has as its image an ellipse as shown in Figure 24. If $\phi = \frac{\pi}{4}$ and $k = l = \sqrt{2}$, then the image of $|x| + |y| = 1$ is the square ***ABCD*** as shown in Figure 25.

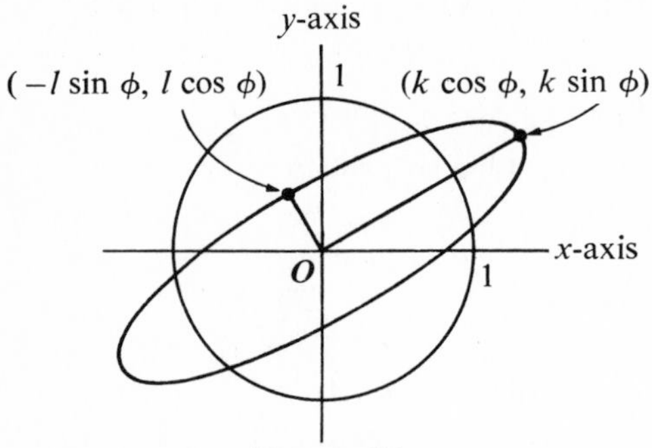

FIGURE 24

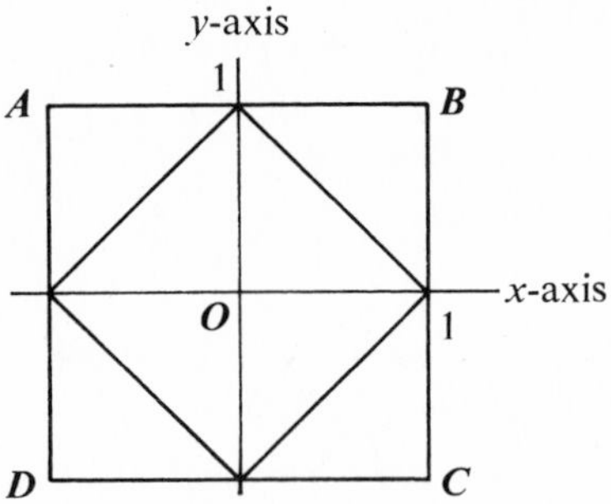

FIGURE 25

The matrix C in Example 6 can be interpreted as the representation of the combined effect of successive mappings: a strain with matrix

$$S = \begin{pmatrix} k & 0 \\ 0 & l \end{pmatrix},$$

followed by a rotation with matrix

$$R = \begin{pmatrix} \cos\phi & -\sin\phi \\ \sin\phi & \cos\phi \end{pmatrix}.$$

For, consider a vector whose coordinate column is

$$U = \begin{pmatrix} x \\ y \end{pmatrix}.$$

Then the mapping represented by R sends SU to $R(SU)$, which equals the coordinate column

$$\begin{pmatrix} xk\cos\phi - yl\sin\phi \\ xk\sin\phi + yl\cos\phi \end{pmatrix}.$$

But this equals CU, namely, the product

$$\begin{pmatrix} k\cos\phi & -l\sin\phi \\ k\sin\phi & l\cos\phi \end{pmatrix}\begin{pmatrix} x \\ y \end{pmatrix}.$$

This type of composition of mappings motivates the definition of "matrix product" for square matrices that we shall introduce later.

The matrix S is conveniently denoted by $S = \operatorname{diag}(k, l)$ because it has zero entries except on the ***diagonal*** (upper left to lower right). Particular cases of this notation are $O = \operatorname{diag}(0, 0)$ and $I = \operatorname{diag}(1, 1)$, for the 2×2 zero matrix and the 2×2 identity matrix, respectively.

PROBLEMS

1. What are the determinants of the matrices in the Examples 1–6?
2. In Example 6, find the equation of the image of the locus of $y = mx$ (m a real number). Find the conditions for $y = x$ to be invariant.
3. Write out the coordinate equations whose coefficient matrices are

$$\text{(a)} \begin{pmatrix} 2 & -1 \\ 0 & 2 \end{pmatrix}, \quad \text{(b)} \begin{pmatrix} 2 & 0 \\ -1 & 2 \end{pmatrix}, \quad \text{(c)} \begin{pmatrix} 1 & 0 & 1 \\ 0 & 1 & 1 \\ 1 & 1 & 0 \end{pmatrix}, \quad \text{(d) diag}\,(k, l, m).$$

Consider these matrices as representations of mappings of the plane, and verify that an invariant line passes through (1, 0) in case (a), through (0, 1) in case (b), and through (1, 1, 1) in case (c). What about case (d)?

2.5 COLUMN AND ROW MATRICES

We have expressed linear coordinate equations, as typified in Equations (2), by a matrix equation $U' = AU$. *The latter equation is a coordinate column statement of the vector equation* $\mathbf{u}' = \boldsymbol{a}\mathbf{u}$. To find appropriate matrix equations corresponding to Equations (5), we first define the *sum of column matrices* and the *scalar multiple of a column matrix* by rules that convert column matrices to column vectors. Thus, suppose

$$U_1 = \begin{pmatrix} x_1 \\ y_1 \end{pmatrix}, \quad U_2 = \begin{pmatrix} x_2 \\ y_2 \end{pmatrix}, \quad U = \begin{pmatrix} x \\ y \end{pmatrix},$$

are column matrices. Then we make column vectors out of them by the rules:

$$U_1 + U_2 = \begin{pmatrix} x_1 + x_2 \\ y_1 + y_2 \end{pmatrix} \quad \text{and} \quad sU = \begin{pmatrix} sx \\ sy \end{pmatrix}. \tag{12}$$

So, *column vectors are column matrices that have been subjected to the rules in Equations* (12); the analogous description can be given of *row vectors*. Now, fix a coordinate system and let U_1, U_2, U be coordinate columns of vectors $\mathbf{u}_1$, $\mathbf{u}_2$, $\mathbf{u}$ at $\boldsymbol{O}$. Using Equations (11) and (12), we can verify directly, with the few *matrix operations* already defined, that

$$\begin{aligned} A(U_1 + U_2) &= AU_1 + AU_2, \\ A(sU) &= s(AU), \end{aligned} \tag{13}$$

because these are the same as the detailed equations

$$\begin{pmatrix} a & b \\ c & d \end{pmatrix}\left[\begin{pmatrix} x_1 \\ y_1 \end{pmatrix} + \begin{pmatrix} x_2 \\ y_2 \end{pmatrix}\right] = \begin{pmatrix} a & b \\ c & d \end{pmatrix}\begin{pmatrix} x_1 \\ y_1 \end{pmatrix} + \begin{pmatrix} a & b \\ c & d \end{pmatrix}\begin{pmatrix} x_2 \\ y_2 \end{pmatrix},$$

$$\begin{pmatrix} a & b \\ c & d \end{pmatrix}\left[s\begin{pmatrix} x \\ y \end{pmatrix}\right] = s\left[\begin{pmatrix} a & b \\ c & d \end{pmatrix}\begin{pmatrix} x \\ y \end{pmatrix}\right].$$

Here, the brackets serve merely as grouping symbols. *Equations* (12) *and* (13) *do not depend on an interpretation of the column matrices as coordinate columns and the matrix A as the representation of a linear transformation.*

However, we wish to emphasize that *Equations* (13) *follow also from the general coordinate correspondence* $\boldsymbol{a}\mathbf{u} \to AU$ *defined by Equation* (10), *which we shall apply to derive matrix identities.* Actually, given a coordinate basis, this correspondence is one-to-one, as we shall show in Section 2.6. In anticipation of this fact let us indicate the correspondence by

$$\boldsymbol{a}\mathbf{u} \leftrightarrow AU. \tag{14}$$

We combine the correspondence (14) with the fact that the vector space at $\boldsymbol{O}$ is isomorphic to the vector space of column vectors, as follows. For any vectors $\mathbf{u}_1$, $\mathbf{u}_2$, $\mathbf{u}$ with coordinate columns U_1, U_2, U we have

$$\mathbf{u}_1 + \mathbf{u}_2 \leftrightarrow U_1 + U_2, \quad s\mathbf{u} \leftrightarrow sU. \tag{15}$$

Hence, if we set $\mathbf{v} = \boldsymbol{a}(\mathbf{u}_1 + \mathbf{u}_2)$ and $\mathbf{w} = \boldsymbol{a}\mathbf{u}_1 + \boldsymbol{a}\mathbf{u}_2$, then the coordinate columns V and W of $\mathbf{v}$ and $\mathbf{w}$ are determined by the correspondences

$$\begin{aligned} \mathbf{v} &= \boldsymbol{a}(\mathbf{u}_1 + \mathbf{u}_2) \leftrightarrow V = A(U_1 + U_2), \\ \mathbf{w} &= \boldsymbol{a}\mathbf{u}_1 + \boldsymbol{a}\mathbf{u}_2 \leftrightarrow W = AU_1 + AU_2. \end{aligned} \tag{16}$$

Also, equal vectors correspond to equal coordinate columns,

$$\mathbf{v} = \mathbf{w} \leftrightarrow V = W,$$

hence we get the correspondence between Equations (5) and the first of Equations (13). Similarly,

$$\boldsymbol{a}(s\mathbf{u}) \leftrightarrow A(sU),$$
$$s(\boldsymbol{a}\mathbf{u}) \leftrightarrow s(AU),$$

implies

$$\boldsymbol{a}(s\mathbf{u}) = s(\boldsymbol{a}\mathbf{u}) \leftrightarrow A(sU) = s(AU).$$

The combined Equation (7) of Section 2.3, which may be written as

$$\boldsymbol{a}(s_1\mathbf{u}_1 + s_2\mathbf{u}_2) = s_1\boldsymbol{a}\mathbf{u}_1 + s_2\boldsymbol{a}\mathbf{u}_2,$$

corresponds to the matrix equation

$$A(s_1U_1 + s_2U_2) = s_1(AU_1) + s_2(AU_2).$$

(Notice that we have begun to discard some of the parentheses in expressions such as $\boldsymbol{a}\mathbf{u}$ and $s\boldsymbol{a}\mathbf{u}$.)

EXAMPLE 1. The definitions of AU, $U_1 + U_2$, and sU generalize readily to square matrices and column matrices of any compatible sizes. As an illustration of these operations, consider the following computations:

$$\begin{pmatrix} 1 & 1 & 0 \\ 0 & 0 & 0 \\ 1 & 0 & 0 \end{pmatrix}\left(\begin{pmatrix} 1 \\ 0 \\ 1 \end{pmatrix} + 2\begin{pmatrix} 0 \\ 1 \\ 1 \end{pmatrix}\right) = \begin{pmatrix} 1 \\ 0 \\ 1 \end{pmatrix} + \begin{pmatrix} 0 \\ 2 \\ 2 \end{pmatrix} = \begin{pmatrix} 1 \\ 2 \\ 3 \end{pmatrix}.$$

In summary, let us first recall that when writing a 2-tuple vector (a, b), we have in mind the order of the entries, not the fact that they are in a row. But for the special purposes of calculation with matrices, we distinguish a row of numbers from a column of the same numbers; the former is a row matrix and the latter is a column matrix. In particular, we distinguish a row matrix whose entries happen to be coordinates from a column matrix whose entries happen to be coordinates; the former is a coordinate row and the latter a coordinate column. Furthermore, by our definition of addition and scalar multiple among row matrices and among column matrices, we create a vector space of row matrices and a vector space of column matrices. These vectors are then called row vectors and column vectors, respectively, which includes what we already have agreed upon when coordinate rows and columns are endowed with the same vector operations.

EXAMPLE 2. *Let the post-multiplication of a* 1×2 *row matrix by a* 2×1 *column matrix be defined by*

$$(m, n)\begin{pmatrix} p \\ q \end{pmatrix} = mp + nq. \tag{17}$$

Then Equations (2) can be expressed as a pair of such products, namely;

$$x' = (a, b)\begin{pmatrix} x \\ y \end{pmatrix},$$
$$y' = (c, d)\begin{pmatrix} x \\ y \end{pmatrix},$$

where the row matrices are formed from the *rows of A*. (The comma between a and b is there merely to avoid reading a product instead of a 2-tuple.) Notice that in Equation (17) the same result (a 1×1 matrix) is obtained if we compute $(p, q)\begin{pmatrix} m \\ n \end{pmatrix}$. Hence, using the *columns of A*, we can express Equations (2) as the pair of products

$$x' = (x, y)\begin{pmatrix} a \\ b \end{pmatrix},$$
$$y' = (x, y)\begin{pmatrix} c \\ d \end{pmatrix},$$

which, *by definition*, is also written as *the single matrix equation*

$$(x', y') = (x, y)\begin{pmatrix} a & c \\ b & d \end{pmatrix}. \tag{18}$$

Notice that the square matrix occurring in Equation (18) is *not* the same as A, but it gives the same numerical information as Equations (10) and (11), Section 2.4. By adapting the rules in Equation (12) to row matrices, we can get the analogue of Equation (13) (see Problem 7 below). However, these analogues will appear later as a consequence of the general process in matrix algebra called *transposition*. We also note that Equation (18) expresses a linear transformation of 2-tuple vector space (see Section 2.4, Example 3) once again, in another matrix form. This time, the 2-tuple vectors are identified with the rows of a matrix rather than with the columns.

EXAMPLE 3. Suppose a 2×2 matrix B has the form

$$B = \begin{pmatrix} sa & sb \\ sc & sd \end{pmatrix}.$$

If one defines sA by

$$sA = \begin{pmatrix} sa & sb \\ sc & sd \end{pmatrix}, \tag{19}$$

then it follows that

$$(sA)U = s(AU) = A(sU). \tag{20}$$

PROBLEMS

1. Verify:

(a) $(x, y)\begin{pmatrix} x \\ y \end{pmatrix} = 0$ if and only if $x = y = 0$ (assume real numbers),

(b) $(ca, cb)\begin{pmatrix} x \\ y \end{pmatrix} = (a, b)\begin{pmatrix} cx \\ cy \end{pmatrix}$,

(c) $(a, b)\begin{pmatrix} x \\ y \end{pmatrix} + (c, d)\begin{pmatrix} x \\ y \end{pmatrix} = (a + c, b + d)\begin{pmatrix} x \\ y \end{pmatrix}$,

(d) $\left[(2, 1)\begin{pmatrix} 1 & 0 \\ 1 & -1 \end{pmatrix}\right]\begin{pmatrix} 3 \\ 2 \end{pmatrix} = (2, 1)\left[\begin{pmatrix} 1 & 0 \\ 1 & -1 \end{pmatrix}\begin{pmatrix} 3 \\ 2 \end{pmatrix}\right]$.

2. Solve for x, y, z and give a geometric interpretation:

$$\begin{pmatrix} 2 & 1 \\ 0 & 2 \end{pmatrix}\begin{pmatrix} x \\ y \end{pmatrix} = z\begin{pmatrix} x \\ y \end{pmatrix}.$$

3. Let $A = \begin{pmatrix} 1 & 2 \\ 2 & 3 \end{pmatrix}$, $B = \begin{pmatrix} -3 & 2 \\ 2 & -1 \end{pmatrix}$, and $U = \begin{pmatrix} x \\ y \end{pmatrix}$. Show that $A(BU) = B(AU) = U$. If $V = \begin{pmatrix} 1 \\ 2 \end{pmatrix}$, solve the equation $AU = V$ by pre-multiplying each side by the matrix B.

4. Find a 3×3 matrix A whose entries are either 0 or 1, and which also satisfies the equation $(a, y, e)A = (y, e, a)$.

5. Consider *the set of all possible tables having p rows and q columns*, with entries from a given field of numbers. *These tables are called $p \times q$ matrices.* Make a vector space out of this set.

6. If A is a 2×2 matrix, show that $|A| \neq 0$ if and only if the columns of A (as vectors) constitute a basis of the vector space of column vectors, and similarly for the rows of A. (The symbol $|A|$ denotes the *determinant of the matrix A*.)

7. Denote the row matrices (x, y) and (x', y') by X and X', respectively, and the matrix $\begin{pmatrix} a & c \\ b & d \end{pmatrix}$ by B. Show that Equation (18) can be written as $X' = XB$ and that Equations (13) can be expressed in the form

$$(X_1 + X_2)B = X_1B + X_2B$$
$$(sX)B = s(XB)$$

2.6 CORRESPONDENCE BETWEEN MATRICES AND LINEAR TRANSFORMATIONS

We have defined a linear transformation $\boldsymbol{a}$ of the vector space at a point $\boldsymbol{O}$ as a mapping which satisfies Equations (5). *Now, let us show that such a mapping can always be specified by linear coordinate equations like Equations* (2), *and that the coefficient matrix is uniquely determined by the coordinate system.* As in Section 1.7, we can select a coordinate system at $\boldsymbol{O}$ by choosing two non-proportional vectors $\mathbf{u}$ and $\mathbf{v}$ at $\boldsymbol{O}$ for a coordinate basis $\{\mathbf{u}, \mathbf{v}\}$ and designating them as the respective unit vectors on coordinate axes at $\boldsymbol{O}$. Every vector $\mathbf{w}$ at $\boldsymbol{O}$ is then a unique linear combination of $\mathbf{u}$ and $\mathbf{v}$,

$$\mathbf{w} = x\mathbf{u} + y\mathbf{v}.$$

Denote the image of $\mathbf{w}$ by $\mathbf{w}'$, so $\mathbf{w}' = \boldsymbol{a}\mathbf{w}$. Also,

$$\mathbf{w}' = x'\mathbf{u} + y'\mathbf{v}$$

for unique scalars x' and y'. Since $\boldsymbol{a}$ is a linear transformation, we have

$$\begin{aligned} \mathbf{w}' &= \boldsymbol{a}\mathbf{w} = \boldsymbol{a}(x\mathbf{u} + y\mathbf{v}) = \boldsymbol{a}(x\mathbf{u}) + \boldsymbol{a}(y\mathbf{v}) \\ &= x\boldsymbol{a}\mathbf{u} + y\boldsymbol{a}\mathbf{v} = x'\mathbf{u} + y'\mathbf{v}. \end{aligned} \tag{21}$$

The images of $\mathbf{u}$ and $\mathbf{v}$ can be expressed as

$$\begin{aligned} \boldsymbol{a}\mathbf{u} &= a\mathbf{u} + c\mathbf{v}, \\ \boldsymbol{a}\mathbf{v} &= b\mathbf{u} + d\mathbf{v}, \end{aligned} \tag{22}$$

where a, b, c, d are unique scalars. Substituting from Equations (22) into Equation (21) and combining the coefficients of $\mathbf{u}$ and $\mathbf{v}$, we obtain the coordinate equations

$$\begin{aligned} x' &= ax + by, \\ y' &= cx + dy, \end{aligned}$$

whose coefficient matrix is

$$A = \begin{pmatrix} a & b \\ c & d \end{pmatrix}.$$

If we denote the coordinate column of $\mathbf{w}$ by W, and that of $\mathbf{w}'$ by W', we have

$$W' = AW, \qquad \text{where} \qquad W = \begin{pmatrix} x \\ y \end{pmatrix}, \qquad W' = \begin{pmatrix} x' \\ y' \end{pmatrix}.$$

We call A the ***matrix representation*** *of* $\boldsymbol{a}$ *with respect to the coordinate basis* $\{\mathbf{u}, \mathbf{v}\}$.

**Note that the columns of A list the coefficients of the linear combinations in Equations* (22)*; that is, these columns are the coordinate columns of* $\boldsymbol{a}\mathbf{u}$ *and* $\boldsymbol{a}\mathbf{v}$. This representation of $\boldsymbol{a}$ by A may also be regarded as the manifestation of a mapping from the set of linear transformations of the given 2-dimensional vector space at $\boldsymbol{O}$ into the set of linear transformations of the vector space of column vectors, that is, into the set of linear transformations of the vector space of 2-tuple vectors considered as column vectors (see Example 3, Section 2.4). We shall see below that this mapping is *one-to-one* and *onto*. To indicate the *representation of* $\boldsymbol{a}$ *by* A, we shall write

$$\boldsymbol{a} \leftrightarrow A.$$

The argument we have used does not depend on real scalars. It applies to any 2-dimensional vector space, and later we extend it easily to finite-dimensional vector spaces. The entries in the matrix A will then be in the field of scalars of the vector space considered.

EXAMPLE 1. With respect to the coordinate basis $\{\mathbf{u}, \mathbf{v}\}$ of the vector space at $\boldsymbol{O}$ shown in Figure 26, let us apply Equations (22) to find the matrix which represents a rotation about $\boldsymbol{O}$ counterclockwise through an angle of ϕ radians. We know (Example 5, Section 2.4) that this rotation is a linear transformation. We need to express $\boldsymbol{a}\mathbf{u}$ and $\boldsymbol{a}\mathbf{v}$ as linear combinations of $\mathbf{u}$ and $\mathbf{v}$. One way to do this is to consider a Cartesian coordinate basis $\{\mathbf{i}, \mathbf{j}\}$ at $\boldsymbol{O}$. Any vector of unit length has the form $\mathbf{i} \cos \theta + \mathbf{j} \sin \theta$, where θ is measured counterclockwise from the direction of $\mathbf{i}$. Hence

$$\mathbf{u} = \mathbf{i}, \quad \mathbf{v} = (\sqrt{2}/2)(\mathbf{i} + \mathbf{j}), \quad \boldsymbol{a}\mathbf{u} = \mathbf{i} \cos \phi + \mathbf{j} \sin \phi,$$

and

$$\boldsymbol{a}\mathbf{v} = \mathbf{i} \cos (\phi + \pi/4) + \mathbf{j} \sin (\phi + \pi/4).$$

Substitute these into Equations (22) and solve for the coefficients a, b, c, d. These turn out to be

$$a = \cos \phi - \sin \phi, \quad b = -\sqrt{2} \sin \phi, \quad c = \sqrt{2} \sin \phi,$$
$$d = \cos \phi + \sin \phi;$$

and $A = \begin{pmatrix} a & b \\ c & d \end{pmatrix}$ is the desired matrix representation with its columns the coordinate columns of $\boldsymbol{a}\mathbf{u}$ and $\boldsymbol{a}\mathbf{v}$ with respect to $\{\mathbf{u}, \mathbf{v}\}$.

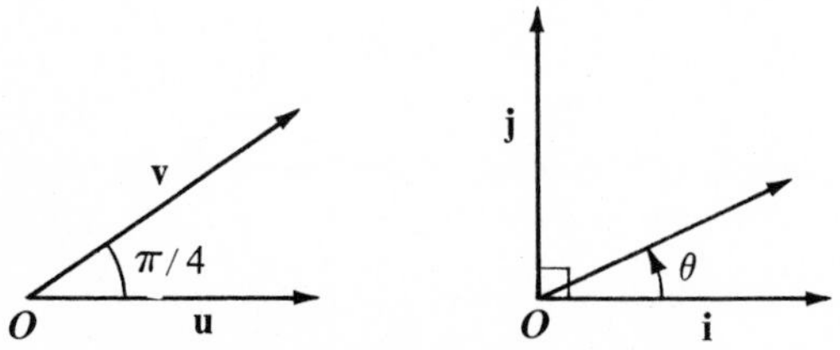

$(|\mathbf{u}| = |\mathbf{v}| = |\mathbf{i}| = |\mathbf{j}| = 1, \mathbf{u} = \mathbf{i})$

FIGURE 26

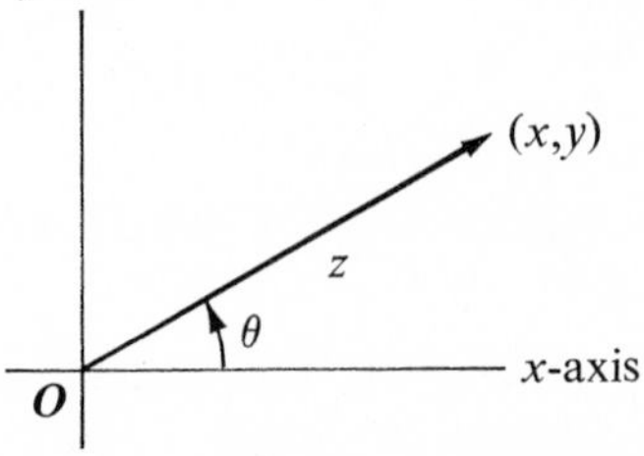

FIGURE 27

EXAMPLE 2. A complex number such as $z = x + iy$ is commonly represented by a position vector in a Cartesian frame, as in Figure 27. The corresponding polar representation is $z = re^{i\theta}$, where $r^2 = x^2 + y^2 = |z|^2$.

The usual addition of complex numbers and their multiplication by *real* numbers corresponds to the same operations on the position vectors, so in this sense the complex numbers constitute vector space. As for multiplication of two complex numbers, it may be regarded as the application of a linear transformation, in fact, as a rotation and a similitude applied successively in either order. For, let $z = re^{i\theta}$ be a variable complex number (a vector in this discussion) and let $ae^{i\phi}$ be a *fixed* complex number, $a \neq 0$. A particular mapping $\boldsymbol{a}$ of the complex numbers (as vectors) into the complex numbers is defined by:

$$z' = \boldsymbol{a}z = ae^{i\phi}re^{i\theta} = are^{i(\theta+\phi)}.$$

This is readily verified to be a linear transformation of the vector space of complex numbers with real scalars. To show that it is a similitude of magnitude a, followed by (or preceded by) a rotation of angle ϕ, use $\{1, i\}$ as a coordinate basis. Then

$$\boldsymbol{a}1 = (a\cos\phi)1 + (a\sin\phi)i,$$
$$\boldsymbol{a}i = (-a\sin\phi)1 + (a\cos\phi)i,$$

from which we get the matrix representation of $\boldsymbol{a}$ with respect to $\{1, i\}$,

$$A = \begin{pmatrix} a\cos\phi & -a\sin\phi \\ a\sin\phi & a\cos\phi \end{pmatrix} = a\begin{pmatrix} \cos\phi & -\sin\phi \\ \sin\phi & \cos\phi \end{pmatrix} = aR.$$

When $a = 0$, then $A = O$; and R was defined in Section 2.4, Example 5.

**Not only is every linear transformation* $\boldsymbol{a}$ *of our vector space represented, with respect to a given coordinate basis, by a uniquely determined matrix whose entries are in the field of scalars of the space, but also, conversely, if we are given a matrix* $A = \begin{pmatrix} a & b \\ c & d \end{pmatrix}$ *with scalar entries, and a coordinate basis* $\{\mathbf{u}, \mathbf{v}\}$, *then* A *is the matrix representation of exactly one linear transformation of the given vector space.*

To prove the latter fact, define two vectors $\mathbf{u}'$ and $\mathbf{v}'$ by

$$\mathbf{u}' = a\mathbf{u} + c\mathbf{v},$$
$$\mathbf{v}' = b\mathbf{u} + d\mathbf{v}.$$

Every vector $\mathbf{w}$ has a unique coordinate row (x, y) such that $\mathbf{w} = x\mathbf{u} + y\mathbf{v}$. *Define the image of* $\mathbf{w}$ *to be the vector* $\mathbf{w}'$, *where*

$$\mathbf{w}' = x\mathbf{u}' + y\mathbf{v}'.$$

Since x and y are unique, this is a mapping. Denote this mapping by $\boldsymbol{a}$, so $\mathbf{w}' = \boldsymbol{a}\mathbf{w}$. In particular, $\boldsymbol{a}\mathbf{u} = \mathbf{u}'$ and $\boldsymbol{a}\mathbf{v} = \mathbf{v}'$. It can be verified that $\boldsymbol{a}$ is a linear transformation by first noticing that

$$\boldsymbol{a}(s\mathbf{u} + t\mathbf{v}) = s\mathbf{u}' + t\mathbf{v}' = s\boldsymbol{a}\mathbf{u} + t\boldsymbol{a}\mathbf{v},$$

for any scalars s and t. Since $\mathbf{u}' = \boldsymbol{a}\mathbf{u}$ and $\mathbf{v}' = \boldsymbol{a}\mathbf{v}$, the matrix $A = \begin{pmatrix} a & b \\ c & d \end{pmatrix}$ is the representation of $\boldsymbol{a}$, according to our definition of a matrix representation. Finally, if $\boldsymbol{b}$ is a linear transformation of the same vector space and is represented by the same matrix, then $\boldsymbol{b}\mathbf{u} = \mathbf{u}'$ and $\boldsymbol{b}\mathbf{v} = \mathbf{v}'$. But this determines $\boldsymbol{b}$, which therefore must coincide with $\boldsymbol{a}$. Using a double-headed arrow to indicate this one-to-one correspondence, *we have, with respect to a coordinate basis, the unique correspondences:*

$$\boldsymbol{a} \leftrightarrow A, \quad \mathbf{u} \leftrightarrow U, \quad \boldsymbol{a}\mathbf{u} \leftrightarrow AU. \tag{23}$$

EXAMPLE 3. We see that a matrix equation $U' = AU$, where U and U' are column matrices and A is a given square matrix whose entries are drawn from the same field as those of U and U', may be regarded as the definition of a mapping, say $\boldsymbol{a}$, of the vector space of column vectors,

$$\boldsymbol{a}U = AU$$

and also that $\boldsymbol{a}$ satisfies Equations (5). Therefore, $\boldsymbol{a}$ is a linear transformation of this vector space. Now, in addition, we show that the matrix A is a matrix representation of $\boldsymbol{a}$, *if it is computed with respect to a suitable coordinate system*. Choose the ***unit column vectors***

$$\left\{\begin{pmatrix}1\\0\end{pmatrix}, \begin{pmatrix}0\\1\end{pmatrix}\right\}$$

as the coordinate basis of the vector space of 2×1 column vectors. Then we know, from the given defining equation $U' = AU$ of $\boldsymbol{a}$, that the images of these particular basis vectors are determined by the equations

$$\boldsymbol{a}\begin{pmatrix}1\\0\end{pmatrix} = a\begin{pmatrix}1\\0\end{pmatrix} + c\begin{pmatrix}0\\1\end{pmatrix},$$
$$\boldsymbol{a}\begin{pmatrix}0\\1\end{pmatrix} = b\begin{pmatrix}1\\0\end{pmatrix} + d\begin{pmatrix}0\\1\end{pmatrix},$$

which shows that A is the representation of $\boldsymbol{a}$ with respect to this coordinate basis. A column vector, when expressed as a linear combination of this basis, has coordinates which coincide with the entries already in the column vector; hence $U' = AU$ also takes on the role of the coordinate equations, in this case.

What happens in Example 3 is simply explained by noting that the unit column vectors are also the coordinate columns of the vectors in any coordinate basis $\{\mathbf{u}, \mathbf{v}\}$ of the vector space at $\boldsymbol{O}$,

$$\mathbf{u} \leftrightarrow \begin{pmatrix}1\\0\end{pmatrix}, \qquad \mathbf{v} \leftrightarrow \begin{pmatrix}0\\1\end{pmatrix}.$$

Thus the correspondence in (23) can be regarded as defining a convenient isomorphic correspondence of the vector space at $\boldsymbol{O}$ with the vector space of column vectors such that the effect of $\boldsymbol{a}$ on a vector $\mathbf{w}$ is faithfully reflected by the effect of A on the column vector W which is the coordinate column of $\mathbf{w}$.

PROBLEMS

1. Suppose that a linear transformation $\boldsymbol{a}$ of 2-dimensional column vector space maps $\begin{pmatrix}1\\1\end{pmatrix}$ onto $\begin{pmatrix}1\\0\end{pmatrix}$ and $\begin{pmatrix}1\\-1\end{pmatrix}$ onto $\begin{pmatrix}0\\1\end{pmatrix}$. Find the matrix representation of $\boldsymbol{a}$ with respect to the coordinate basis $\left\{\begin{pmatrix}1\\1\end{pmatrix}, \begin{pmatrix}1\\-1\end{pmatrix}\right\}$, and also with respect to $\left\{\begin{pmatrix}1\\0\end{pmatrix}, \begin{pmatrix}0\\1\end{pmatrix}\right\}$.
2. A linear transformation $\boldsymbol{a}$ of 2-dimensional row vector space maps $(1, 0)$ onto (a, c) and $(0, 1)$ onto (b, d). Find the matrix representation of $\boldsymbol{a}$ with respect to the coordinate basis $\{(1, 0), (0, 1)\}$.
3. Treat the set of numbers $\{a + b\sqrt{2}\}$, a and b rational, the way the complex numbers were treated in Example 2, using $\{1, \sqrt{2}\}$ as a coordinate basis. Show that $\sqrt{2}$ is represented by $\begin{pmatrix}0 & 2\\1 & 0\end{pmatrix}$.
4. Show that the correspondence between complex numbers and linear transformations in Example 2 is one-to-one.
5. Suppose that $\{\mathbf{u}, \mathbf{v}, \mathbf{w}\}$ is a coordinate basis of a 3-dimensional vector space. Let $\boldsymbol{a}$ be a linear transformation of this space. Write the equations corresponding to Equations (22) and find the matrix representation of $\boldsymbol{a}$.
6. Find A in Example 1 by solving for $\mathbf{i}$ and $\mathbf{j}$ in terms of $\mathbf{u}$ and $\mathbf{v}$, then substituting in the expressions for $\boldsymbol{a}\mathbf{u}$ and $\boldsymbol{a}\mathbf{v}$.

2.7 PRODUCTS

Let $\boldsymbol{a}$ and $\boldsymbol{b}$ be any two mappings of a vector space into itself. For every vector $\mathbf{u}$, the vector $\boldsymbol{b}\mathbf{u}$ is in the domain of $\boldsymbol{a}$, hence $\boldsymbol{a}(\boldsymbol{b}\mathbf{u})$ is a vector whose connection to $\mathbf{u}$ can be indicated schematically by $\mathbf{u} \to \boldsymbol{b}\mathbf{u} \to \boldsymbol{a}(\boldsymbol{b}\mathbf{u})$. *If $\boldsymbol{a}(\boldsymbol{b}\mathbf{u})$ is taken as the image of* $\mathbf{u}$, *it defines a third mapping of the vector space into itself which is called the* ***product*** *of* $\boldsymbol{a}$ *and* $\boldsymbol{b}$. *This product is denoted by*

$$\boldsymbol{ab}$$

in order to indicate that we applied $\boldsymbol{b}$ *first, then* $\boldsymbol{a}$, which means that

$$(\boldsymbol{ab})\mathbf{u} = \boldsymbol{a}(\boldsymbol{b}\mathbf{u}). \tag{24}$$

If $\boldsymbol{a}$ and $\boldsymbol{b}$ are linear transformations, then $\boldsymbol{ab}$ is a linear transformation (Problem 1 below).

EXAMPLE 1. Multiplication of linear transformations has some of the properties of multiplication among scalars. But one of the differences is that, in general, $\boldsymbol{ab} \neq \boldsymbol{ba}$. This non-commutativity is already illustrated in Section 2.4, Example 5, where we do not get the same result by first rotating and then straining unless the constants assume special values.

EXAMPLE 2. Other differences are illustrated by projections onto coordinate axes. For instance, a projection onto the x-axis followed by a projection onto the y-axis is equivalent to the zero linear transformation of the plane, even though neither projection is itself the zero mapping. Furthermore, if $\boldsymbol{a}$ is a projection on one of the axes, there is no linear transformation $\boldsymbol{b}$ such that $\boldsymbol{ab}$ or $\boldsymbol{ba}$ equals $\boldsymbol{i}$.

Since $\boldsymbol{ab}$ is a linear transformation, there is a unique matrix which represents it with respect to a given coordinate basis. Let $\{\mathbf{u}, \mathbf{v}\}$ be a coordinate basis. Suppose that $\boldsymbol{a}$ is represented by $A = \begin{pmatrix} a & b \\ c & d \end{pmatrix}$ and $\boldsymbol{b}$ is represented by $B = \begin{pmatrix} e & f \\ g & h \end{pmatrix}$, and recall that the columns of these matrices are coordinate columns of the images of $\mathbf{u}$ and $\mathbf{v}$. Denote $\boldsymbol{ab}$ by $\boldsymbol{c}$. Then

$$\begin{aligned} \boldsymbol{c}\mathbf{u} &= \boldsymbol{a}(\boldsymbol{b}\mathbf{u}) = \boldsymbol{a}(e\mathbf{u} + g\mathbf{v}) = e(a\mathbf{u} + c\mathbf{v}) + g(b\mathbf{u} + d\mathbf{v}) \\ &= (ae + bg)\mathbf{u} + (ce + dg)\mathbf{v}, \\ \boldsymbol{c}\mathbf{v} &= \boldsymbol{a}(\boldsymbol{b}\mathbf{v}) = \boldsymbol{a}(f\mathbf{u} + h\mathbf{v}) = f(a\mathbf{u} + c\mathbf{v}) + h(b\mathbf{u} + d\mathbf{v}) \\ &= (af + bh)\mathbf{u} + (cf + dh)\mathbf{v}. \end{aligned}$$

If we denote the matrix representation of $\boldsymbol{c}$ *by* C, *then*

$$C = \begin{pmatrix} ae + bg & af + bh \\ ce + dg & cf + dh \end{pmatrix}.$$

For any vector $\mathbf{w}$, let W, W', W'' be coordinate columns of $\mathbf{w}$, $\mathbf{w}'$, $\mathbf{w}''$, respectively, where $\mathbf{w}' = \boldsymbol{b}\mathbf{w}$, and

$$\mathbf{w}'' = \boldsymbol{a}\mathbf{w}' = \boldsymbol{a}(\boldsymbol{b}\mathbf{w}) = \boldsymbol{c}\mathbf{w}.$$

Then, by application of the correspondences (23) in Section 2.6, we have $W' = BW$, and

$$W'' = AW' = A(BW) = CW.$$

The matrix C *is called the* ***product*** *of* A *and* B *in the order indicated by the notation*

$$C = AB. \tag{25}$$

Hence

$$CW = (AB)W = A(BW)$$

for every coordinate column W. If we again use a double-headed arrow to indicate a one-to-one correspondence, we may summarize as follows: *With respect to a coordinate basis, we have the unique correspondences:*

$$\begin{gathered} \boldsymbol{a} \leftrightarrow A, \quad \boldsymbol{b} \leftrightarrow B, \quad \boldsymbol{ab} \leftrightarrow AB, \\ \mathbf{u} \leftrightarrow U, \quad (\boldsymbol{ab})\mathbf{u} = \boldsymbol{a}(\boldsymbol{b}(\mathbf{u})) \leftrightarrow (AB)U = A(BU). \end{gathered} \tag{26}$$

EXAMPLE 3. Since $\boldsymbol{a}$ and $\boldsymbol{b}$ can be specified by coordinate equations, say

$$\begin{aligned} x'' &= ax' + by', \\ y'' &= cx' + dy', \end{aligned} \quad \text{and} \quad \begin{aligned} x' &= ex + fy, \\ y' &= gx + hy, \end{aligned}$$

respectively, we can derive the matrix representation C of $\boldsymbol{c}$ by eliminating x' and y' between these two systems.

EXAMPLE 4. If $A = \begin{pmatrix} 1 & 1 \\ 1 & 1 \end{pmatrix}$ and $B = \begin{pmatrix} 1 & 1 \\ -1 & -1 \end{pmatrix}$ then $AB = 0$, but $BA = \begin{pmatrix} 2 & 2 \\ -2 & -2 \end{pmatrix}$.

EXAMPLE 5. Let $A = \begin{pmatrix} \cos\phi & -\sin\phi \\ \sin\phi & \cos\phi \end{pmatrix}$, $B = \begin{pmatrix} \cos\phi & \sin\phi \\ -\sin\phi & \cos\phi \end{pmatrix}$, and $C = \begin{pmatrix} \cos\psi & -\sin\psi \\ \sin\psi & \cos\psi \end{pmatrix}$. Then

$$AB = BA = I,\ AC = CA = \begin{pmatrix} \cos(\phi + \psi) & -\sin(\phi + \psi) \\ \sin(\phi + \psi) & \cos(\phi + \psi) \end{pmatrix}.$$

EXAMPLE 6. We have already introduced the product of a row matrix with a column matrix, in that order (Section 2.5, Example 2). Let us denote the rows (brief for row matrices) of a 2×2 matrix A by A_1 and A_2; that is, *A is regarded as a 2×1 column matrix whose entries are the two row matrices A_1 and A_2.* Symbolically, we write

$$A = \begin{pmatrix} A_1 \\ A_2 \end{pmatrix}.$$

Also, let us denote the columns of the 2×2 matrix B by B_1 and B_2, so

$$B = (B_1, B_2),$$

where the comma is used to avoid confusion with a product. Then $C = AB$ can be written, with careful attention to order of the factors, in the form

$$C = \begin{pmatrix} A_1B_1 & A_1B_2 \\ A_2B_1 & A_2B_2 \end{pmatrix}.$$

The more general case of Example 6 is that of two $p \times p$ matrices A and B ***partitioned*** *into row matrices and into column matrices*, respectively. Let this be indicated by

$$A = \begin{pmatrix} A_1 \\ \vdots \\ A_p \end{pmatrix} \quad \text{and} \quad B = (B_1, \ldots, B_p).$$

Then we have the following rules for the product AB: *The i-th **row** of AB is a linear combination of the rows of B using the entries in the i-th row of A as coefficients.* That is, the i-th row of AB equals A_iB, where

$$A_iB = (A_iB_1, A_iB_2, \ldots, A_iB_p),$$

as in Section 2.5, Equation (18) and Problem 7, so we can express AB in the forms

$$AB = \begin{pmatrix} A_1B \\ \vdots \\ A_pB \end{pmatrix} = \begin{pmatrix} A_1B_1 & A_1B_2 & \cdots \\ A_2B_1 & A_2B_2 & \cdots \\ \vdots & \vdots & \end{pmatrix}.$$

The j-th **column** *of AB is a linear combination of the columns of A using the entries in the j-th column of B as coefficients.* That is, the j-th column of AB equals AB_j. Thus, we can express AB in the form

$$AB = (AB_1, \ldots, AB_p).$$

EXAMPLE 7. If R is a 1×2 row matrix and T is a 2×1 column matrix, then for any 2×2 matrix A it is easily verified that $R(AT) = (RA)T$. This kind of mixed associativity involving row matrices and column matrices is a special case of the associativity of multiplication of general rectangular matrices (which represent mappings of a type we shall consider later). Here we note that an expression like $x^2 - 2xy + y^2$ can be written as the entry of a 1×1 matrix

$$(x, y)\begin{pmatrix} 1 & -1 \\ -1 & 1 \end{pmatrix}\begin{pmatrix} x \\ y \end{pmatrix}.$$

If $\boldsymbol{a}$, $\boldsymbol{b}$, $\boldsymbol{c}$ are mappings of a vector space into itself, *we define a product*

$$\boldsymbol{abc}$$

as a mapping $\mathbf{d}$ *equivalent to the successive application of* $\mathbf{c}$, $\boldsymbol{b}$, $\boldsymbol{a}$ *in that order.* That is,

$$\mathbf{d}\mathbf{u} = \boldsymbol{a}(\boldsymbol{b}(\mathbf{c}\mathbf{u})) \quad \text{for every } \mathbf{u}.$$

If we use the definition of $\boldsymbol{ab}$, we can write $\boldsymbol{d}\mathbf{u}$ in two ways:

$$\boldsymbol{a}(\boldsymbol{b}(\mathbf{c}\mathbf{u})) = \boldsymbol{a}((\boldsymbol{bc})\mathbf{u}) = (\boldsymbol{a}(\boldsymbol{bc}))\mathbf{u},$$
$$\boldsymbol{a}(\boldsymbol{b}(\mathbf{c}\mathbf{u})) = (\boldsymbol{ab})(\mathbf{c}\mathbf{u}) = ((\boldsymbol{ab})\boldsymbol{c})\mathbf{u}.$$

Hence we get the associative law $\boldsymbol{a}(\boldsymbol{bc}) = (\boldsymbol{ab})\boldsymbol{c}$, which justifies the notation $\boldsymbol{abc}$.

Now suppose A, B, C are matrices which represent $\boldsymbol{a}$, $\boldsymbol{b}$, $\boldsymbol{c}$ with respect to some coordinate basis. We know that AB and BC represent $\boldsymbol{ab}$ and $\boldsymbol{bc}$, respectively. Hence $(AB)C$ and $A(BC)$ represent $(\boldsymbol{ab})\boldsymbol{c}$ and $\boldsymbol{a}(\boldsymbol{bc})$, respectively. From the associative law of linear transformations and the uniqueness of representing matrices (given a coordinate basis), we find

$$(AB)C = A(BC).$$

This is the *associative law for matrix multiplication*, which justifies the notation ABC. *Hence we have the correspondences:*

$$\boldsymbol{a} \leftrightarrow A, \quad \boldsymbol{b} \leftrightarrow B, \quad \boldsymbol{c} \leftrightarrow C, \quad \boldsymbol{abc} \leftrightarrow ABC. \tag{27}$$

EXAMPLE 8. Let

$$A = \begin{pmatrix} 1 & 0 \\ g/e & 1 \end{pmatrix}, \quad B = \begin{pmatrix} e & 0 \\ 0 & d/e \end{pmatrix}, \quad C = \begin{pmatrix} 1 & f/e \\ 0 & 1 \end{pmatrix}, \quad D = \begin{pmatrix} e & f \\ g & h \end{pmatrix},$$

where $e \neq 0$ and $d = eh - fg$. Then the matrix D can be factored into $D = ABC$. This corresponds to the geometric interpretation of D as a *shear*, followed by a *strain*, followed by another *shear*, when $d \neq 0$.

EXAMPLE 9. Let U, V, W, X be column matrices of the same size, and A, B, C square matrices for which $V = CU$, $W = BV$, and $X = AW$. Then

$$X = A(B(CU)) = A((BC)U) = (A(BC))U,$$

and since CU is a column matrix,

$$X = (AB)(CU) = ((AB)C)U.$$

Thus

$$((AB)C)U = (A(BC))U$$

for every U. So, again, we deduce the associativity of the product of three square matrices, this time by using the mixed associative law for matrices: $(AB)U = A(BU)$.

PROBLEMS

1. If $\boldsymbol{a}, \boldsymbol{b}$ are linear transformations, apply $\boldsymbol{ab}$ to $s\mathbf{u} + t\mathbf{v}$ to prove that $\boldsymbol{ab}$ is a linear transformation.

2. Solve for the unknown entries:

(a) $\begin{pmatrix} a & b \\ 1 & 1 \end{pmatrix}\begin{pmatrix} 2 & 0 \\ 0 & 3 \end{pmatrix} = \begin{pmatrix} 1 & 1 \\ 2 & c \end{pmatrix}$, (b) $\begin{pmatrix} a & b \\ c & d \end{pmatrix}\begin{pmatrix} 2 & 0 \\ 0 & 3 \end{pmatrix} = \begin{pmatrix} 4 & 0 \\ 0 & 9 \end{pmatrix}$,

(c) $\begin{pmatrix} a & b \\ c & d \end{pmatrix}\begin{pmatrix} 2 & 1 \\ 0 & -1 \end{pmatrix} = \begin{pmatrix} 1 & 0 \\ 0 & 1 \end{pmatrix}$, (d) $\begin{pmatrix} 0 & 1 & 0 \\ 0 & b & 0 \\ 1 & 0 & c \end{pmatrix}\begin{pmatrix} 1 & 1 & 1 \\ d & e & f \\ 1 & 1 & 0 \end{pmatrix} = \begin{pmatrix} 1 & 1 & 1 \\ 1 & 1 & 1 \\ 1 & 1 & 1 \end{pmatrix}$,

(e) $\begin{pmatrix} a & b \\ c & d \end{pmatrix}\begin{pmatrix} a & c \\ b & d \end{pmatrix} = \begin{pmatrix} 1 & 0 \\ 0 & 1 \end{pmatrix}$ (real numbers).

3. Find all the 2×2 matrices which commute with $\begin{pmatrix} 1 & 1 \\ 0 & 1 \end{pmatrix}$. Do the same for $\begin{pmatrix} \cos\phi & -\sin\phi \\ \sin\phi & \cos\phi \end{pmatrix}$. What does the latter result mean geometrically?

4. Let $A = \begin{pmatrix} A_1 \\ A_2 \end{pmatrix}$, $C = (C_1, C_2)$, and B be 2×2 matrices. Show that

$$ABC = \begin{pmatrix} A_1BC_1 & A_1BC_2 \\ A_2BC_1 & A_2BC_2 \end{pmatrix}.$$

5. Show that $\boldsymbol{abcd}$ has the same meaning no matter how the factors are grouped. (Associativity of the product of four linear transformations.)

2.8 LINEAR TRANSFORMATIONS AS VECTORS

The *set of all linear transformations* of a vector space qualifies as vector space too if the following useful definitions of addition and scalar multiple are adopted.

(a) *Addition and its consequences.* If $\boldsymbol{a}$ and $\boldsymbol{b}$ are linear transformations, then the ***sum*** $\boldsymbol{a} + \boldsymbol{b}$ *denotes that mapping in which the image of a vector* $\mathbf{u}$ *is the sum* $\boldsymbol{a}\mathbf{u} + \boldsymbol{b}\mathbf{u}$. That is,

$$(\boldsymbol{a} + \boldsymbol{b})\mathbf{u} = \boldsymbol{a}\mathbf{u} + \boldsymbol{b}\mathbf{u} \tag{28}$$

for every vector $\mathbf{u}$, as illustrated in Figure 28. One readily verifies that $\boldsymbol{a} + \boldsymbol{b}$ is a linear transformation (Problem 1 below).

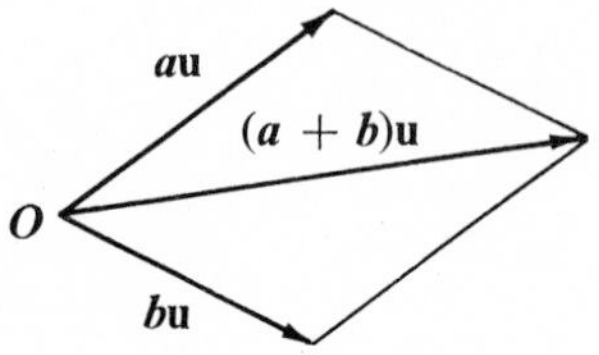

FIGURE 28

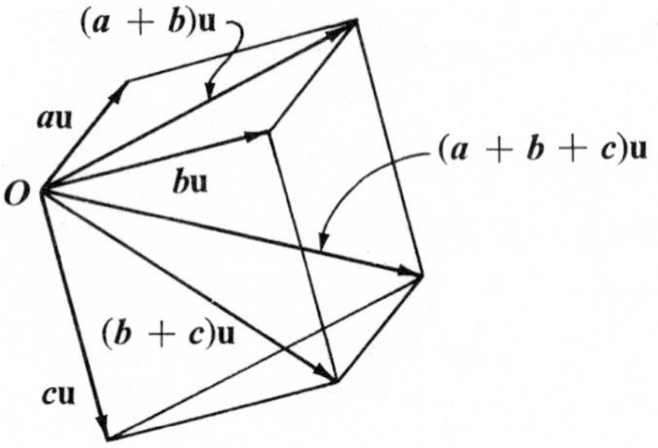

FIGURE 29

EXAMPLE 1. In Figure 29, we show geometrically that addition of linear transformations is associative; that is,

$$(\boldsymbol{a} + \boldsymbol{b}) + \boldsymbol{c} = \boldsymbol{a} + (\boldsymbol{b} + \boldsymbol{c}).$$

Since $\boldsymbol{a} + \boldsymbol{b}$ is a linear transformation, we know it has a unique matrix with respect to a coordinate basis $\{\mathbf{u}, \mathbf{v}\}$. To find this matrix, we suppose $A = \begin{pmatrix} a & b \\ c & d \end{pmatrix}$ and $B = \begin{pmatrix} e & f \\ g & h \end{pmatrix}$ represent $\boldsymbol{a}$ and $\boldsymbol{b}$, respectively, with respect to $\{\mathbf{u}, \mathbf{v}\}$. Then, if we denote $\boldsymbol{a} + \boldsymbol{b}$ by $\boldsymbol{c}$,

$$\begin{aligned}
\boldsymbol{c}\mathbf{u} &= \boldsymbol{a}\mathbf{u} + \boldsymbol{b}\mathbf{u} = (a\mathbf{u} + c\mathbf{v}) + (e\mathbf{u} + g\mathbf{v}) \\
&= (a + e)\mathbf{u} + (c + g)\mathbf{v}, \\
\boldsymbol{c}\mathbf{v} &= \boldsymbol{a}\mathbf{v} + \boldsymbol{b}\mathbf{v} = (b\mathbf{u} + d\mathbf{v}) + (f\mathbf{u} + h\mathbf{v}) \\
&= (b + f)\mathbf{u} + (d + h)\mathbf{v}.
\end{aligned}$$

This shows that the *matrix C which represents* $\boldsymbol{c}$ *is*

$$C = \begin{pmatrix} a + e & b + f \\ c + g & d + h \end{pmatrix}.$$

We therefore *define the* ***matrix sum*** $A + B$ *by*

$$C = A + B. \tag{29}$$

This readily generalizes to any two $p \times p$ matrices. *With respect to a coordinate basis, we have the correspondences:*

$$\boldsymbol{a} \leftrightarrow A, \quad \boldsymbol{b} \leftrightarrow B, \quad \boldsymbol{a} + \boldsymbol{b} \leftrightarrow A + B. \tag{30}$$

EXAMPLE 2. We could have approached the definition of the sum $A + B$ by the matrix computation

$$AU + BU = \begin{pmatrix} ax + by \\ cx + dy \end{pmatrix} + \begin{pmatrix} ex + fy \\ gx + hy \end{pmatrix} = CU.$$

If we apply (30) to Equation (28) we get $AU + BU = (A + B)U$. This is a mixed distributive law. *Therefore, with respect to a coordinate basis, we have:*

$$\begin{gathered} \boldsymbol{a} \leftrightarrow A, \quad \boldsymbol{b} \leftrightarrow B, \quad \mathbf{u} \leftrightarrow U, \\ (\boldsymbol{a} + \boldsymbol{b})\mathbf{u} = \boldsymbol{a}\mathbf{u} + \boldsymbol{b}\mathbf{u} \leftrightarrow (A + B)U = AU + BU. \end{gathered} \tag{31}$$

EXAMPLE 3. Let $\boldsymbol{a}$, $\boldsymbol{b}$, $\boldsymbol{c}$ be linear transformations. Then $(\boldsymbol{a} + \boldsymbol{b})\boldsymbol{c}$ also is a linear transformation. We have

$$\begin{aligned} \big((\boldsymbol{a} + \boldsymbol{b})\boldsymbol{c}\big)\mathbf{u} &= (\boldsymbol{a} + \boldsymbol{b})(\boldsymbol{c}\mathbf{u}) = \boldsymbol{a}(\boldsymbol{c}\mathbf{u}) + \boldsymbol{b}(\boldsymbol{c}\mathbf{u}) = (\boldsymbol{a}\boldsymbol{c})\mathbf{u} + (\boldsymbol{b}\boldsymbol{c})\mathbf{u} \\ &= (\boldsymbol{a}\boldsymbol{c} + \boldsymbol{b}\boldsymbol{c})\mathbf{u} \text{ for every } \mathbf{u}. \end{aligned}$$

This yields a *right distributive law for linear transformations:* $(\boldsymbol{a} + \boldsymbol{b})\boldsymbol{c} = \boldsymbol{a}\boldsymbol{c} + \boldsymbol{b}\boldsymbol{c}$. A left distributive law, $\boldsymbol{a}(\boldsymbol{b} + \boldsymbol{c}) = \boldsymbol{a}\boldsymbol{b} + \boldsymbol{a}\boldsymbol{c}$, is also easily derived. A matrix equivalent for each then follows. So, *with respect to a coordinate basis, we have:*

$$\begin{gathered} \boldsymbol{a} \leftrightarrow A, \quad \boldsymbol{b} \leftrightarrow B, \quad \boldsymbol{c} \leftrightarrow C, \\ (\boldsymbol{a} + \boldsymbol{b})\boldsymbol{c} = \boldsymbol{a}\boldsymbol{c} + \boldsymbol{b}\boldsymbol{c} \leftrightarrow (A + B)C = AC + BC, \\ \boldsymbol{a}(\boldsymbol{b} + \boldsymbol{c}) = \boldsymbol{a}\boldsymbol{b} + \boldsymbol{a}\boldsymbol{c} \leftrightarrow A(B + C) = AB + AC. \end{gathered} \tag{32}$$

(b) *Scalar multiples.* Let s be a scalar and $\boldsymbol{a}$ a linear transformation of the vector space. *If to each vector* $\mathbf{u}$ *we assign the image vector* $s(\boldsymbol{a}\mathbf{u})$, *then a mapping is defined. This mapping is denoted by* $s\boldsymbol{a}$ *and is called a* **scalar multiple of** $\boldsymbol{a}$ *by* s, so

$$(s\boldsymbol{a})\mathbf{u} = s(\boldsymbol{a}\mathbf{u}). \tag{33}$$

That the scalar multiple $s\boldsymbol{a}$ is a linear transformation, follows from the computations:

$$(s\boldsymbol{a})(\mathbf{u} + \mathbf{v}) = s\big(\boldsymbol{a}(\mathbf{u} + \mathbf{v})\big) = s(\boldsymbol{a}\mathbf{u} + \boldsymbol{a}\mathbf{v}) = s(\boldsymbol{a}\mathbf{u}) + s(\boldsymbol{a}\mathbf{v}) = (s\boldsymbol{a})\mathbf{u} + (s\boldsymbol{a})\mathbf{v},$$

and

$$(s\boldsymbol{a})(t\mathbf{u}) = s\big(\boldsymbol{a}(t\mathbf{u})\big) = s\big(t(\boldsymbol{a}\mathbf{u})\big) = (st)(\boldsymbol{a}\mathbf{u}) = (ts)(\boldsymbol{a}\mathbf{u}) = t\big(s(\boldsymbol{a}\mathbf{u})\big) = t\big((s\boldsymbol{a})\mathbf{u}\big).$$

Incidentally, we have the mixed associative law

$$(st)\boldsymbol{a} = s(t\boldsymbol{a})$$

for all scalars s and t.

Denote sa by b. Since b is a linear transformation, we can find its unique matrix representation with respect to a coordinate basis $\{\mathbf{u}, \mathbf{v}\}$ as usual by computing $b\mathbf{u}$ and $b\mathbf{v}$. Thus,

$$b\mathbf{u} = s(a\mathbf{u}) = (sa)\mathbf{u} + (sc)\mathbf{v},$$
$$b\mathbf{v} = s(a\mathbf{v}) = (sb)\mathbf{u} + (sd)\mathbf{v},$$

which yields the matrix

$$B = \begin{pmatrix} sa & sb \\ sc & sd \end{pmatrix}$$

as the representation of b. *We have already agreed to write this as sA, and it becomes our definition of the* ***scalar multiple of a matrix.*** Since a scalar multiple of a column matrix has already been defined, *we have, with respect to a coordinate basis:*

$$a \leftrightarrow A, \quad \mathbf{u} \leftrightarrow U, \quad sa \leftrightarrow sA, \quad (sa)\mathbf{u} = s(a\mathbf{u}) \leftrightarrow (sA)U = s(AU). \tag{34}$$

EXAMPLE 4. The linear transformation associated with a complex number in Section 2.6, Example 2 is a scalar multiple of a rotation. Its matrix in a Cartesian frame is a scalar multiple aR of the 2×2 rotation matrix R (Section 2.4, Example 5).

A scalar multiple of the identity, say si, has the matrix sI. So for any linear transformation a, we have (see Problem 2 below),

$$sa = (si)a = a(si) \leftrightarrow sA = sIA = \begin{pmatrix} s & 0 \\ 0 & s \end{pmatrix} A = A \begin{pmatrix} s & 0 \\ 0 & s \end{pmatrix} = A(sI).$$

It is easy to verify that for any two linear transformations a and b, and any scalars s and t, the mappings $s(a + b)$ and $(s + t)a$ are linear transformations. *So we have, with respect to a coordinate basis:*

$$a \leftrightarrow A, \quad b \leftrightarrow B, \quad s(a + b) = sa + sb \leftrightarrow s(A + B) = sA + sB,$$
$$(s + t)a = sa + ta \leftrightarrow (s + t)A = sA + tA. \tag{35}$$

EXAMPLE 5. The linear transformation associated with $e^{i\phi}$ (a rotation) can now be analyzed as a *linear combination of linear transformations.* The particular representation R can be written $(\cos \phi)I + (\sin \phi)J$, where $J = \begin{pmatrix} 0 & -1 \\ 1 & 0 \end{pmatrix}$, so $J^2 = -I$. This corresponds to the equation

$$e^{i\phi} = \cos \phi + i \sin \phi.$$

The linear transformation represented by J (with respect to the same Cartesian basis) is a counterclockwise rotation through $\pi/2$ radians, with coordinate equations $x' = -y$, $y' = x$.

The set of all 2×2 matrices (in fact, all $p \times p$ matrices, for any positive integer p), with entries drawn from the field of scalars of a given vector space, itself constitutes a vector space, as does the set of linear transformations represented by these matrices. The representation $\boldsymbol{a} \leftrightarrow A$ with respect to a coordinate basis, matches multiplication, addition, and scalar multiple uniquely.

**Any expression (in a linear transformation) created by these operations can be replaced by a corresponding expression in any representing matrix, and vice versa, all with respect to a fixed coordinate basis.*

The operations we have defined on the matrices have meaning even if the entries are not restricted to the field of scalars of a given vector space. Although there always exists a vector space (say column vectors) for which the matrix represents a linear transformation, we need not consider the matrix in connection with linear transformations. *Matrices can obviously be manipulated independently of their role as representations of linear transformations*, in which case, they constitute a mathematical system from whose formal properties we can deduce consequences applicable in contexts other than vector spaces.

EXAMPLE 6. Suppose A and B are $p \times p$ matrices with the property that the entries in each row add up to the number 1. Then the same is true for AB. For, let U be the $p \times 1$ column matrix whose entries each equal 1. Then

$$(AB)U = A(BU) = AU = U.$$

EXAMPLE 7. *Define $\boldsymbol{a}^0$ by $\boldsymbol{a}^0 = \boldsymbol{i}$. Powers of $\boldsymbol{a}$ are then determined for positive integers by $\boldsymbol{a}^n = \boldsymbol{a}^{n-1}\boldsymbol{a}$.* From this one can prove that $\boldsymbol{a}^m\boldsymbol{a}^n = \boldsymbol{a}^{m+n}$ for non-negative integers m and n. (In fact, $\boldsymbol{a}$ need be only a mapping.) *For the corresponding matrix representation we have* (with $A^0 = I$):

$$\boldsymbol{a} \leftrightarrow A, \quad \boldsymbol{a}^m\boldsymbol{a}^n = \boldsymbol{a}^{m+n} \leftrightarrow A^{m+n} = A^mA^n. \tag{36}$$

EXAMPLE 8. Let $p(\boldsymbol{a}) = \sum c_i\boldsymbol{a}^i$ be a polynomial in $\boldsymbol{a}$. If $\boldsymbol{a} \leftrightarrow A$, then $\boldsymbol{a}^i \leftrightarrow A^i$ and $c_i\boldsymbol{a}^i \leftrightarrow c_iA^i$, hence $p(\boldsymbol{a}) \leftrightarrow p(A)$. *Therefore*

$$p(\boldsymbol{a}) = \boldsymbol{o} \quad \textit{if and only if} \quad p(A) = O.$$

When $p(\boldsymbol{a}) = \boldsymbol{o}$, one speaks of $\boldsymbol{a}$ as a *zero* of the polynomial $p(x)$, and similarly for $p(A) = O$ and A.

PROBLEMS

1. Show that $\boldsymbol{a} + \boldsymbol{b}$, $(\boldsymbol{a} + \boldsymbol{b})\boldsymbol{c}$, $\boldsymbol{a}(\boldsymbol{b} + \boldsymbol{c})$ are linear transformations if $\boldsymbol{a}, \boldsymbol{b}, \boldsymbol{c}$ are. Also, check $0\boldsymbol{a}$ and $1\boldsymbol{a}$. Verify these directly on 2×2 matrices.
2. Show that $s(\boldsymbol{ab}) = (s\boldsymbol{a})\boldsymbol{b} = \boldsymbol{a}(s\boldsymbol{b})$, and give the corresponding property for matrices.
3. Show that $s\boldsymbol{a}^{m+n} = (s\boldsymbol{a}^m)\boldsymbol{a}^n = \boldsymbol{a}^m(s\boldsymbol{a}^n)$, and $(st)\boldsymbol{a}^{m+n} = s\boldsymbol{a}^m t\boldsymbol{a}^n$, where $\boldsymbol{a}$ is a linear transformation.

4. If R is the 2×2 rotation matrix, compute $R^2 - (2\cos\phi)R + I$, hence find a corresponding result for the rotation mapping.

5. If $A = \begin{pmatrix} a & -b \\ b & a \end{pmatrix}$, compute $A^2 - 2aA + |A|I$.

6. Show that the set of matrices $\begin{pmatrix} a & -b \\ b & a \end{pmatrix}$, where a and b vary over the real numbers, has all the field properties of the field of complex numbers under the correspondence

$$a + bi \leftrightarrow \begin{pmatrix} a & -b \\ b & a \end{pmatrix}.$$

2.9 POLYNOMIALS

All the rules we have found for the algebra of linear transformations and matrices can be extended to cover expressions involving any finite number of summands, factors, and scalar multipliers. We assume these facts, which can be proved by induction, and proceed to the construction and manipulation of polynomials and polynomial equations formed from a linear transformation or from a square matrix.

EXAMPLE 1. To illustrate some of the extended rules, let $\boldsymbol{a}$ be a linear transformation and c_0, c_1, c_2, c_3, c_4 be scalars. Then we can write

$$\begin{aligned}\boldsymbol{a}(\boldsymbol{a}(\boldsymbol{a}(\boldsymbol{a}(\boldsymbol{a} + c_4\boldsymbol{i}) + c_3\boldsymbol{i}) + c_2\boldsymbol{i}) + c_1\boldsymbol{i}) + c_0\boldsymbol{i} \\ = \boldsymbol{a}^5 + c_4\boldsymbol{a}^4 + c_3\boldsymbol{a}^3 + c_2\boldsymbol{a}^2 + c_1\boldsymbol{a} + c_0\boldsymbol{i}.\end{aligned}$$

A corresponding equation can be written with a square matrix A in place of $\boldsymbol{a}$, if the entries in A and the c_i's are in a common field, as is certainly the case when A represents $\boldsymbol{a}$.

Suppose $f(x) = \sum a_i x^i$ and $g(x) = \sum b_i x^i$ are polynomials in a symbol x with coefficients that are among the scalars of a given vector space. The usual arithmetic of polynomials in a variable x is imposed on these polynomials with the understanding that equality occurs if and only if like powers of x have equal coefficients. *If $\boldsymbol{a}$ is a linear transformation, we can associate a mapping $f(\boldsymbol{a})$ with $f(x)$ and a mapping $g(\boldsymbol{a})$ with $g(x)$, where,* to get the mappings, *x is replaced by $\boldsymbol{a}$, a_0 by $a_0\boldsymbol{i}$, and b_0 by $b_0\boldsymbol{i}$.* Now, $f(\boldsymbol{a}) = \sum a_i\boldsymbol{a}^i$ and $g(\boldsymbol{a}) = \sum b_i\boldsymbol{a}^i$ are linear combinations of linear transformations. *Hence $f(\boldsymbol{a})$ and $g(\boldsymbol{a})$ are themselves linear transformations.* Since

$$\begin{aligned}\sum(a_i + b_i)\boldsymbol{a}^i &= f(\boldsymbol{a}) + g(\boldsymbol{a}),\\ \sum\left(\sum a_j b_{i-j}\right)\boldsymbol{a}^i &= f(\boldsymbol{a})g(\boldsymbol{a}),\end{aligned}$$

we have a mapping (not one-to-one) from the set of polynomials in x onto the set of polynomials in $\boldsymbol{a}$,

$$f(x) \to f(\boldsymbol{a}),$$

such that $f(\boldsymbol{a}) + g(\boldsymbol{a})$ is the image of $f(x) + g(x)$ and $f(\boldsymbol{a})g(\boldsymbol{a})$ is the image of $f(x)g(x)$. Then any polynomial equation in x implies one in $\boldsymbol{a}$, as well as in any square matrix A whose entries are in a field containing the coefficients involved in the equation (because A represents some $\boldsymbol{a}$).

If A is any square matrix whose entries are in a field which contains the coefficients of our polynomials in x, then we can bypass the correspondence $f(\boldsymbol{a}) \leftrightarrow f(A)$ and get a mapping (not one-to-one) directly from polynomials in x to polynomials in A,

$$f(x) \rightarrow f(A),$$

with $f(A) + g(A)$ the image of $f(x) + g(x)$ and $f(A)g(A)$ the image of $f(x)g(x)$. For, *the algebra induced in the set of square matrices* (of same size and field of entries) *by the theory of linear transformations can be independently imposed directly on the matrices.* In fact, much of this matrix algebra applies even when the entries are from sets other than fields.

EXAMPLE 2. Suppose that the entries k, l in the matrix $A = \text{diag}\,(k, l)$, and the coefficients of a polynomial $f(x)$, are scalars from a common field. Then $f(A) = \text{diag}\,\big(f(k), f(l)\big)$. If k and l are replaced by square matrices A_1 and A_2, then we get a generalization to a ***diagonal-block matrix***

$$A = \text{diag}\,(A_1, A_2) = \begin{pmatrix} A_1 & O \\ O & A_2 \end{pmatrix}, \qquad f(A) = \text{diag}\,\big(f(A_1), f(A_2)\big).$$

Here, as wherever it occurs, the zero matrix O is of whatever shape the context requires.

EXAMPLE 3. Suppose a linear transformation $\boldsymbol{a}$ is represented by A, where $A = \begin{pmatrix} 0 & 1 \\ 2 & 0 \end{pmatrix}$. Then, assuming $\sqrt{2}$ is a permissible scalar, we have (Section 2.8, Example 8) the equivalent facts:

$$\boldsymbol{a}^2 - 2\boldsymbol{i} = (\boldsymbol{a} - \sqrt{2}\,\boldsymbol{i})(\boldsymbol{a} + \sqrt{2}\,\boldsymbol{i}) = \boldsymbol{o},$$
$$A^2 - 2I = (A - \sqrt{2}\,I)(A + \sqrt{2}\,I) = O.$$

The equations in A can be checked directly from the polynomial equation $x^2 - 2 = (x - \sqrt{2})(x + \sqrt{2})$ and the structure of the matrix A.

EXAMPLE 4. Suppose $A = \begin{pmatrix} 0 & 1 \\ 0 & 0 \end{pmatrix}$ and that A represents a linear transformation $\boldsymbol{a}$. Although $x^3 \neq x^2$, yet $A^3 = A^2 = O$ and so $\boldsymbol{a}^3 = \boldsymbol{a}^2 = \boldsymbol{o}$.

EXAMPLE 5. If a and b are non-zero integers, then a greatest common divisor, say d, can be expressed as $d = pa + qb$, where p and q also are integers. Among polynomials in x with coefficients drawn from a prescribed field, a greatest common divisor of any two non-zero polynomials also exists and can be expressed analogously to the integer case. Thus, $x^3 + 8$ and $x^2 - 4$ have a particular greatest common divisor $4(x + 2)$, and

$$4(x + 2) = 1(x^3 + 8) - x(x^2 - 4),$$

where 1 and $-x$ act like p and q in the integer case above. From this equation, we can conclude that any linear transformation $\boldsymbol{a}$ of a vector space with rational scalars satisfies the equation

$$4(\boldsymbol{a} + 2\boldsymbol{i}) = \boldsymbol{a}^3 + 8\boldsymbol{i} - \boldsymbol{a}(\boldsymbol{a}^2 - 4\boldsymbol{i}),$$

and so does any square matrix A. Among polynomials, it is customary to mean by *the* greatest common divisor, one with the *coefficient of its highest degree term equal to* 1 (a *monic* polynomial), which in this example is $x + 2$.

EXAMPLE 6. It is sometimes convenient to label the coefficients in a polynomial as follows:

$$a_0x^n + a_1x^{n-1} + \cdots + a_n = \sum_{i=0}^{n} a_ix^{n-i}.$$

Here, the subscript and exponent of a term add up to n. With this notation we see that

$$\left(\sum a_ix^{n-i}\right)\left(\sum b_ix^{m-i}\right) = \sum \left(\sum_{j=0}^{i} a_jb_{i-j}\right) x^{n+m-i}.$$

PROBLEMS

1. If $A = \begin{pmatrix} a & 0 & 0 \\ d & b & 0 \\ f & e & c \end{pmatrix}$, compute $(A - aI)(A - bI)(A - cI)$.
2. If $A = \begin{pmatrix} 0 & 1 & 0 \\ 0 & 0 & 1 \\ s & 0 & 0 \end{pmatrix}$, show that $A^3 = sI$. Find the analogous structure for a $p \times p$ matrix A such that $A^p = sI$.
3. If $A = \text{diag}(k, l)$ where k and l are distinct numbers, show that every 2×2 diagonal matrix, whose entries are from the same field as k and l, is a polynomial in A. Modify this for the case $A = \text{diag}(k, l, m)$.
4. Show that $f(\boldsymbol{a})$ is a linear transformation if $f(x)$ is a polynomial with scalar coefficients and $\boldsymbol{a}$ is a linear transformation, using induction on the degree of $f(x)$ and assuming $\boldsymbol{a}^n$ is a linear transformation for every $n \geq 0$.
5. If $f(x)$ and $g(x)$ are polynomials with scalar coefficients, show that $f(\boldsymbol{a})g(\boldsymbol{a}) = g(\boldsymbol{a})f(\boldsymbol{a})$ for any linear transformation $\boldsymbol{a}$, and that $f(A)g(A) = g(A)f(A)$, provided suitable restrictions are made on the entries of the square matrix A.

2.10 SUBSPACES

We have seen (Section 1.8, Example 2 and Problem 4) that a subset of a given vector space, not equal to the whole space nor to the zero space, may itself be a vector space with respect to the *same scalar field and vector operations.*

In general, *a subset of a given vector space is called a* ***subspace*** *of the vector space if it has the following property: With respect to the same scalar field and the same processes of addition and scalar multiple used in the given vector space, this subset is itself a vector space.* In other words, if **u** and **v** are any vectors in the subset and if s and t are any scalars, then $s\mathbf{u} + t\mathbf{v}$ is in the subset. We note that checking all linear combinations $s\mathbf{u} + t\mathbf{v}$ is equivalent to checking all sums $\mathbf{u} + \mathbf{v}$ and all scalar multiples $s\mathbf{u}$.

EXAMPLE 1. In real 3-dimensional space there are four types of subspaces of the vector space at a point $\boldsymbol{O}$:

(a) The whole space.
(b) The zero space $\{\mathbf{o}\}$ that consists of just the zero vector and which we have already called a zero-dimensional vector space.
(c) The subset consisting of all position vectors to the points on a line through $\boldsymbol{O}$.
(d) The subset consisting of all position vectors to the points on a plane through $\boldsymbol{O}$.

In type (c), let **u** be any non-zero vector in the subspace. Then the vectors in this subspace are exactly all the scalar multiples of **u**. In type (d), let **u** and **v** be any two non-proportional vectors in the subspace. Then the vectors in this subspace are exactly all the linear combinations of **u** and **v**.

EXAMPLE 2. Let a and b be two constants chosen from the scalar field of a 2-tuple vector space. Consider the subset

$$\{(x, y) \mid ax + by = 0\},$$

that is, *the collection of* 2*-tuple vectors* (x, y) *for which* $ax + by = 0$. This subset is a subspace. For, if (x_1, y_1) and (x_2, y_2) are in the subset and if s and t are any scalars, then

$$a(sx_1 + tx_2) + b(sy_1 + ty_2) = 0.$$

This equation shows that $s(x_1, y_1) + t(x_2, y_2)$ is in the subset if (x_1, y_1) and (x_2, y_2) are in the subset.

EXAMPLE 3. Let $\boldsymbol{a}$ be a linear transformation of a vector space. The subset $\{\mathbf{u} \mid \boldsymbol{a}\mathbf{u} = \mathbf{o}\}$, which is the collection of vectors for which $\boldsymbol{a}\mathbf{u} = \mathbf{o}$, is a subspace: for, if $\boldsymbol{a}\mathbf{u} = \boldsymbol{a}\mathbf{v} = \mathbf{o}$, then $\boldsymbol{a}(s\mathbf{u} + t\mathbf{v}) = \mathbf{o}$. Furthermore, the subset $\{\mathbf{v} \mid \mathbf{v} = \boldsymbol{a}\mathbf{u} \text{ for some } \mathbf{u}\}$, which is the *range* of $\boldsymbol{a}$, is also a subspace:

for, if $\mathbf{u}' = \boldsymbol{a}\mathbf{u}$ and $\mathbf{v}' = \boldsymbol{a}\mathbf{v}$, then $s\mathbf{u}' + t\mathbf{v}' = \boldsymbol{a}(s\mathbf{u} + t\mathbf{v})$. In Figure 30 we illustrate a linear transformation $\boldsymbol{a}$ of the plane whose coordinate equations are $x' = kx$, $y' = 0$, $(k > 1)$. We see that $\boldsymbol{a}\mathbf{u} = \mathbf{o}$ for every position vector to a point on the y-axis, and that the range is the set of position vectors to the points on the x-axis. This mapping is a projection and a strain applied successively (in either order).

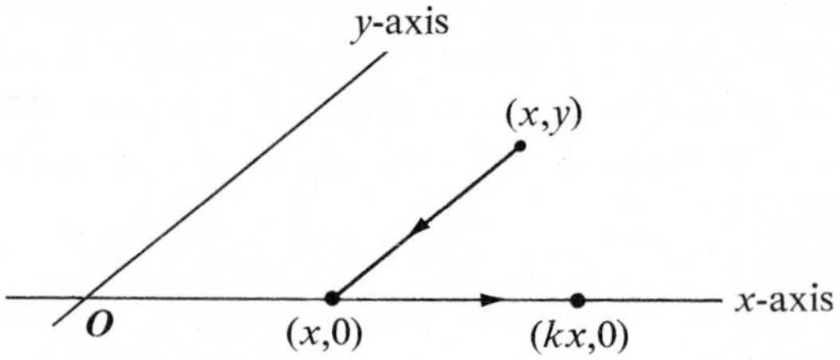

FIGURE 30

The simplest kind of subspace, other than the zero space, is the 1-dimensional type. It is *generated by a single non-zero vector*, say $\mathbf{u}$, which means that it consists of all scalar multiples of $\mathbf{u}$. Every line through the origin $\boldsymbol{O}$ of our vector space at $\boldsymbol{O}$ defines such a subspace. *We denote it by* $[\mathbf{u}]$ and remark that it can be expressed in set notation by

$$[\mathbf{u}] = \{\mathbf{w} \mid \mathbf{w} = s\mathbf{u}, \quad s \text{ a scalar}\}; \tag{37}$$

that is, $[\mathbf{u}]$ *consists of all scalar multiples of* $\mathbf{u}$.

The *invariant lines through* $\boldsymbol{O}$ that we have encountered in some of our mappings illustrate a particular class of 1-dimensional subspaces which will receive our special attention.

PROBLEMS

1. Show that any two subspaces of a given vector space have at least the zero space as a common subspace. Show that the subset consisting of those vectors which are in common to two subspaces of a given vector space is a subspace. Illustrate in real 3-dimensional space by considering pairs of planes through $\boldsymbol{O}$.
2. In 3-tuple vector space show that the subset

$$\{(x, y, z) \mid ax + by + cz = 0; \quad a, b, c \quad \text{constant}\}$$

is a subspace.

3. Find a basis of the subspace which is common to the following two subspaces of 3-tuple vector space:

$$\{(x, y, z) \mid x - y + 2z = 0\} \quad \text{and} \quad \{(x, y, z) \mid x + y + z = 0\}.$$

4. If $\mathbf{u} \neq \mathbf{o}$ show that every basis of $[\mathbf{u}]$ has exactly one non-zero vector.
5. Let $\mathbf{u}$ and $\mathbf{v}$ be any two vectors at $\boldsymbol{O}$ in real 3-dimensional space. Show that $\{s\mathbf{u} + t\mathbf{v} \mid s, t \text{ real scalars}\}$ is a subspace. When does it correspond to a point, a line, or a plane?

6. Show that the set $\{\mathbf{u} \mid \boldsymbol{a}\mathbf{u} = \mathbf{v}$ for some $\mathbf{v}$ in a given subspace$\}$ is a subspace (*the complete counterimage of the given subspace*). Compare this to the first subspace in Example 3.

2.11 KERNEL AND IMAGE

For any mapping $\boldsymbol{a}$ of a vector space, *the subset* $\{\mathbf{u} \mid \boldsymbol{a}\mathbf{u} = \mathbf{o}\}$ *is called the* ***kernel*** *of* $\boldsymbol{a}$ *and is denoted by* ker $\boldsymbol{a}$. Also *the subset* $\{\mathbf{v} \mid \mathbf{v} = \boldsymbol{a}\mathbf{u}$ for some $\mathbf{u}\}$ *is called the* ***image*** *of* $\boldsymbol{a}$ *and is denoted by* im $\boldsymbol{a}$. We have already noted that ker $\boldsymbol{a}$ and im $\boldsymbol{a}$ are subspaces when $\boldsymbol{a}$ is a linear transformation. The term ***null-space*** is also used for ker $\boldsymbol{a}$. In summary,

$$\ker \boldsymbol{a} = \text{null-space of } \boldsymbol{a} = \{\mathbf{u} \mid \boldsymbol{a}\mathbf{u} = \mathbf{o}\},$$
$$\text{im } \boldsymbol{a} = \text{range of } \boldsymbol{a} = \{\mathbf{v} \mid \mathbf{v} = \boldsymbol{a}\mathbf{u} \text{ for some } \mathbf{u}\}.$$

EXAMPLE 1. Suppose the coordinate equations of a linear transformation $\boldsymbol{a}$ of the plane are $x' = x + y$, $y' = 2x + 2y$. Then

$$\ker \boldsymbol{a} = \{\text{position vectors to points on } x + y = 0\}$$

and

$$\text{im } \boldsymbol{a} = \{\text{position vectors to points on } y = 2x\}.$$

Notice that *each of these lines is invariant.* A point $(k, 2k)$ on $y = 2x$ is mapped onto $3(k, 2k)$. In Figure 31 we see how $\boldsymbol{a}$ may be regarded a projection and a strain successively applied (in either order).

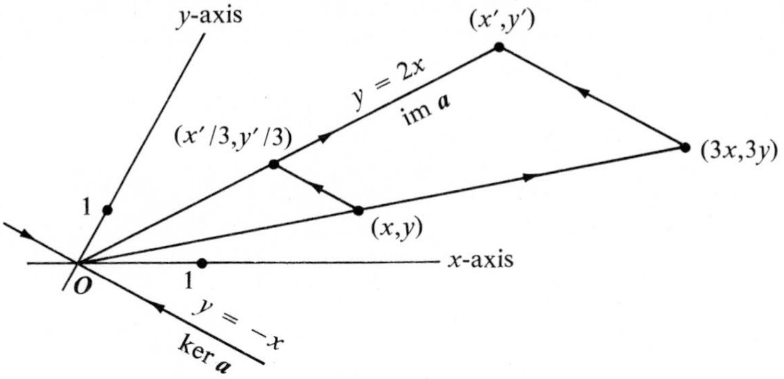

FIGURE 31

EXAMPLE 2. In real 3-dimensional space, a certain linear transformation $\boldsymbol{a}$ has coordinate equations $x' = y' = z' = x$. Then

$$\text{im } \boldsymbol{a} = \{\text{position vectors to points on the line } x = y = z\}$$

and

$$\ker \boldsymbol{a} = \{\text{position vectors to points on the } yz\text{-plane}\}.$$

*When we have a matrix representation A of a linear transformation $\boldsymbol{a}$, then the coordinate equation $U' = AU$ shows that im $\boldsymbol{a}$ *consists exactly of all those vectors whose coordinate columns* U' *are a linear combination of the columns of* A. Also, ker $\boldsymbol{a}$ *consists of those vectors whose coordinate columns* U *satisfy* $AU = O$. This is readily checked in Examples 1 and 2.

EXAMPLE 3. If we recall the results of Section 2.1, Example 6, Problems 5, 6, and Section 2.5, Problem 6, we see that the *following properties of a linear transformation* $\boldsymbol{a}$ *of the 2-dimensional vector space at* $\boldsymbol{O}$ *were shown to be equivalent*:

(a) ker $\boldsymbol{a} = \{\mathbf{o}\}$.
(b) im $\boldsymbol{a} =$ {whole vector space}.
(c) If $\boldsymbol{a} \leftrightarrow A$ then $|A| \neq 0$.
(d) $\boldsymbol{a}$ is a one-to-one (equivalently, onto).
(e) Column matrices formed from A and considered as vectors, are a basis of column vector space, and the same statement for row matrices.

PROBLEMS

1. Suppose $\boldsymbol{a}$ is a linear transformation of the plane with coordinate equations $x' = ey$, $y' = fy (f \neq 0)$. Describe this mapping, and, in particular, find ker $\boldsymbol{a}$ and im $\boldsymbol{a}$.
2. Give an example of a linear transformation $\boldsymbol{a}$ such that ker $\boldsymbol{a} =$ im $\boldsymbol{a}$.
3. Suppose $\boldsymbol{a}$ is a linear transformation of the plane, with a representing matrix A. Suppose also that $|A| = 0$ and $A \neq 0$. Find the dimensions of ker $\boldsymbol{a}$ and im $\boldsymbol{a}$. Show that with respect to a suitable coordinate basis, $\boldsymbol{a}$ is represented by diag $(k, 0)$, $k \neq 0$, or by
$$\begin{pmatrix} 0 & k \\ 0 & 0 \end{pmatrix}.$$
4. Show that: (a) $\boldsymbol{ab} = \boldsymbol{o}$ if and only if ker $\boldsymbol{a}$ contains im $\boldsymbol{b}$, (b) ker $\boldsymbol{ab} =$ ker $\boldsymbol{b}$ if and only if ker $\boldsymbol{a}$ and im $\mathbf{b}$ have only the zero subspace in common.
5. Suppose that a linear transformation $\boldsymbol{a}$ of the plane leaves three distinct lines through $\boldsymbol{O}$ invariant. Show that $\boldsymbol{a} = s\boldsymbol{i}$ for some scalar s.

2.12 ONE-TO-ONE AND ONTO

We have called a mapping $\boldsymbol{a}$ of a vector space *one-to-one* if distinct vectors have distinct images. This condition amounts to the requirement that

$$\mathbf{u} = \mathbf{u}' \quad \text{whenever} \quad \boldsymbol{a}\mathbf{u} = \boldsymbol{a}\mathbf{u}'. \tag{38}$$

When a mapping is a linear transformation, the criterion for one-to-oneness is equivalent to ker $\boldsymbol{a} = \{\mathbf{o}\}$, because for a linear transformation $\boldsymbol{a}\mathbf{u} = \boldsymbol{a}\mathbf{u}'$ means $\boldsymbol{a}(\mathbf{u} - \mathbf{u}') = \mathbf{o}$.

EXAMPLE 1. Let $\boldsymbol{a}$ be a linear transformation of *any* vector space. Suppose some vector $\mathbf{v}$ in the im $\boldsymbol{a}$ has a *unique* counterimage $\mathbf{u}$, so $\mathbf{v} = \boldsymbol{a}\mathbf{u}$ for one vector $\mathbf{u}$ only. If $\boldsymbol{a}\mathbf{w} = \mathbf{o}$ for some $\mathbf{w} \neq \mathbf{o}$, then $\mathbf{u} + \mathbf{w} \neq \mathbf{u}$ and $\mathbf{v} = \boldsymbol{a}(\mathbf{u} + \mathbf{w})$, in contradiction to the uniqueness of the counterimage of $\mathbf{v}$. Hence ker $\boldsymbol{a} = \{\mathbf{o}\}$. Now if $\mathbf{u}$ and $\mathbf{u}'$ are counterimages of some vector $\mathbf{w}$, that is, $\mathbf{w} = \boldsymbol{a}\mathbf{u} = \boldsymbol{a}\mathbf{u}'$, then $\boldsymbol{a}(\mathbf{u} - \mathbf{u}') = \mathbf{o}$. But ker $\boldsymbol{a} = \{\mathbf{o}\}$, hence $\mathbf{u} - \mathbf{u}' = \mathbf{o}$. Thus *every vector* $\mathbf{v}$ *in* im $\boldsymbol{a}$ *has a unique counterimage if one vector does.*

EXAMPLE 2. Let A be a square matrix and let U and V be column matrices with the same number of rows as A, all three with entries in a common field. We can regard the equation $AU = V$ as a matrix representation of $\boldsymbol{a}\mathbf{u} = \mathbf{v}$, where $\boldsymbol{a}$ is a linear transformation of a finite-dimensional vector space with this common field as its scalar field (for instance, a vector space of column vectors with unit column vectors as a basis, as in Section 2.6, Example 3). Hence by Example 1, whenever $AU = V$ with V fixed has a solution for U (with entries in the same field), then the solution is unique if and only if $AU = O$ has no solution other than $U = O$. Since A is not necessarily 2×2, we are not yet in position to say that our hypotheses on $\boldsymbol{a}$ and A mean that the linear transformation $\boldsymbol{a}$ is onto, and that $|A| \neq 0$.

EXAMPLE 3. We have seen (Section 2.1, Example 6) that when A is a 2×2 matrix the equation $AU = V$ represents a one-to-one (which in this case is also onto) mapping if and only if $|A| \neq 0$. Let us review some relevant determinant theory for the 3×3 case, since it is typical of the general case. The double subscript notation is handy. *Let* a_{ij} *denote an entry in* A, *where* i *is the row index and* j *is the column index.* In the 3×3 case we have

$$A = \begin{pmatrix} a_{11} & a_{12} & a_{13} \\ a_{21} & a_{22} & a_{23} \\ a_{31} & a_{32} & a_{33} \end{pmatrix}.$$

When the i-th row and j-th column of A are deleted, we may consider the determinant of the remaining 2×2 array. This second-order determinant is called *the* ***minor*** *of* a_{ij}. When this minor is multiplied by $(-1)^{i+j}$, it is called *the* ***cofactor*** *of* a_{ij} and is denoted by cof-a_{ij}. For instance, if $i = 1$ and $j = 3$, then

$$\text{cof-}a_{13} = (-1)^{1+3} \begin{vmatrix} a_{21} & a_{22} \\ a_{31} & a_{32} \end{vmatrix} = a_{21}a_{32} - a_{22}a_{31}.$$

$|A|$ can be "expanded" in six ways as a linear combination of cofactors: three of these use cofactors of entries in a row, the other three of these use cofactors of entries in a column. For instance, the expansion by row 2 is

$$|A| = \sum_{j=1}^{3} a_{2j} \times \text{cof-}a_{2j},$$

and by column 3 it is

$$|A| = \sum_{i=1}^{3} a_{i3} \times \text{cof-}a_{i3}.$$

Cramer's Rule for the solution of $AU = V$ (for U) when $|A| \neq 0$ can be expressed as:

$$x_i = |A_i|/|A| \qquad (i = 1, 2, 3),$$

where the x_i's are the entries in U and each A_i is derived from A by replacing the i-th column of A by the column V, in turn. *We assume acquaintance with the fact that Cramer's Rule works for every $p \times p$ matrix A such that $|A| \neq 0$. The proof of Cramer's Rule also implies that it gives the only solution.*

If we replace the entry a_{ij} of A by cof-a_{ij} for every i and j, the resulting *matrix of cofactors* is denoted by cof-A. *If a_{ij} is replaced by* cof-a_{ji} *rather than by* cof-a_{ij}, *the resulting* ***transposed matrix of cofactors*** *is denoted by* (cof-A)^t. Then we can express the above solution for U by Cramer's Rule in the matrix form:

$$U = (1/|A|)(\text{cof-}A)^t V. \tag{39}$$

Later we shall see that for all $p \times p$ matrices the condition $|A| \neq 0$ is actually the necessary and sufficient condition that $AU = V$ define a one-to-one (and as it turns out, also onto) mapping.

It does not follow, in general, that a mapping of a vector space which is one-to-one is also onto, even if it is a linear transformation. We have, however, verified that it is true for a linear transformation of the plane, in fact for any 2-dimensional space, and we shall reconsider the question after the following examples.

EXAMPLE 4. Consider as a vector space the set of real polynomials in x, including the constant polynomials (Section 1.8, Example 1). It can be shown that this space is not finite-dimensional. A particular mapping is determined by assigning to each polynomial $f(x)$ its *derivative* $f'(x)$. Denote this mapping by $\boldsymbol{a}$. Then $\boldsymbol{a}$ is a linear transformation which is onto, but not one-to-one. For instance, every constant is a counterimage of 0. (If $f(x) = \sum a_i x^i$, then $f'(x) = \sum i a_i x^{i-1}$.)

EXAMPLE 5. Consider the same space as in Example 4. Define a mapping $\boldsymbol{a}$ by assigning to $f(x)$ the image $xf(x)$. Then $\boldsymbol{a}$ is a linear transformation which is one-to-one but not onto. For instance, no constant other than zero has a counterimage.

*Let us now show, in a way (see Section 2.11, Example 3) that will readily generalize to any finite-dimensional vector space, that *a linear transformation of a 2-dimensional vector space is onto if and only if it is one-to-one.*

Suppose $\{\mathbf{u}, \mathbf{v}\}$ is a basis. By previous results (Section 1.9), we know that any set of three or more vectors cannot be a basis. So if $\mathbf{w}$ is any vector of the space there must exist three scalars *not all zero* such that

$$r\mathbf{w} + s\boldsymbol{a}\mathbf{u} + t\boldsymbol{a}\mathbf{v} = \mathbf{o}.$$

If $r \neq 0$, then

$$\mathbf{w} = \boldsymbol{a}\big(-(s/r)\mathbf{u} - (t/r)\mathbf{v}\big),$$

which implies that $\mathbf{w}$ is an image. But if $r = 0$, then

$$s\boldsymbol{a}\mathbf{u} + t\boldsymbol{a}\mathbf{v} = \boldsymbol{a}(s\mathbf{u} + t\mathbf{v}) = \mathbf{o},$$

and at least one of s and t is not zero; this would imply that $\boldsymbol{a}$ is *not* one-to-one (because $\ker \boldsymbol{a} \neq \{\mathbf{o}\}$). Hence we may conclude that *if $\boldsymbol{a}$ is one-to-one, then it is also onto.* Conversely, *suppose $\boldsymbol{a}$ is onto*, that is, im $\boldsymbol{a}$ is the whole space. Suppose $\mathbf{w}$ is a non-zero vector in $\ker \boldsymbol{a}$ (so $\boldsymbol{a}\mathbf{w} = \mathbf{o}$ with $\mathbf{w} \neq \mathbf{o}$). We can choose a basis $\{\mathbf{u}, \mathbf{v}\}$ in which $\mathbf{u} = \mathbf{w}$, and $\mathbf{v}$ is a vector that is not a scalar multiple of $\mathbf{u}$. Then $\boldsymbol{a}(s\mathbf{u} + t\mathbf{v}) = t\boldsymbol{a}\mathbf{v}$ for all scalars s and t. This means that im $\boldsymbol{a} = [\boldsymbol{a}\mathbf{v}]$. But a 2-dimensional vector space *cannot* be generated by one vector. This contradiction shows that $\ker \boldsymbol{a} = \{\mathbf{o}\}$, which means that $\boldsymbol{a}$ is one-to-one. Therefore, we have that *$\boldsymbol{a}$ is one-to-one if it is onto.* Altogether we have our desired result: *$\boldsymbol{a}$ is one-to-one if and only if $\boldsymbol{a}$ is onto.* The 1-dimensional case is readily verified directly; the higher dimensional cases will follow from the dimension theory in Chapter 4.

PROBLEMS

1. Show that the mappings in Examples 4, 5 are linear transformations.
2. Write out cof-A when A is a general 2×2 matrix, and also when A is a general 3×3 matrix. Define a workable cof-A when A is 1×1.
3. Solve the system $AU = V$ for U, using $(\text{cof-}A)^t$ as a matrix pre-multiplier, if

$$A = \begin{pmatrix} a & b & c \\ 0 & d & e \\ 0 & 0 & f \end{pmatrix}, \qquad V = \begin{pmatrix} p \\ q \\ r \end{pmatrix}, \qquad adf \neq 0.$$

4. In the 3×3 case, verify that: (a) $|sA| = s^3|A|$, (b) $|A^t| = |A|$ where A^t is the *transpose of A obtained by interchanging a_{ij} with a_{ji}* for every pair of indices i, j, (c) $|A| = 0$ if any row or column consists of zeros, or if any pair of rows or if any pair of columns are equal, (d) $(\text{cof-}A)^t = \text{cof-}A^t$.
5. If ω is an imaginary cube root of 1, show that

$$\begin{vmatrix} a_1 & a_2 & a_3 \\ a_3 & a_1 & a_2 \\ a_2 & a_3 & a_1 \end{vmatrix} = (a_1 + a_2 + a_3)(a_1 + \omega a_2 + \omega^2 a_3)(a_1 + \omega^2 a_2 + \omega a_3).$$

2.13 INVERTIBILITY

Suppose $\boldsymbol{a}$ is a linear transformation of the vector space at $\boldsymbol{O}$, or of any 1-, 2-, or 3-dimensional vector space. *Assume that* $\boldsymbol{a}$ *is an onto mapping.* We now know, at least in the 1- and 2-dimensional case, that this is equivalent to assuming that $\boldsymbol{a}$ is one-to-one. Therefore, as $\mathbf{u}$ varies over the vector space, the image $\boldsymbol{a}\mathbf{u}$ runs through all vectors (because $\boldsymbol{a}$ is onto) without repetition (because $\boldsymbol{a}$ is one-to-one). Hence, *we can define a mapping* $\boldsymbol{b}$ *by*

$$\boldsymbol{b}(\boldsymbol{a}\mathbf{u}) = \mathbf{u} \quad \text{for every } \mathbf{u}. \tag{40}$$

This is the same as having a mapping $\boldsymbol{b}$ such that $\boldsymbol{ba} = \boldsymbol{i}$, and, as we shall see, it implies $\boldsymbol{ab} = \boldsymbol{i}$ also.

The mapping $\boldsymbol{b}$, *defined by Equation* (40), *is a linear transformation too.* First of all, corresponding to any vectors $\mathbf{u}$ and $\mathbf{v}$ there are vectors $\mathbf{u}'$ and $\mathbf{v}'$ such that $\mathbf{u} = \boldsymbol{a}\mathbf{u}'$ and $\mathbf{v} = \boldsymbol{a}\mathbf{v}'$, so

$$\boldsymbol{b}(\mathbf{u} + \mathbf{v}) = \boldsymbol{b}(\boldsymbol{a}\mathbf{u}' + \boldsymbol{a}\mathbf{v}') = (\boldsymbol{ba})(\mathbf{u}' + \mathbf{v}') = \boldsymbol{i}\mathbf{u}' + \boldsymbol{i}\mathbf{v}' = (\boldsymbol{ba})\mathbf{u}' + (\boldsymbol{ba})\mathbf{v}' = \boldsymbol{b}\mathbf{u} + \boldsymbol{b}\mathbf{v}.$$

Secondly,

$$\boldsymbol{b}(s\mathbf{u}) = \boldsymbol{b}(s\boldsymbol{a}\mathbf{u}') = \boldsymbol{b}\big(\boldsymbol{a}(s\mathbf{u}')\big) = s\mathbf{u}' = s\big((\boldsymbol{ba})\mathbf{u}'\big) = s\boldsymbol{b}\mathbf{u}.$$

If there exists another mapping $\boldsymbol{c}$ such that $\boldsymbol{ca} = \boldsymbol{i}$, then $\boldsymbol{c}(\boldsymbol{a}\mathbf{u}) = \mathbf{u} = \boldsymbol{b}(\boldsymbol{a}\mathbf{u})$ for every $\mathbf{u}$. But we are still assuming that $\boldsymbol{a}$ is onto, hence $\boldsymbol{c}\mathbf{v} = \boldsymbol{b}\mathbf{v}$ for every vector $\mathbf{v}$, that is $\boldsymbol{c} = \boldsymbol{b}$. So, *the linear transformation* $\boldsymbol{b}$ *is the only mapping* $\boldsymbol{b}$ *for which* $\boldsymbol{ba} = \boldsymbol{i}$.

This linear transformation $\boldsymbol{b}$ is itself onto because $\boldsymbol{b}(\boldsymbol{a}\mathbf{u}) = \boldsymbol{i}\mathbf{u} = \mathbf{u}$ for every $\mathbf{u}$. Hence, as is the case for $\boldsymbol{a}$, there exists a mapping $\boldsymbol{c}$ for which $\boldsymbol{cb} = \boldsymbol{i}$. This leads to the equalities

$$\boldsymbol{c} = \boldsymbol{c}(\boldsymbol{ba}) = (\boldsymbol{cb})\boldsymbol{a} = \boldsymbol{a}.$$

So in summary, *when* $\boldsymbol{a}$ *is an onto* (which is equivalent to one-to-one) *linear transformation there exists a unique mapping* $\boldsymbol{b}$ *such that* $\boldsymbol{ba} = \boldsymbol{i}$; *this mapping* $\boldsymbol{b}$ *is a linear transformation which is onto* (one-to-one), *and* $\boldsymbol{ab} = \boldsymbol{i}$. So far, we have proved these facts in the 1- and 2-dimensional cases, but they are true in any finite-dimensional case.

EXAMPLE 1. Suppose the linear transformation $\boldsymbol{a}$ is represented by A and $\boldsymbol{b}$ by B, with respect to some coordinate basis, where $\boldsymbol{a}$ is onto and $\boldsymbol{ba} = \boldsymbol{i}$ as above. Since $\boldsymbol{ab} = \boldsymbol{ba} = \boldsymbol{i}$, we must have $AB = BA = I$. (For instance in Section 2.4, Example 5 take $\psi = -\phi$. Also see Section 2.5, Problem 3.)

If we do not assume that the linear transformation $\boldsymbol{a}$ is onto, but only that there exists a mapping $\boldsymbol{c}$ such that $\boldsymbol{ca} = \boldsymbol{i}$, then we see that $\boldsymbol{a}\mathbf{u} = \boldsymbol{a}\mathbf{u}'$ if and only if $\mathbf{u} = \mathbf{u}'$. But this implies $\boldsymbol{a}$ is one-to-one, and since $\boldsymbol{a}$ is a linear transformation of a finite-dimensional vector space, it is onto (at least in the 1- and 2-dimensional cases). Therefore $\boldsymbol{c}$ coincides with $\boldsymbol{b}$ above. So we have the result: *A linear transformation* $\boldsymbol{a}$ *of the vector space at* $\boldsymbol{O}$ *is one-to-one (onto) if and only if there exists a mapping* $\boldsymbol{b}$ *such that* $\boldsymbol{ba} = \boldsymbol{i}$.

A linear transformation $\boldsymbol{a}$ *is called* ***invertible*** *if and only if there exists a linear transformation* $\boldsymbol{b}$ *such that*

$$\boldsymbol{ab} = \boldsymbol{ba} = \boldsymbol{i}. \tag{41}$$

Therefore, when $\boldsymbol{a}$ is a linear transformation of the vector space at $\boldsymbol{O}$ we know that $\boldsymbol{a}$ *is invertible if and only if* $\boldsymbol{a}$ *is one-to-one* (*or equivalently, onto*). *The uniquely determined linear transformation* $\boldsymbol{b}$ *in Equation* (41) *is called the* ***inverse*** *of* $\boldsymbol{a}$ *and is denoted by* $\boldsymbol{a}^{-1}$.

A similar terminology and notation is used for the representing matrices. If A represents $\boldsymbol{a}$, then A^{-1} will denote the matrix which represents $\boldsymbol{a}^{-1}$. *In terms of this notation we have the correspondences:*

$$\boldsymbol{a} \leftrightarrow A, \quad \boldsymbol{a}^{-1} \leftrightarrow A^{-1}, \quad \boldsymbol{aa}^{-1} = \boldsymbol{a}^{-1}\boldsymbol{a} = \boldsymbol{i} \leftrightarrow AA^{-1} = A^{-1}A = I. \tag{42}$$

A square matrix A *is called* ***invertible*** *if and only if there exists a square matrix* A^{-1} *such that the last two equalities in* (42) *hold.* A^{-1} *is called the* ***inverse*** *of* A.

We shall show later (Section 6.2, Example 2) that the determinant of the product AB of two square matrices has the property $|AB| = |A|\,|B|$, which is easy to verify directly in the 1×1 and 2×2 cases. Let us assume this fact, at least for $p \times p$ matrices with $p \leq 3$. Now, when A is invertible then $AA^{-1} = I$, so $|A|\,|A^{-1}| = |I| = 1$. *In particular, this implies that* $|A| \neq 0$ *when* A *is invertible.*

Conversely, if $|A| \neq 0$ and we invoke Cramer's Rule, Section 2.12, Equation (39), then the equation $AU = O$ has the unique solution $U = O$. Hence the kernel of a corresponding linear transformation $\boldsymbol{a}$ (represented by A) is $\{\mathbf{o}\}$, so $\boldsymbol{a}$ is one-to-one. This means that $\boldsymbol{a}^{-1}$ exists and therefore so does A^{-1}. Or, we can actually construct A^{-1} from Equation (39) as shown in Example 2 below, without having to assume that (42) holds for $p = 3$.

In particular, we now see that *if we interpret a square matrix* A *as the representation of a linear transformation* $\boldsymbol{a}$, *then* $\boldsymbol{a}$ *is invertible if and only if* $|A| \neq 0$.

EXAMPLE 2. When A is invertible, then for any equation $AU = V$ from which U is sought, we get the unique solution $U = A^{-1}AU = A^{-1}V$. *But suppose we know only that* $|A| \neq 0$. If we assume Cramer's Rule, then U in Equation (39) is a solution of $AU = V$ for every V. Consider the key matrix $(\text{cof-}A)^t$. It is commonly called the ***adjugate*** or ***adjoint*** of A, so non-committally and briefly, let us denote it by adj-A,

$$\text{adj-}A = (\text{cof-}A)^t = \begin{pmatrix} \text{cof-}a_{11} & \text{cof-}a_{21} & \cdots \\ \text{cof-}a_{12} & & \\ \vdots & & \end{pmatrix}.$$

Now, when we substitute from Equation (39) into $AU = V$, we get

$(A \operatorname{adj-}A)V = |A|V$ for every V, which implies $A \operatorname{adj-}A = |A|I$. But this means that A is invertible, with

$$A^{-1} = (1/|A|)(\text{cof-}A)^t = (1/|A|) \operatorname{adj-}A. \tag{43}$$

In the 2×2 case, $A = \begin{pmatrix} a & b \\ c & d \end{pmatrix}$, the cofactors are very simple:

$$\text{cof-}A = \begin{pmatrix} d & -c \\ -b & a \end{pmatrix} \quad \text{and} \quad A^{-1} = (1/|A|)\begin{pmatrix} d & -b \\ -c & a \end{pmatrix}.$$

Note that $AA^{-1} = A^{-1}A = I$ is the case $|A| \neq 0$ of

$$A \operatorname{adj-}A = (\operatorname{adj-}A)A = |A|I. \tag{44}$$

These equalities (44) *are true even when* $|A| = 0$. (See Problem 2.)

EXAMPLE 3. For a 3×3 matrix A the computation of cof-A is still rather easy. Suppose

$$A = \begin{pmatrix} 1 & 0 & 1 \\ 1 & 2 & 0 \\ 0 & 0 & -1 \end{pmatrix}.$$

This matrix A is invertible, for instance, because $|A| = -2 \neq 0$. A brief computation yields:

$$\text{cof-}A = \begin{pmatrix} -2 & 1 & 0 \\ 0 & -1 & 0 \\ -2 & 1 & 2 \end{pmatrix},$$

$$A^{-1} = -(\tfrac{1}{2})(\text{cof-}A)^t = -(\tfrac{1}{2})\begin{pmatrix} -2 & 0 & -2 \\ 1 & -1 & 1 \\ 0 & 0 & 2 \end{pmatrix} = \begin{pmatrix} 1 & 0 & 1 \\ -\frac{1}{2} & \frac{1}{2} & -\frac{1}{2} \\ 0 & 0 & -1 \end{pmatrix}.$$

This may be checked by computing AA^{-1} or $A^{-1}A$.

EXAMPLE 4. Let $\{\mathbf{u}, \mathbf{v}\}$ and $\{\mathbf{u}', \mathbf{v}'\}$ be two coordinate bases for a 2-dimensional vector space. Then we know that there exist unique scalars such that

$$\begin{aligned} \mathbf{u}' &= a\mathbf{u} + c\mathbf{v}, \\ \mathbf{v}' &= b\mathbf{u} + d\mathbf{v}, \end{aligned} \quad \text{and} \quad \begin{aligned} \mathbf{u} &= a'\mathbf{u}' + c'\mathbf{v}', \\ \mathbf{v} &= b'\mathbf{u}' + d'\mathbf{v}'. \end{aligned} \tag{45}$$

Let

$$A = \begin{pmatrix} a & b \\ c & d \end{pmatrix} \quad \text{and} \quad A' = \begin{pmatrix} a' & b' \\ c' & d' \end{pmatrix}.$$

These are the *transposes of the coefficient matrices* of the above pairs of equations, which is consistent with our previous use of the term *transpose*. If we substitute $\mathbf{u}$ and $\mathbf{v}$ from the right-hand system into the left-hand system, we get $A'A = I$, so

$$A' = A^{-1}.$$

This property for a pair of bases generalizes to any finite dimensional vector space. From the point of view of linear transformations, *the matrices* A *and* $A'(=A^{-1})$ *also determine a natural pair of invertible linear transformations* $\boldsymbol{a}$ *and* $\boldsymbol{a}^{-1}$, *respectively;* for, in Equations (45) we may regard $\mathbf{u}'$, $\mathbf{v}'$ as images $\boldsymbol{a}\mathbf{u}$, $\boldsymbol{a}\mathbf{v}$, and, similarly, we may regard $\mathbf{u}$, $\mathbf{v}$ as images $\boldsymbol{a}^{-1}\mathbf{u}'$, $\boldsymbol{a}^{-1}\mathbf{v}'$ (Problem 5 below).

PROBLEMS

1. If $A = \begin{pmatrix} \cos\theta & -\sin\theta \\ \sin\theta & \cos\theta \end{pmatrix}$, show that $A^{-1} = A^t$.

2. Show that for a $p \times p$ matrix A, $p \leq 3$ (at least),

$$\sum_j a_{ij} \text{ cof-}a_{kj} = \begin{Bmatrix} 0 & \text{if } i \neq k \\ |A| & \text{if } i = k \end{Bmatrix} = \sum_j a_{ji} \text{ cof-}a_{jk}.$$

3. Show that if $\boldsymbol{a}$ and $\boldsymbol{b}$ are invertible, then so is $\boldsymbol{ab}$, and its inverse is $\boldsymbol{b}^{-1}\boldsymbol{a}^{-1}$.

4. Show that when A is invertible then $(A^{-1})^t = (A^t)^{-1}$.

5. In Example 4, show why A determines an invertible linear transformation under which $\mathbf{u}'$ is the image of $\mathbf{u}$ and $\mathbf{v}'$ is the image of $\mathbf{v}$.

6. Show that a 2×2 matrix is invertible if and only if its columns, considered as column vectors, constitute a basis of the column vector space. Is this true for the rows?

7. If $|A| = 0$, is $|\text{adj-}A| = 0$?

2.14 DIRECT SUMS

It is convenient to denote a vector space by a special symbol such as $\mathbf{V}$ or $\mathbf{W}$. However, we continue to keep the vector space at a point $\boldsymbol{O}$ of real 2- or 3-dimensional space in mind.

As already noted, each vector $\mathbf{u}$ in a vector space $\mathbf{V}$ *generates* a subspace $[\mathbf{u}]$ consisting of all the scalar multiples of $\mathbf{u}$. *More generally, this bracket notation will indicate the subspace* ***generated*** *by a subset of* $\mathbf{V}$. For instance, a finite subset $\{\mathbf{u}_1, \ldots, \mathbf{u}_t\}$ of $\mathbf{V}$ gives rise to the subspace

$$[\mathbf{u}_1, \ldots, \mathbf{u}_t] = \{\textstyle\sum c_i\mathbf{u}_i \mid c_i\text{'s} \quad \text{scalars}\},$$

which is *the collection of all possible linear combinations of the* $\mathbf{u}_i$'s.

EXAMPLE 1. Let $\mathbf{V}$ be a 2-dimensional vector space. If $\mathbf{u}$ and $\mathbf{v}$ are two vectors in $\mathbf{V}$, then $\{\mathbf{u}, \mathbf{v}\}$ is a basis of $\mathbf{V}$ if and only if $\mathbf{V} = [\mathbf{u}, \mathbf{v}]$. For, we know that $\{\mathbf{u}, \mathbf{v}\}$ is a basis if and only if neither vector is a scalar multiple of the other, and that every basis must have two vectors.

In a 2-dimensional vector space $\mathbf{V}$ with basis $\{\mathbf{u}, \mathbf{v}\}$, every vector is uniquely expressible as the sum of a vector from $[\mathbf{u}]$ and a vector from $[\mathbf{v}]$. This is merely another way of saying that $\{\mathbf{u}, \mathbf{v}\}$ is a basis of $\mathbf{V}$, but this time *in terms of subspaces. We denote this fact by*

$$\mathbf{V} = [\mathbf{u}] \dotplus [\mathbf{v}]$$

and call it a ***decomposition*** *of* $\mathbf{V}$ *into a* ***direct sum*** *of the subspaces* $[\mathbf{u}]$ *and* $[\mathbf{v}]$.

If $\mathbf{V}$ is 3-dimensional with a basis $\{\mathbf{u}, \mathbf{v}, \mathbf{w}\}$, then a corresponding decomposition is

$$\mathbf{V} = [\mathbf{u}] \dotplus [\mathbf{v}] \dotplus [\mathbf{w}],$$

a direct sum of three subspaces. But it is also true that every vector is uniquely expressible as the sum of a vector from $[\mathbf{u}]$ and a vector from $[\mathbf{v}, \mathbf{w}]$, so

$$\mathbf{V} = [\mathbf{u}] \dotplus [\mathbf{v}, \mathbf{w}],$$

which expresses the fact that $\mathbf{V}$ is a direct sum of the two indicated subspaces. There are, of course, many ways to choose a basis and for each choice there are different ways to *decompose* $\mathbf{V}$ into a *direct sum of subspaces.*

In general, we say that $\mathbf{V}$ *is a* ***direct sum*** *of two subspaces* $\mathbf{V}_1$ *and* $\mathbf{V}_2$ *if and only if every vector* $\mathbf{v}$ *in* $\mathbf{V}$ *is uniquely expressible as* $\mathbf{v} = \mathbf{v}_1 + \mathbf{v}_2$ *with* $\mathbf{v}_1$ in $\mathbf{V}_1$ *and* $\mathbf{v}_2$ *in* $\mathbf{V}_2$. *Then we write*

$$\mathbf{V} = \mathbf{V}_1 \dotplus \mathbf{V}_2.$$

This definition generalizes to any finite number of subspaces.

EXAMPLE 2. In Figure 32 let $\{\mathbf{u}, \mathbf{v}, \mathbf{w}\}$ be any three vectors at $\boldsymbol{O}$. The label $[\mathbf{u}]$ on a line means that the points on this line are used to define the subspace $[\mathbf{u}]$ of position vectors to these points. A similar interpretation is meant for the other labels.

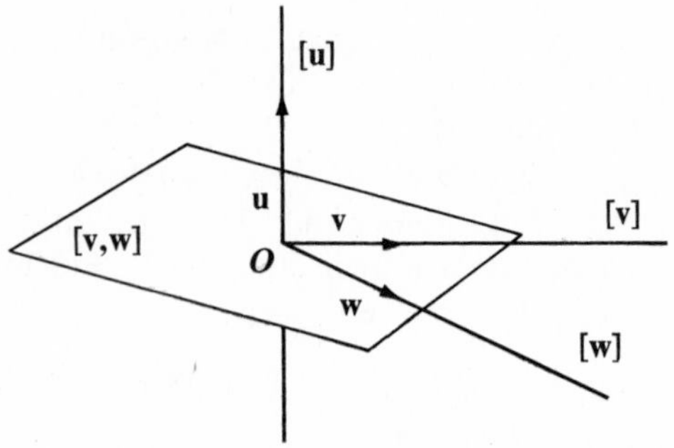

FIGURE 32

PROBLEMS

1. If $\mathbf{V}$ is a 3-tuple vector space, show that

$$\mathbf{V} = [(1, 1, -1)] \dotplus [(1, -1, 1), \quad (-1, 1, 1)].$$

2. If $\mathbf{W}$ is a subspace of $\mathbf{V}$, and $\mathbf{W}$ contains a given finite subset $\{\mathbf{u}_1, \ldots, \mathbf{u}_t\}$ of vectors from $\mathbf{V}$, show that $\mathbf{W}$ contains all the vectors in the subspace $[\mathbf{u}_1, \ldots, \mathbf{u}_t]$.

3. Complete the proof of the fact that, in the 3-dimensional case, $\mathbf{V} = [\mathbf{u}] \dotplus [\mathbf{v}, \mathbf{w}]$ if $\{\mathbf{u}, \mathbf{v}, \mathbf{w}\}$ is a basis. Is the converse true?

4. In each case add a suitable direct summand:
(a) vector space of 1×4 row vectors $= [(1, 1, 1, 1), (1, 1, 1, 0)] \dotplus [?]$,
(b) vector space of polynomials $= [\{f(x) \mid f(r) = 0 \text{ for a fixed scalar } r\}] \dotplus [?]$.

2.15 INVARIANT SUBSPACES

Let $\mathbf{W}$ be a subspace of a vector space $\mathbf{V}$. Suppose further that a given linear transformation $\boldsymbol{a}$ of $\mathbf{V}$ has the property:

$$\boldsymbol{a}\mathbf{w} \text{ is in } \mathbf{W} \text{ for every vector } \mathbf{w} \text{ in } \mathbf{W}.$$

Then *the subspace* $\mathbf{W}$ *is said to be* ***invariant*** *with respect to* $\boldsymbol{a}$.

EXAMPLE 1. In real 3-dimensional space let $\boldsymbol{a}$ be a rotation about an axis (line). Let $\boldsymbol{O}$ be a point on this axis and let us select a basis of the vector space $\mathbf{V}$ at $\boldsymbol{O}$ as follows: Choose a vector $\mathbf{u}$ at $\boldsymbol{O}$ along the axis of rotation and two non-proportional vectors $\mathbf{v}$ and $\mathbf{w}$ at $\boldsymbol{O}$ in the plane perpendicular to this axis, as in Figure 33. Then the line $[\mathbf{u}]$ and the plane $[\mathbf{v}, \mathbf{w}]$ are subspaces of $\mathbf{V}$ such that $\mathbf{V} = [\mathbf{u}] \dotplus [\mathbf{v}, \mathbf{w}]$. But each of these direct summands is also invariant with respect to $\boldsymbol{a}$: for, $\boldsymbol{a}\mathbf{u} = \mathbf{u}$, and $\boldsymbol{a}(s\mathbf{v} + t\mathbf{w})$ is in $[\mathbf{v}, \mathbf{w}]$ for every choice of scalars s, t. Since this mapping induces a rotation of the plane $[\mathbf{v}, \mathbf{w}]$, the mapping is a linear transformation.

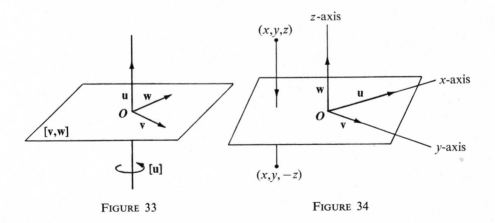

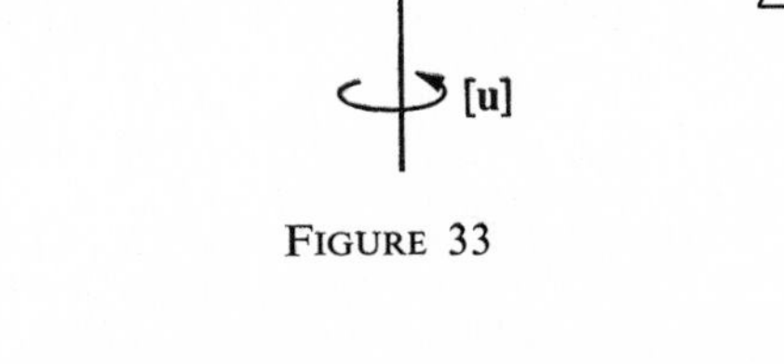

FIGURE 33

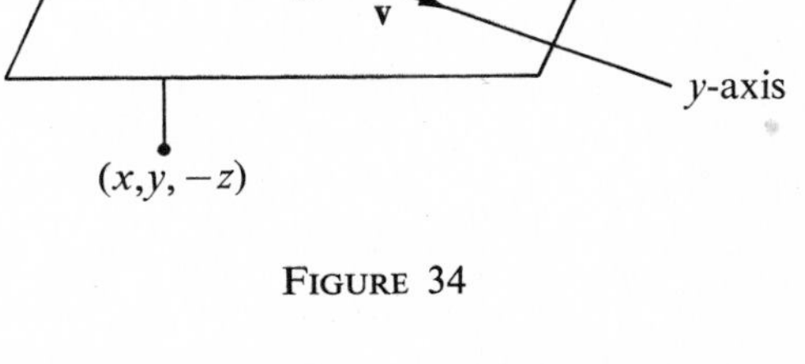

FIGURE 34

The determination of *the invariant subspaces of a vector space* $\mathbf{V}$ *with respect to a given linear transformation* $\boldsymbol{a}$ *and the decomposition of* $\mathbf{V}$ *into a direct sum of invariant subspaces* are central problems in linear algebra. One of our goals is to characterize linear transformations by their behavior on invariant subspaces. But there are also useful consequences for computation with matrices. For instance, *when* **V** *is a direct sum of invariant subspaces, the selection of a coordinate basis by choosing vectors from the invariant summands, in turn, leads to simplified matrix representations of the linear transformation* ***a***.

EXAMPLE 2. If in Example 1 we use $\{\mathbf{u}, \mathbf{v}, \mathbf{w}\}$ as a coordinate basis, then $\boldsymbol{a}$ is represented by a matrix of the form diag $(1, B)$, where B is a 2×2 matrix, as the invariant subspaces show. If from the invariant subspace $[\mathbf{v}, \mathbf{w}]$ we select a pair of mutually perpendicular unit length vectors $\{\mathbf{v}', \mathbf{w}'\}$ and use $\{\mathbf{u}, \mathbf{v}', \mathbf{w}'\}$ as a coordinate basis, then $\boldsymbol{a}$ will be represented by the diagonal-block matrix

$$\operatorname{diag}(1, B) = \begin{pmatrix} 1 & 0 & 0 \\ 0 & \cos\phi & -\sin\phi \\ 0 & \sin\phi & \cos\phi \end{pmatrix}.$$

EXAMPLE 3. Another example is given by the linear transformation which reflects every point (of real 3-dimensional space) perpendicularly across a fixed plane. Select any point $\boldsymbol{O}$ in this plane and consider the vector space **V** at $\boldsymbol{O}$. Two invariant subspaces are the fixed plane and the line through $\boldsymbol{O}$ perpendicular to the fixed plane (Fig. 34, p. 67). **V** is a direct sum of these two invariant subspaces, and with a coordinate basis $\{\mathbf{u}, \mathbf{v}, \mathbf{w}\}$, chosen as in Figure 34, $\boldsymbol{a}$ is represented by $A = \operatorname{diag}(1, 1, -1)$.

PROBLEMS

1. Show that $\boldsymbol{a}$ in Example 3 is a linear transformation, even if the reflection is not perpendicular to the plane.
2. Write out the indicated coordinate equations for the mappings in Examples 2 and 3.
3. Let **V** be a 4-tuple vector space. Show that the assignment of (z, w, x, y) as the image of (x, y, z, w) defines a linear transformation. Find a matrix representation which uses the decomposition of this space into the direct sum

$$[(1, 0, 0, 0),\quad (0, 0, 1, 0)] \dotplus [(0, 1, 0, 0),\quad (0, 0, 0, 1)].$$

4. Let $\mathbf{V} = \mathbf{V}_1 \dotplus \mathbf{V}_2$ be a direct sum decomposition of a real vector space **V**. Show that each of the following mappings is a linear transformation of **V**, and find invariant subspaces other than **V** and $\{\mathbf{o}\}$:
   (a) $\boldsymbol{a}(\mathbf{v}_1 + \mathbf{v}_2) = \mathbf{v}_1$, $\mathbf{v}_i$ in $\mathbf{V}_i$,
   (b) $\boldsymbol{a}(\mathbf{v}_1 + \mathbf{v}_2) = \mathbf{v}_1 - \mathbf{v}_2$, $\mathbf{v}_i$ in $\mathbf{V}_i$.

2.16 CHARACTERISTIC VECTORS

When $\boldsymbol{a}$ is a linear transformation of a vector space **V**, we have seen that there may be a non-zero vector **u** such that

$$\boldsymbol{a}\mathbf{u} = s\mathbf{u}$$

for some scalar s (where the term *scalar* means, as usual, a number in the scalar field of $\mathbf{V}$). When such a non-zero vector $\mathbf{u}$ does exist, then the scalar s is obviously unique, and for every scalar t we have $\boldsymbol{a}t\mathbf{u} = t\boldsymbol{a}\mathbf{u} = ts\mathbf{u}$. Hence the subspace $[\mathbf{u}]$ is mapped into itself by $\boldsymbol{a}$, so $[\mathbf{u}]$ is a 1-dimensional *invariant* subspace of $\mathbf{V}$. The invariant lines through $\boldsymbol{O}$ that have occurred in many of our examples correspond to such 1-dimensional invariant subspaces.

For a given linear transformation $\boldsymbol{a}$, there may not be any non-zero vector $\mathbf{u}$ satisfying $\boldsymbol{a}\mathbf{u} = s\mathbf{u}$, no matter what the value of the scalar s. *But if, for some scalar s, there is such a vector, then we call s a* ***characteristic number*** *of* $\boldsymbol{a}$ *and we call* $\mathbf{u}$ *a* ***characteristic vector*** *of* $\boldsymbol{a}$ *belonging to s. A characteristic vector* $\mathbf{u}$ *generates a 1-dimensional invariant subspace* $[\mathbf{u}]$ *which, apart from the zero vector, consists entirely of characteristic vectors belonging to the characteristic number s:* for,

$$\boldsymbol{a}(t\mathbf{u}) = s(t\mathbf{u})$$

and $t\mathbf{u}$ is in $[\mathbf{u}]$.

*If we rewrite $\boldsymbol{a}\mathbf{u} = s\mathbf{u}$ in the equivalent form

$$(s\boldsymbol{i} - \boldsymbol{a})\mathbf{u} = \mathbf{o}, \tag{46}$$

then we see that *the characteristic vectors of* $\boldsymbol{a}$ *which belong to the characteristic number s of* $\boldsymbol{a}$ *are exactly the non-zero vectors in the subspace* ker $(s\boldsymbol{i} - \boldsymbol{a})$.

EXAMPLE 1. Suppose a linear transformation $\boldsymbol{a}$ of a 2-dimensional vector space $\mathbf{V}$ has two characteristic vectors $\mathbf{u}_1$ and $\mathbf{u}_2$ belonging to characteristic numbers s_1 and s_2, respectively; that is,

$$\boldsymbol{a}\mathbf{u}_1 = s_1\mathbf{u}_1 \quad \text{and} \quad \boldsymbol{a}\mathbf{u}_2 = s_2\mathbf{u}_2, \quad \mathbf{u}_1 \neq \mathbf{o} \neq \mathbf{u}_2.$$

Furthermore, suppose that $\mathbf{V} = [\mathbf{u}_1, \mathbf{u}_2]$. Since $\mathbf{V}$ is 2-dimensional, we can choose $\{\mathbf{u}_1, \mathbf{u}_2\}$ as a coordinate basis of $\mathbf{V}$. With respect to this coordinate basis, $\boldsymbol{a}$ has a matrix representation

$$A = \operatorname{diag}(s_1, s_2).$$

If our field of scalars is real, then such a linear transformation $\boldsymbol{a}$ may be regarded as a plane strain with magnitudes s_1 and s_2 in the directions of $\mathbf{u}_1$ and $\mathbf{u}_2$, respectively.

EXAMPLE 2. Under the influence of a rotation $\boldsymbol{a}$ about an axis through a point $\boldsymbol{O}$ in real 3-dimensional space, every non-zero vector $\mathbf{u}$ in the direction of the axis of rotation is a characteristic vector of $\boldsymbol{a}$ belonging to the characteristic number 1; that is, $\boldsymbol{a}\mathbf{u} = \mathbf{u}$. The fact that the characteristic number here equals 1 means that *each point* on the axis is invariant (fixed under $\boldsymbol{a}$).

EXAMPLE 3. In the case of a perpendicular reflection $\boldsymbol{a}$ in a plane containing the point $\boldsymbol{O}$, every non-zero vector at $\boldsymbol{O}$ that lies in this plane is a characteristic vector of $\boldsymbol{a}$ belonging to the characteristic number 1, while every non-zero vector at $\boldsymbol{O}$ which is perpendicular to this plane is a characteristic vector of $\boldsymbol{a}$ belonging to the characteristic number -1. In this case, the characteristic vectors belonging to 1 constitute the non-zero vectors of a 2-dimensional invariant subspace.

EXAMPLE 4. A similitude (uniform positive strain with point $\boldsymbol{O}$ fixed) of magnitude k has every non-zero vector at $\boldsymbol{O}$ as a characteristic vector belonging to the characteristic number k. Every coordinate basis yields the same coordinate representation $A = kI$.

EXAMPLE 5. If $\boldsymbol{a}$ is a general strain of magnitudes k, l, m in three non-coplanar directions from a point $\boldsymbol{O}$, then there are three characteristic vectors, $\mathbf{u}$, $\mathbf{v}$, $\mathbf{w}$ of $\boldsymbol{a}$ belonging to the characteristic numbers k, l, m, respectively. If $\{\mathbf{u}, \mathbf{v}, \mathbf{w}\}$ is used as a coordinate basis, then $\boldsymbol{a}$ is represented by

$$A = \operatorname{diag}(k, l, m),$$

because

$$\boldsymbol{a}\mathbf{u} = k\mathbf{u},\ \boldsymbol{a}\mathbf{v} = l\mathbf{v},\ \boldsymbol{a}\mathbf{w} = m\mathbf{w}.$$

EXAMPLE 6. Among the decompositions of the vector space $\mathbf{V}$ used in Examples 2–5, are the following:

Ex. 2: $\mathbf{V} =$ [a characteristic vector belonging to 1] $\dotplus$ {plane perpendicular to the axis, at $\boldsymbol{O}$}.
Ex. 3: $\mathbf{V} =$ [two non-proportional characteristic vectors belonging to 1] $\dotplus$ [a characteristic vector belonging to -1].
Ex. 4: $\mathbf{V} = [\mathbf{u}] \dotplus [\mathbf{v}] \dotplus [\mathbf{w}]$, for any three non-coplanar vectors at $\boldsymbol{O}$.
Ex. 5: $\mathbf{V} = [\mathbf{u}] \dotplus [\mathbf{v}] \dotplus [\mathbf{w}]$, for characteristic vectors $\mathbf{u}$, $\mathbf{v}$, $\mathbf{w}$ belonging to k, l, m, respectively.

In each case, the subspaces are invariant.

PROBLEMS

1. Give an example of a linear transformation which has no characteristic vectors. Is this possible in real 3-dimensional space?
2. Compare the characteristic vectors and characteristic numbers of $\boldsymbol{a}$, $\boldsymbol{a}^{-1}$, $s\boldsymbol{a}$, and $\boldsymbol{a}^2$.
3. If s is not a characteristic number of $\boldsymbol{a}$, show that $s\boldsymbol{i} - \boldsymbol{a}$ is invertible.
4. In Example 1, suppose $s_1 \neq s_2$. Show that this implies $\mathbf{V} = [\mathbf{u}_1, \mathbf{u}_2]$.
5. Show that in real 3-dimensional space *every* linear transformation can be represented by a matrix of the form

$$\begin{pmatrix} s & s' & s'' \\ 0 & & \\ 0 & \multicolumn{2}{c}{B} \end{pmatrix}$$

where s is a characteristic number and B is 2×2.

2.17 CHARACTERISTIC POLYNOMIAL

Let $\boldsymbol{a}$ be a linear transformation of a 2-dimensional vector space $\mathbf{V}$. Suppose $\mathbf{u}$ is a characteristic vector of $\boldsymbol{a}$ belonging to the characteristic number s of $\boldsymbol{a}$. If, with respect to some coordinate basis, the matrix $A = \begin{pmatrix} a & b \\ c & d \end{pmatrix}$ represents $\boldsymbol{a}$ and the coordinate column $U = \begin{pmatrix} x \\ y \end{pmatrix} \neq O$ represents $\mathbf{u}$, then we have the correspondence

$$\boldsymbol{a}\mathbf{u} = s\mathbf{u} \leftrightarrow AU = sU,$$

or, equivalently,

$$(s\boldsymbol{i} - \boldsymbol{a})\mathbf{u} = \mathbf{o} \leftrightarrow (sI - A)U = O. \tag{47}$$

In more detail, the matrix equation $(sI - A)U = O$ in Equation (47) is

$$\begin{pmatrix} s - a & -b \\ -c & s - d \end{pmatrix} \begin{pmatrix} x \\ y \end{pmatrix} = \begin{pmatrix} 0 \\ 0 \end{pmatrix},$$

which describes the homogeneous system

$$(s - a)x - by = 0,$$
$$-cx + (s - d)y = 0.$$

On the other hand, let s be any number in the scalar field of $\mathbf{V}$, and let A be a given matrix with entries from this same field. Then an equation of the form $(sI - A)U = O$ has a non-zero solution for a column U of scalars if and only if $|sI - A| = 0$. Let $\boldsymbol{a} \leftrightarrow A$ for some linear transformation $\boldsymbol{a}$ of $\mathbf{V}$. Since a vector $\mathbf{u}$ is zero if and only if its coordinate column is zero, we conclude that *$\boldsymbol{a}$ has a characteristic vector belonging to the scalar s if and only if*

$$|sI - A| = 0. \tag{48}$$

EXAMPLE 1. Suppose a certain linear transformation $\boldsymbol{a}$ of the plane is represented by $A = \begin{pmatrix} 1 & -1 \\ -1 & 1 \end{pmatrix}$. We observe that if $U = \begin{pmatrix} 1 \\ -1 \end{pmatrix}$, then $AU = 2U$. So $\boldsymbol{a}$ has a characteristic vector $\mathbf{u}$ (with coordinate column U) belonging to the characteristic number 2, hence satisfying $(2\boldsymbol{i} - \boldsymbol{a})\mathbf{u} = \mathbf{o}$. The determinant of the matrix $2I - A$ is zero and $2\boldsymbol{i} - \boldsymbol{a}$ is not invertible.

If x is a variable, then those scalars (in the scalar field of $\mathbf{V}$ as usual) *which are roots of the polynomial*

$$|xI - A| = 0 \tag{49}$$

constitute all the characteristic numbers of the linear transformation $\boldsymbol{a}$ (represented by A). For, as we have seen above, given any scalar s, the condition $|sI - A| = 0$ is the necessary and sufficient condition for $(sI - A)U = O$ to have a non-zero solution for a coordinate column U.

*Thus, *if $\boldsymbol{a} \leftrightarrow A$* and *s is any characteristic number of $\boldsymbol{a}$, then the characteristic vectors of $\boldsymbol{a}$ belonging to s are exactly those vectors whose coordinate columns* *are non-zero solutions of* $(sI - A)U = O$. On the other hand, if $\boldsymbol{a} \leftrightarrow A$, then *each characteristic vector* $\mathbf{u}$ *of* $\boldsymbol{a}$ *has a non-zero coordinate column that is a solution of* $(sI - A)U = O$ *for a unique scalar s which is a root of* $|xI - A| = 0$, *and then s is therefore the characteristic number of* $\boldsymbol{a}$ *to which* $\mathbf{u}$ *belongs.*

The polynomial $|xI - A|$ *is called the* ***characteristic polynomial*** *of the matrix* A. However, we shall see later that the coefficients of the characteristic polynomial of a linear transformation $\boldsymbol{a}$ are independent of which representing matrix (that is, of which coordinate basis) we use. Hence if $\boldsymbol{a} \leftrightarrow A$, then $|xI - A|$ *is also called the* ***characteristic polynomial*** *of the linear transformation* $\boldsymbol{a}$ *which is represented by A. Equation* (49) *is, therefore, called the* ***characteristic equation*** *of A and of* $\boldsymbol{a}$, both.

Although only those roots of $|xI - A| = 0$ which are in the scalar field of $\mathbf{V}$ are characteristic numbers of the linear transformation $\boldsymbol{a}$ represented by A, yet *every root s of* $|xI - A| = 0$ *is called a characteristic number of A and every non-zero solution of* $(sI - A)U = O$ *is called a* ***characteristic column vector*** *of A*. This is a convenience in matrix algebra. It also reflects the fact that there always exists a vector space whose field of scalars includes *all* the roots of $|xI - A| = 0$, as well as all the entries of a given matrix A. Hence, there exists a linear transformation which is represented by A and for which *all* the roots of $|xI - A| = 0$ are characteristic numbers. (*A column vector space with the right kind of scalar field will do.* However, dually, it can be shown that $\boldsymbol{a}$ itself can be regarded as a linear transformation of a vector space which contains $\mathbf{V}$ and has a scalar field which contains all the roots of $|xI - A| = 0$.)

EXAMPLE 2. If $A = \begin{pmatrix} a & b \\ c & d \end{pmatrix}$, then

$$|xI - A| = x^2 - (a + d)x + |A|.$$

When the discriminant of this quadratic is negative, then any linear transformation $\boldsymbol{a}$ of a vector space with *real* scalars which A may happen to represent has no characteristic numbers or vectors. But of course the matrix A does. For instance, $A = \begin{pmatrix} 0 & 1 \\ -1 & 0 \end{pmatrix}$ has a characteristic equation $x^2 + 1 = 0$ and characteristic numbers $\pm i$ (where $i^2 = -1$). Solving $(sI - A)U = O$ for U, *with* $s = \pm i$ *in turn*, we get a characteristic column vector $\begin{pmatrix} 1 \\ i \end{pmatrix}$ of A belonging to the characteristic number i of A and a characteristic column vector $\begin{pmatrix} 1 \\ -i \end{pmatrix}$ of A belonging to the characteristic number $-i$ of A. Any non-zero scalar multiples of these vectors are again characteristic vectors.

EXAMPLE 3. If

$$A = \begin{pmatrix} a & b & c \\ d & e & f \\ g & h & i \end{pmatrix}$$

then

$$|xI - A| = x^3 - (a + e + i)x^2 + \left(\begin{vmatrix} a & b \\ d & e \end{vmatrix} + \begin{vmatrix} a & c \\ g & i \end{vmatrix} + \begin{vmatrix} e & f \\ h & i \end{vmatrix}\right)x - |A|,$$

where we have indicated how the coefficients are related to the so-called ***principal minors*** of A. (These minors result from striking out rows and columns that have like indices.)

EXAMPLE 4. Let

$$A = \begin{pmatrix} a & b \\ b & c \end{pmatrix}.$$

This matrix is called ***symmetric*** because the entries that are symmetrically located with respect to the ***diagonal*** (which in every matrix extends from the upper left to the lower right) are equal. In terms of our *transpose* terminology, *the condition which characterizes symmetry of the matrix A has the form*

$$A = A^t.$$

If we assume real entries and compute the discriminant of $|xI - A|$, we find

$$(a + c)^2 - 4(ac - b^2) = (a - c)^2 + 4b^2 \geq 0.$$

Thus the characteristic numbers of A are real. So, if a linear transformation $\boldsymbol{a}$ of a real (2-dimensional here) vector space is represented by a symmetric matrix with respect to some coordinate basis, then $\boldsymbol{a}$ has two characteristic numbers and they are real. If $a = c$, then these numbers are $a + b$ and $a - b$; only when $b = 0$ are the latter equal, and then both equal a.

PROBLEMS

1. In Example 1, find the characteristic numbers and vectors of the linear transformation $\boldsymbol{a}$. Is this different from those of A?
2. Compare the characteristic numbers of a matrix $A = \begin{pmatrix} a & b \\ c & d \end{pmatrix}$ with the characteristic numbers of its transpose, $A^t = \begin{pmatrix} a & c \\ b & d \end{pmatrix}$. Do the 3×3 case too. Compare the characteristic vectors, if possible.
3. Find the characteristic numbers and vectors of the symmetric matrix
$$\begin{pmatrix} 0 & 1 & 1 \\ 1 & -1 & 0 \\ 1 & 0 & 1 \end{pmatrix}.$$
4. If the scalar field is real and $\boldsymbol{a} \leftrightarrow \begin{pmatrix} 0 & b \\ -b & 0 \end{pmatrix}$, find the characteristic numbers and vectors of $\boldsymbol{a}$ and of A.
5. If the 3×3 matrix A of Example 3 is real and such that $A = -A^t$, then expand $|A|$ and describe the characteristic numbers of A.

2.18 SPECIAL COORDINATE BASES IN 2-DIMENSIONAL SPACE

Let us consider how a linear transformation $\boldsymbol{a}$ is involved in the generation of a 2-dimensional vector space $\mathbf{V}$. We can divide the problem into two cases as follows:

(a) $\mathbf{V} = [\mathbf{u}, \boldsymbol{a}\mathbf{u}]$ for some $\mathbf{u}$ in $\mathbf{V}$.
(b) $\boldsymbol{a}\mathbf{u}$ is in $[\mathbf{u}]$ for every $\mathbf{u}$ in $\mathbf{V}$.

In case (a), $\mathbf{V}$ is called a ***cyclic space*** with respect to $\boldsymbol{a}$. If we choose $\{\mathbf{u}, \boldsymbol{a}\mathbf{u}\}$ as a coordinate basis then $\boldsymbol{a}^2\mathbf{u} = b\mathbf{u} + d(\boldsymbol{a}\mathbf{u})$ for unique scalars b and d. The matrix A which represents $\boldsymbol{a}$ with respect to this coordinate basis is therefore

$$A = \begin{pmatrix} 0 & b \\ 1 & d \end{pmatrix}.$$

In case (b), $\boldsymbol{a}\mathbf{u} = s\mathbf{u}$ for every $\mathbf{u}$, where the scalar s apparently depends on $\mathbf{u}$. However, suppose $\mathbf{V} = [\mathbf{u}_1, \mathbf{u}_2]$ and consider $\mathbf{u} = \mathbf{u}_1 + \mathbf{u}_2 \neq \mathbf{o}$. Then

$$\boldsymbol{a}\mathbf{u} = s\mathbf{u} = \boldsymbol{a}\mathbf{u}_1 + \boldsymbol{a}\mathbf{u}_2 = s_1\mathbf{u}_1 + s_2\mathbf{u}_2.$$

Therefore $s_1 = s_2 = s$. So for every coordinate basis, we get the same matrix representation of $\boldsymbol{a}$, by the scalar matrix

$$A = sI.$$

Now, let us consider the same problem with emphasis on the characteristic vectors of $\boldsymbol{a}$. *Assume the scalars of* $\mathbf{V}$ *are real numbers.* There are three cases here.

(a′) $\mathbf{V} = [\mathbf{u}_1, \mathbf{u}_2]$ with $\mathbf{u}_1$ and $\mathbf{u}_2$ characteristic vectors of $\boldsymbol{a}$ belonging to the (real) characteristic numbers s_1 and s_2, respectively. So $\mathbf{V} = [\mathbf{u}_1] \dotplus [\mathbf{u}_2]$, with $\boldsymbol{a}\mathbf{u}_1 = s_1\mathbf{u}_1$ and $\boldsymbol{a}\mathbf{u}_2 = s_2\mathbf{u}_2$.

(b′) The characteristic vectors of $\boldsymbol{a}$ all lie in a 1-dimensional subspace, say $[\mathbf{u}]$.

(c′) The linear transformation $\boldsymbol{a}$ has no characteristic vectors.

In case (a′), choose $\{\mathbf{u}_1, \mathbf{u}_2\}$ as a coordinate basis. Then $\boldsymbol{a}$ is represented by

$$A = \operatorname{diag}(s_1, s_2).$$

In case (b′), the vector $\mathbf{u}$ must be a characteristic vector of $\boldsymbol{a}$ belonging to a real characteristic number s. Our hypothesis implies that s is the only characteristic number of $\boldsymbol{a}$ and the vectors belonging to s constitute the non-zero vectors of $[\mathbf{u}]$. If $\{\mathbf{u}, \mathbf{v}\}$ is any coordinate basis which starts with $\mathbf{u}$, then $\mathbf{v}$ is not in $[\mathbf{u}]$. So $\boldsymbol{a}\mathbf{v} = e\mathbf{u} + f\mathbf{v}$ for $e \neq 0$. Replace $\mathbf{v}$ by $\mathbf{v}' = (1/e)\mathbf{v}$. With respect to the coordinate basis $\{\mathbf{u}, \mathbf{v}'\}$, $\boldsymbol{a}$ is represented by $A = \begin{pmatrix} s & 1 \\ 0 & f \end{pmatrix}$. But then f is a (real) characteristic number *of the matrix A*, and since f is real it must be a characteristic number of $\boldsymbol{a}$. But this means that $f = s$, and hence

$$A = \begin{pmatrix} s & 1 \\ 0 & s \end{pmatrix}.$$

In case (c′), $\boldsymbol{a}\mathbf{u}$ is not in $[\mathbf{u}]$ for any non-zero vector $\mathbf{u}$. Therefore $\mathbf{V} = [\mathbf{u}, \boldsymbol{a}\mathbf{u}]$ for any $\mathbf{u} \neq \mathbf{o}$, which is the (real) case (a) above with the discriminant of $|xI - A|$ negative, that is, $d^2 + 4b < 0$.

PROBLEMS

1. In (b′), show that s is the only characteristic number.
2. If $\{\mathbf{u}, \mathbf{v}'\}$ is a basis of $\mathbf{V}$, $\boldsymbol{a}\mathbf{u} = s\mathbf{u}$, $\boldsymbol{a}\mathbf{v}' = \mathbf{u} + f\mathbf{v}'$, and $f \neq s$, then show that $\mathbf{u} + (f - s)\mathbf{v}'$ is a characteristic vector of $\boldsymbol{a}$ belonging to f. (Do not use matrices.) Thus vary the discussion in (b′).
3. In the real 2-dimensional vector space of complex numbers (Section 2.6, Example 2), let $z = x + iy$ be a fixed imaginary number ($y \neq 0$) and choose $\{1, z\}$ as a basis. Show that if z is also regarded as a linear transformation, then it is represented with respect to this basis by

$$\begin{pmatrix} 0 & -|z|^2 \\ 1 & 2x \end{pmatrix}.$$

3

Similarity

3.1 SIMILAR LINEAR TRANSFORMATIONS

Two linear transformations $\boldsymbol{a}$ and $\boldsymbol{b}$ of a vector space $\mathbf{V}$ are equal if and only if $\boldsymbol{a}\mathbf{u} = \boldsymbol{b}\mathbf{u}$ for every vector $\mathbf{u}$ in $\mathbf{V}$. When two unequal linear transformations are referred to the same coordinate basis, their representing matrices will be unequal. However, we have already noted (for instance, Section 2.4, Example 1) that *a single matrix with entries from the scalar field of* $\mathbf{V}$ *can represent many different linear transformations of* $\mathbf{V}$ *if the latter are separately referred to suitable different coordinate bases.*

EXAMPLE 1. Let $\boldsymbol{a}$ be the linear transformation of the vector space at $\boldsymbol{O}$ which, with respect to some coordinate basis $\{\mathbf{u}, \mathbf{v}\}$, has a representing matrix $A = \text{diag}(1, 2)$; that is, $\boldsymbol{a}\mathbf{u} = \mathbf{u}$ and $\boldsymbol{a}\mathbf{v} = 2\mathbf{v}$. Also, let $\boldsymbol{b}$ be the linear transformation which, with respect to the *same* coordinate basis $\{\mathbf{u}, \mathbf{v}\}$, is represented by $B = \text{diag}(2, 1)$; that is $\boldsymbol{b}\mathbf{u} = 2\mathbf{u}$ and $\boldsymbol{b}\mathbf{v} = \mathbf{v}$. But if we refer $\boldsymbol{b}$ to the *different* coordinate basis $\{\mathbf{v}, \mathbf{u}\}$, then $\boldsymbol{b}$ is represented by the matrix $A = \text{diag}(1, 2)$.

An insight into the general situation is obtained by considering the 2-dimensional case. Suppose $\{\mathbf{u}_1, \mathbf{u}_2\}$ and $\{\mathbf{v}_1, \mathbf{v}_2\}$ are two coordinate bases of a 2-dimensional vector space $\mathbf{V}$. As we have seen (Section 2.13, Example 4), one can define an invertible linear transformation $\boldsymbol{p}$ of $\mathbf{V}$ by the equations

$$\mathbf{v}_i = \boldsymbol{p}\mathbf{u}_i \quad (i = 1, 2).$$

Now, suppose that a linear transformation $\boldsymbol{a}$ of $\mathbf{V}$ is represented with respect to $\{\mathbf{u}_1, \mathbf{u}_2\}$ by the *same matrix*

$$M = \begin{pmatrix} m_{11} & m_{12} \\ m_{21} & m_{22} \end{pmatrix}$$

which represents a linear transformation $\boldsymbol{b}$ of $\mathbf{V}$ with respect to the other basis $\{\mathbf{v}_1, \mathbf{v}_2\}$. This means that

$$\boldsymbol{a}\mathbf{u}_i = \textstyle\sum \mathbf{u}_j m_{ji}, \quad \boldsymbol{b}\mathbf{v}_i = \sum \mathbf{v}_j m_{ji} \quad (i = 1, 2).$$

Therefore,

$$\boldsymbol{bp}\mathbf{u}_i = \boldsymbol{b}\mathbf{v}_i = \sum \mathbf{v}_j m_{ji} = \sum \boldsymbol{p}\mathbf{u}_j m_{ji} = \boldsymbol{p}\sum \mathbf{u}_j m_{ji} = \boldsymbol{pa}\mathbf{u}_i \quad (i = 1, 2).$$

Since a linear transformation is determined by its effect on a coordinate basis, we deduce that

$$\boldsymbol{pa} = \boldsymbol{bp}. \tag{1}$$

Because $\boldsymbol{p}$ is invertible, we may restate Equation (1) in either of the equivalent forms:

$$\boldsymbol{b} = \boldsymbol{pap}^{-1} \quad \text{or} \quad \boldsymbol{a} = \boldsymbol{p}^{-1}\boldsymbol{bp}.$$

When two linear transformations $\boldsymbol{a}$ *and* $\boldsymbol{b}$ *of* $\mathbf{V}$ *are related, as in Equation* (1), *by an invertible linear transformation* $\boldsymbol{p}$, *then* $\boldsymbol{a}$ *and* $\boldsymbol{b}$ *are called* ***similar linear transformations*** *connected by* $\boldsymbol{p}$.

EXAMPLE 2. In Example 1, define $\boldsymbol{p}$ by the equations $\boldsymbol{p}\mathbf{u} = \mathbf{v}$ and $\boldsymbol{p}\mathbf{v} = \mathbf{u}$. Then we have $\boldsymbol{pa} = \boldsymbol{bp}$ (with $\boldsymbol{a}$ and $\boldsymbol{b}$ as given there). The matrix representations of $\boldsymbol{a}$, $\boldsymbol{b}$, and $\boldsymbol{p}$ with respect to the coordinate basis $\{\mathbf{u}, \mathbf{v}\}$ are $A = \begin{pmatrix} 1 & 0 \\ 0 & 2 \end{pmatrix}$, $B = \begin{pmatrix} 2 & 0 \\ 0 & 1 \end{pmatrix}$, and $P = \begin{pmatrix} 0 & 1 \\ 1 & 0 \end{pmatrix}$. They satisfy the matrix equation $PA = BP$, which is a coordinate counterpart of $\boldsymbol{pa} = \boldsymbol{bp}$, with respect to $\{\mathbf{u}, \mathbf{v}\}$: $\boldsymbol{pa} = \boldsymbol{bp} \leftrightarrow PA = BP$. (The latter equations should not be confounded with a formula that we shall begin to use in Section 3.3, where a single linear transformation will be studied with respect to different bases.)

Similar linear transformations $\boldsymbol{a}$ and $\boldsymbol{b}$ are related to each other in a special geometric way which has nothing to do directly with coordinate bases. Roughly stated, $\boldsymbol{b}$ acts on the images under $\boldsymbol{p}$ in faithful imitation of the way $\boldsymbol{a}$ acts on the counterimages. More precisely, $\boldsymbol{a}$ *and* $\boldsymbol{b}$ *are similar linear transformations of* $\mathbf{V}$ *if and only if there exists an invertible linear transformation* $\boldsymbol{p}$ *of* $\mathbf{V}$ *such that, if* $\boldsymbol{a}$ *maps* $\mathbf{u}$ *onto* $\mathbf{v}$ *then* $\boldsymbol{b}$ *maps* $\boldsymbol{p}\mathbf{u}$ *onto* $\boldsymbol{p}\mathbf{v}$. (Because $\boldsymbol{p}$ is invertible, the roles of $\boldsymbol{a}$ and $\boldsymbol{b}$ are interchangeable, with $\boldsymbol{p}$ replaced by $\boldsymbol{p}^{-1}$.) This description merely restates Equation (1) in the form: $\boldsymbol{pa}\mathbf{u} = \boldsymbol{bp}\mathbf{u}$, for every $\mathbf{u}$ in $\mathbf{V}$ and some invertible $\boldsymbol{p}$. See Figure 35 for a schematic description of the mappings.

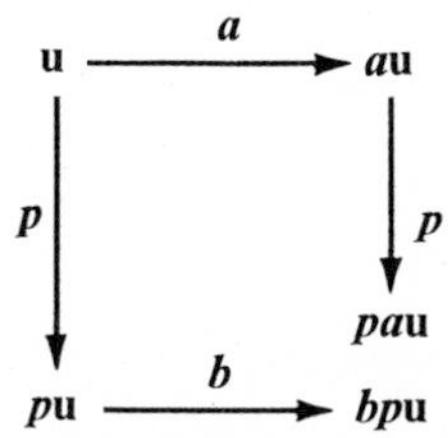

FIGURE 35

Suppose that $\boldsymbol{a}$ and $\boldsymbol{b}$ are similar linear transformations of $\mathbf{V}$, that is, $\boldsymbol{pa} = \boldsymbol{bp}$ for some invertible linear transformation $\boldsymbol{p}$ of $\mathbf{V}$. Let $\{\mathbf{u}_1, \mathbf{u}_2\}$ be any coordinate basis of $\mathbf{V}$. *Set* $\mathbf{v}_i = \boldsymbol{p}\mathbf{u}_i$ $(i = 1, 2)$ *and take* $\{\mathbf{v}_1, \mathbf{v}_2\}$ *as another coordinate basis of* $\mathbf{V}$. Then there exist two unique sets of scalars $\{a_{11}, a_{12}, a_{21}, a_{22}\}$ and $\{b_{11}, b_{12}, b_{21}, b_{22}\}$ such that for $i = 1, 2$, we have

$$\sum \mathbf{v}_j b_{ji} = \boldsymbol{b}\mathbf{v}_i = \boldsymbol{bp}\mathbf{u}_i = \boldsymbol{pa}\mathbf{u}_i = \boldsymbol{p}\sum \mathbf{u}_j a_{ji} = \sum(\boldsymbol{p}\mathbf{u}_j)a_{ji} = \sum \mathbf{v}_j a_{ji}.$$

Hence $b_{ji} = a_{ji}$ for all i, j, which implies that ***a** and **b** are represented with respect to* $\{\mathbf{u}_1, \mathbf{u}_2\}$ *and* $\{\mathbf{v}_1, \mathbf{v}_2\}$, *respectively, by the same matrix.*

*Therefore, we may state that *two linear transformations **a** and **b** of* $\mathbf{V}$ *are similar if and only if there exist two coordinate bases of* $\mathbf{V}$ *with respect to which **a** and **b** are represented, respectively, by the same matrix.*

Note that *any* linear transformation $\boldsymbol{c}$ of $\mathbf{V}$ which is similar to a fixed linear transformation, say $\boldsymbol{a}$, can be represented by the same matrix A which represents $\boldsymbol{a}$. For, if $\boldsymbol{qa} = \boldsymbol{cq}$ where $\boldsymbol{q}$ is an invertible linear transformation of $\mathbf{V}$, then we merely use the connecting linear transformation $\boldsymbol{q}$ to define a suitable basis, as above, with respect to which $\boldsymbol{c}$ will be represented by A also. Thus, if $\boldsymbol{a} \leftrightarrow A$ with respect to $\{\mathbf{u}_1, \mathbf{u}_2\}$, then $\boldsymbol{c} \leftrightarrow A$ with respect to $\{\boldsymbol{q}\mathbf{u}_1, \boldsymbol{q}\mathbf{u}_2\}$.

EXAMPLE 3. In the plane, consider the mapping (reflection across the line $y = x$) with the coordinate equations $x' = y$, $y' = x$. The matrix of coefficients is $A = \begin{pmatrix} 0 & 1 \\ 1 & 0 \end{pmatrix}$. Suppose $\{\mathbf{u}_1, \mathbf{u}_2\}$ and $\{\mathbf{v}_1, \mathbf{v}_2\}$ are two coordinate bases of the vector space at a point $\boldsymbol{O}$, such that $\mathbf{v}_1 = 3\mathbf{u}_1$ and $\mathbf{v}_2 = \mathbf{u}_2$ *as shown in* Figure 36. When (x, y) is regarded as a coordinate row with respect to $\{\mathbf{u}_1, \mathbf{u}_2\}$, let us denote by $\boldsymbol{a}$ the linear transformation represented by A; when (x, y) is regarded as a coordinate row with respect to $\{\mathbf{v}_1, \mathbf{v}_2\}$, let us denote by $\boldsymbol{b}$ the linear transformation represented by A. Finally, define an invertible linear transformation $\boldsymbol{p}$ by $\mathbf{v}_i = \boldsymbol{p}\mathbf{u}_i$ $(i = 1, 2)$. Then we have the interpretation of $\boldsymbol{a}$ and $\boldsymbol{b}$ as similar linear transformations of the plane in which $\boldsymbol{p}$ is the invertible linear transformation which matches images and counterimages. In Figure 36, only the end-points of these vectors are labeled. With respect to $\{\mathbf{u}_1, \mathbf{u}_2\}$, we note that

$$\boldsymbol{p} \leftrightarrow P = \operatorname{diag}(3, 1), \quad \boldsymbol{b} \leftrightarrow B = \begin{pmatrix} 0 & 3 \\ \frac{1}{3} & 0 \end{pmatrix}.$$

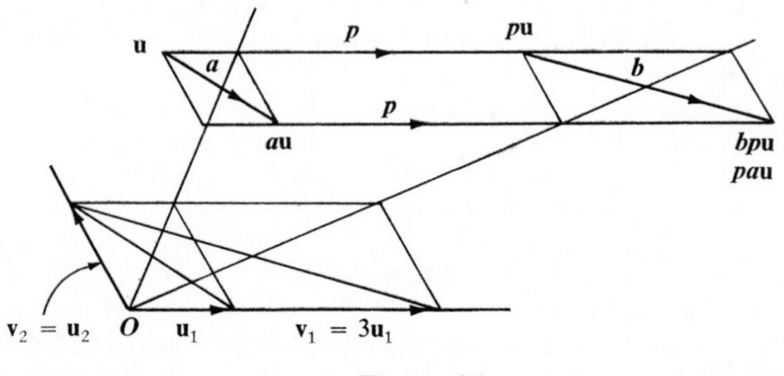

FIGURE 36

Let $\boldsymbol{a}$ and $\boldsymbol{b}$ be similar linear transformations with a connecting invertible linear transformation $\boldsymbol{p}$, and suppose A, B, P represent these linear transformations with respect to the same fixed coordinate basis. Then the equation $\boldsymbol{pa} = \boldsymbol{bp}$ is represented by the matrix equation $PA = BP$ with P invertible, as in Examples 2 and 3.

Now, *when any pair of matrices A and B are related by an equation of the form $PA = BP$, where P is an invertible matrix and the entries in all three lie in a common field, we call the matrices A and B* **similar matrices** *connected by P*. For, we can regard P as the matrix representation, with respect to some fixed coordinate basis of a suitable vector space, of an invertible linear transformation $\boldsymbol{p}$, and regard the equation $PA = BP$ as the matrix representation, with respect to the same coordinate basis, of an equation $\boldsymbol{pa} = \boldsymbol{bp}$ connecting the linear transformations $\boldsymbol{a}$ and $\boldsymbol{b}$ determined by A and B. In other words, $PA = BP$ is a coordinate representation with respect to a single basis of the similarity of two linear transformations.

*Thus we may state that *$\boldsymbol{a}$ and $\boldsymbol{b}$ are similar linear transformations of* **V** *if and only if, with respect to the same coordinate basis, they are represented by similar matrices* (connected by an invertible matrix with scalar entries). The restriction on the entries of the connecting invertible matrix can be weakened because, as we shall see in Chapter 7, when such an invertible matrix exists, with its entries perhaps not in the given scalar field, but in a larger containing field, then there also exists one whose entries are scalars of the given vector space **V**.

PROBLEMS

1. (a) If $\boldsymbol{a}$ is a similitude of magnitude k (>0), show that it is similar only to itself. (b) If $\boldsymbol{p}$ is a similitude and $\boldsymbol{a}$, $\boldsymbol{b}$ are a pair of linear transformations, show that $\boldsymbol{pa} = \boldsymbol{bp}$ if and only if $\boldsymbol{a} = \boldsymbol{b}$. Extend these to "negative" similitudes ($k < 0$).
2. Treat the following cases as in Example 3 and Figure 36, using the same pair of coordinate bases and again showing the images of a typical vector: (a) $A = \operatorname{diag}(1, 2)$, (b) $A = \operatorname{diag}(1/3, 1)$, (c) $A = \begin{pmatrix} 0 & 1 \\ -1 & 0 \end{pmatrix}$. Note that $P = \operatorname{diag}(3, 1)$, and verify $PA = BP$.
3. If $\boldsymbol{a}$ is similar to $\boldsymbol{b}$, show that (a) $\boldsymbol{a}^2$ is similar to $\boldsymbol{b}^2$, (b) $f(\boldsymbol{a})$ is similar to $f(\boldsymbol{b})$, where $f(\boldsymbol{a})$ is any polynomial in $\boldsymbol{a}$ with scalar coefficients, (c) when $\boldsymbol{a}^2$ is similar to $\boldsymbol{b}^2$, then $\boldsymbol{a}$ need not be similar to $\boldsymbol{b}$.
4. Let $\boldsymbol{a}$ be similar to $\boldsymbol{b}$ by an invertible linear transformation $\boldsymbol{p}$. If $\boldsymbol{a}\mathbf{u} = s\mathbf{u}$, show that s is a characteristic number of $\boldsymbol{b}$ and that $\boldsymbol{p}\mathbf{u}$ is a characteristic vector of $\boldsymbol{b}$ belonging to s.
5. For each linear transformation $\boldsymbol{a}$ of a vector space **V**, define a subset of the set of all linear transformations of **V** by $\mathrm{S}(\boldsymbol{a}) = \{\boldsymbol{c} \mid \boldsymbol{c} \text{ is similar to } \boldsymbol{a}\}$. Show that if $\boldsymbol{b}$ is in $\mathrm{S}(\boldsymbol{a})$ then $\mathrm{S}(\boldsymbol{a}) = \mathrm{S}(\boldsymbol{b})$, but if $\boldsymbol{b}$ is *not* in $\mathrm{S}(\boldsymbol{a})$, then $\mathrm{S}(\boldsymbol{a})$ and $\mathrm{S}(\boldsymbol{b})$ have *no* linear transformations in common.
6. Let $\boldsymbol{p}$ be invertible. Show that if $\boldsymbol{pa} = \boldsymbol{a'p}$ and $\boldsymbol{pb} = \boldsymbol{b'p}$, then $\boldsymbol{p}(\boldsymbol{a} + \boldsymbol{b}) = (\boldsymbol{a'} + \boldsymbol{b'})\boldsymbol{p}$ and $\boldsymbol{pab} = \boldsymbol{a'b'p}$.

7. In connection with Example 1, suppose c is a linear transformation whose matrix with respect to $\{\mathbf{u} + \mathbf{v}, \mathbf{u} - 2\mathbf{v}\}$ is $A = \text{diag}(1, 2)$. Show that c is similar to a and b, and that

$$c\mathbf{u} + c\mathbf{v} = \mathbf{u} + \mathbf{v}, \quad c\mathbf{u} - 2c\mathbf{v} = 2\mathbf{u} - 4\mathbf{v},$$

from which we can find the matrix of c with respect to $\{\mathbf{u}, \mathbf{v}\}$, namely,

$$C = \tfrac{1}{3}\begin{pmatrix} 4 & -1 \\ -2 & 5 \end{pmatrix}.$$

Compute P and verify $PA = CP$, where P expresses $\{\mathbf{u} + \mathbf{v}, \mathbf{u} - 2\mathbf{v}\}$ in terms of $\{\mathbf{u}, \mathbf{v}\}$.

3.2 COORDINATE REPRESENTATIONS OF VECTORS

Because an invertible matrix may be regarded as defining a change of coordinate basis, it is possible to consider *similar matrices* as representations of the *same linear transformation. We must first compare the two coordinate columns of a vector* $\mathbf{w}$ *in a vector space* $\mathbf{V}$ *when computed with respect to two coordinate bases.* Let these bases be $\{\mathbf{u}_1, \mathbf{u}_2\}$ and $\{\mathbf{v}_1, \mathbf{v}_2\}$, respectively, as illustrated in Figure 37 for the vector space at O. Then there are unique linear combinations

$$\mathbf{w} = x_1\mathbf{u}_1 + x_2\mathbf{u}_2 = y_1\mathbf{v}_1 + y_2\mathbf{v}_2$$

with corresponding coordinate columns

$$X = \begin{pmatrix} x_1 \\ x_2 \end{pmatrix} \quad \text{and} \quad Y = \begin{pmatrix} y_1 \\ y_2 \end{pmatrix}.$$

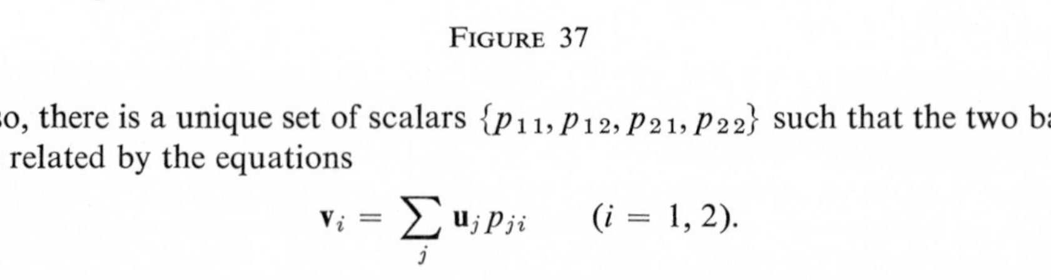

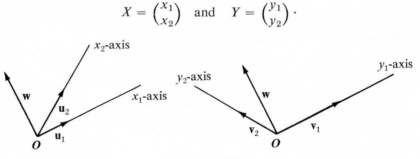

FIGURE 37

Also, there is a unique set of scalars $\{p_{11}, p_{12}, p_{21}, p_{22}\}$ such that the two bases are related by the equations

$$\mathbf{v}_i = \sum_j \mathbf{u}_j p_{ji} \qquad (i = 1, 2). \tag{2}$$

The transpose of the matrix of coefficients of these equations is an invertible matrix

$$P = \begin{pmatrix} p_{11} & p_{12} \\ p_{21} & p_{22} \end{pmatrix}.$$

If we substitute for $\mathbf{v}_i$ in our expression for $\mathbf{w}$ above, we get

$$\mathbf{w} = x_1\mathbf{u}_1 + x_2\mathbf{u}_2 = (y_1p_{11} + y_2p_{12})\mathbf{u}_1 + (y_1p_{21} + y_2p_{22})\mathbf{u}_2,$$

which is equivalent to the coordinate column equation

$$X = PY. \tag{3}$$

It is handy to think of X as the *first* coordinate column and Y as the *second*, corresponding to the habit of calling $\{\mathbf{u}_1, \mathbf{u}_2\}$ the *first* coordinate basis because $\{\mathbf{v}_1, \mathbf{v}_2\}$ is derived from it by Equation (2). Thus, *Equation* (3) *expresses the first coordinate column of* $\mathbf{w}$ *in terms of the second coordinate column, whereas, by Equation* (2), *the columns of P display the coordinates of the vectors in the second coordinate basis with respect to the first coordinate basis.*

EXAMPLE 1. If we use Equations (2) to define a linear transformation $\boldsymbol{p}$ associated with the two bases by the equations $\mathbf{v}_i = \boldsymbol{p}\mathbf{u}_i$ $(i = 1, 2)$, then Equation (3) may be deduced from the equivalent computation

$$\begin{aligned}\mathbf{w} &= \sum_j x_j\mathbf{u}_j = \sum_i y_i\mathbf{v}_i = \sum_i y_i(\boldsymbol{p}\mathbf{u}_i)\\ &= \sum_{i,j} y_i\mathbf{u}_j p_{ji} = \sum_j \left(\sum_i p_{ji}y_i\right)\mathbf{u}_j.\end{aligned}$$

We have used the double subscript notation for the entries in some of our matrices. It is convenient to apply this general notation for entries by using the abbreviations

$$A = (a_{ij}), \quad B = (b_{ij}),$$

and so forth, when the meaning is clear. Also, we extend the use of *transpose* to all tables. For instance, we define the ***transpose of a column matrix*** X, where

$$X = \begin{pmatrix} x_1 \\ x_2 \end{pmatrix},$$

to be the row matrix X^t, where

$$X^t = (x_1, x_2),$$

and we express the column matrix X in horizontal detail by indicating that it is the ***transpose of a row matrix*** (x_1, x_2),

$$X = (x_1, x_2)^t.$$

Hence the equation $X = PY$ can also be expressed in partial detail, on one line, as $(x_1, x_2)^t = P(y_1, y_2)^t$, or in the transposed matrix form $X^t = Y^tP^t$.

In general,

$$B = A^t \quad \textit{means} \quad b_{ij} = a_{ji}, \quad \textit{all } i, j,$$

and A^t *is called the* ***transpose*** *of* A.

EXAMPLE 2. The transpose of a 1×1 matrix equals the same matrix. So if X and Y are column matrices of same size, then $X^tY = (X^tY)^t = Y^tX$.

As we have often remarked, there is a correspondence between the set of changes that can be made in a coordinate basis of $\mathbf{V}$ and the set of invertible linear transformations of $\mathbf{V}$. Every invertible matrix whose entries are scalars of

$\mathbf{V}$ defines a unique change from a given coordinate basis and vice versa. We shall reconsider this correspondence in Chapter 5.

EXAMPLE 3. When $\{\mathbf{u}_1, \mathbf{u}_2\}$, $\{\mathbf{v}_1, \mathbf{v}_2\}$ are two coordinate bases and $\boldsymbol{p}$ is the invertible linear transformation determined by $\mathbf{v}_i = \boldsymbol{p}\mathbf{u}_i$ $(i = 1, 2)$, then $\boldsymbol{p}$ is represented by some matrix $P = (p_{ij})$ with respect to $\{\mathbf{u}_1, \mathbf{u}_2\}$. If we seek the representation of $\boldsymbol{p}$ with respect to $\{\mathbf{v}_1, \mathbf{v}_2\}$, we find

$$\boldsymbol{p}\mathbf{v}_i = \boldsymbol{p}\sum \mathbf{u}_j p_{ji} = \sum(\boldsymbol{p}\mathbf{u}_j)p_{ji} = \sum \mathbf{v}_j p_{ji} \quad (i = 1, 2),$$

which implies that $\boldsymbol{p}$ is again represented by P.

EXAMPLE 4. Every permutation of the vectors in a coordinate basis yields another coordinate basis. If $\{\mathbf{u}, \mathbf{v}\}$ is a coordinate basis of a 2-dimensional vector space $\mathbf{V}$, then the invertible matrices $I = \text{diag}(1, 1)$ and $P = \begin{pmatrix} 0 & 1 \\ 1 & 0 \end{pmatrix}$ correspond to the two possible permutations of $\{\mathbf{u}, \mathbf{v}\}$. (Of course, I yields the same basis again.) Instead of permutations of the basis vectors, we may consider the effect of adding a scalar multiple of one basis vector to a *different* basis vector, for instance a change from $\{\mathbf{u}, \mathbf{v}\}$ to

$$\{\mathbf{u} + k\mathbf{v}, \mathbf{v}\} \quad \text{or} \quad \{\mathbf{u}, \mathbf{v} + k\mathbf{u}\}.$$

The corresponding invertible matrices are, respectively,

$$P = \begin{pmatrix} 1 & 0 \\ k & 1 \end{pmatrix} \quad \text{and} \quad P = \begin{pmatrix} 1 & k \\ 0 & 1 \end{pmatrix}.$$

Finally, consider a change from $\{\mathbf{u}, \mathbf{v}\}$ to

$$\{\mathbf{u}, k\mathbf{v}\} \quad \text{or} \quad \{k\mathbf{u}, \mathbf{v}\} \quad (k \neq 0).$$

The corresponding invertible matrices are, respectively,

$$P = \begin{pmatrix} 1 & 0 \\ 0 & k \end{pmatrix} \quad \text{and} \quad P = \begin{pmatrix} k & 0 \\ 0 & 1 \end{pmatrix} \qquad (k \neq 0).$$

PROBLEMS

1. A coordinate basis $\{\mathbf{u}, \mathbf{v}, \mathbf{w}\}$ of a 3-dimensional vector space $\mathbf{V}$ can be permuted into six distinct coordinate bases (one of which is the same as the original). Find the corresponding invertible matrix representations and describe the effects on the coordinate column of a vector in $\mathbf{V}$. Find their determinants.
2. Find the types of invertible matrices which correspond to each of the following changes of a coordinate basis in a 3-dimensional vector space: (a) Interchange two basis vectors. (b) Multiply one basis vector by a non-zero scalar. (c) Add a scalar multiple of one basis vector to a different basis vector. Show the effects on a coordinate column. Find their determinants.
3. Prove that $(X + Y)^t = X^t + Y^t$, $(cX)^t = cX^t$ for column matrices of same height. Prove that $(A + B)^t = A^t + B^t$, $(AB)^t = B^tA^t$, and $(cA)^t = cA^t$, for square matrices of same size.

3.3 MATRIX REPRESENTATIONS OF A SINGLE LINEAR TRANSFORMATION

We now consider a single linear transformation $\boldsymbol{a}$ *and compare its matrix representations when computed with respect to two coordinate bases.* Let $\{\mathbf{u}_1, \mathbf{u}_2\}$ and $\{\mathbf{v}_1, \mathbf{v}_2\}$ be coordinate bases of a 2-dimensional vector space $\mathbf{V}$ and let $\boldsymbol{p}$ be the invertible linear transformation determined by $\mathbf{v}_i = \boldsymbol{p}\mathbf{u}_i$ $(i = 1, 2)$. Suppose $\boldsymbol{a}$ is represented by $A = (a_{ij})$ *with respect to* $\{\mathbf{u}_1, \mathbf{u}_2\}$, and by $B = (b_{ij})$ *with respect to* $\{\mathbf{v}_1, \mathbf{v}_2\}$. This means that we have

$$\boldsymbol{a}\mathbf{v}_i = \sum_j \mathbf{v}_j b_{ji} = \sum_k \mathbf{u}_k \left(\sum_j p_{kj} b_{ji}\right),$$

and

$$\boldsymbol{a}\mathbf{v}_i = \boldsymbol{a}\boldsymbol{p}\mathbf{u}_i = \boldsymbol{a}\sum_j \mathbf{u}_j p_{ji} = \sum_j (\boldsymbol{a}\mathbf{u}_j) p_{ji} = \sum_k \mathbf{u}_k \left(\sum_j a_{kj} p_{ji}\right).$$

Hence $PB = AP$, *where the invertible matrix* $P = (p_{ij})$ *represents* $\boldsymbol{p}$ *with respect to either basis* (Section 3.2, Example 3). We have already designated such a pair of matrices A and B as *similar matrices*, regardless of the source of the connecting matrix P. Therefore, we have that *the matrix representations of* $\boldsymbol{a}$ *with respect to the two coordinate bases* $\{\mathbf{u}_1, \mathbf{u}_2\}$, $\{\boldsymbol{p}\mathbf{u}_1, \boldsymbol{p}\mathbf{u}_2\}$, *are similar matrices, connected by the representation of the invertible linear transformation* $\boldsymbol{p}$. If X is the coordinate column of a vector with respect to $\{\mathbf{u}_1, \mathbf{u}_2\}$, then we may relate the above coordinate facts by the diagram in Figure 38.

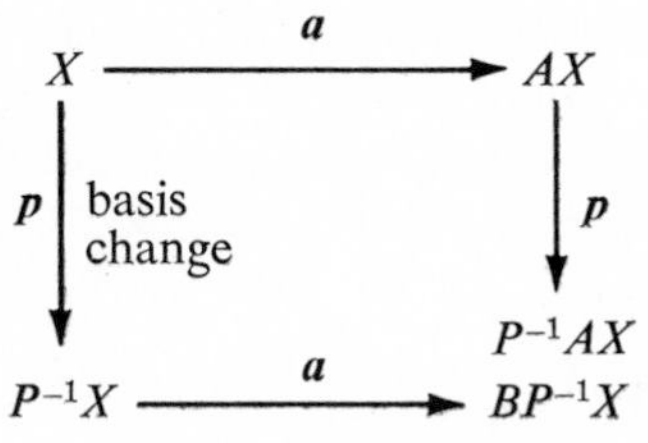

FIGURE 38

*Our present matrix equation

$$PB = AP$$

expresses the similarity of two matrices A and B which are computed with respect to the two coordinate bases $\{\mathbf{u}_1, \mathbf{u}_2\}$ and $\{\boldsymbol{p}\mathbf{u}_1, \boldsymbol{p}\mathbf{u}_2\}$ of $\mathbf{V}$, and *both matrices represent* $\boldsymbol{a}$. The coordinate equation $PA = BP$ of Section 3.1 expresses the similarity of two matrices A and B which are computed with respect to the same coordinate basis $\{\mathbf{u}_1, \mathbf{u}_2\}$ of $\mathbf{V}$ and *they represent the two similar linear transformations* $\boldsymbol{a}$ *and* $\boldsymbol{b}$, respectively. If we had used $\boldsymbol{p}^{-1}$ instead of $\boldsymbol{p}$ in Section 3.1, then our equations would have looked the same. Beginning with the present section, we shall favor the $PB = AP$ form for similar matrices when $\boldsymbol{a} \leftrightarrow A$ with respect to the *first* coordinate basis and $\boldsymbol{a} \leftrightarrow B$ with respect to the *second* coordinate basis.

Notice that in the product $P^{-1}AP$, the factor $P^{-1}A$ has columns which are the coordinate columns of the images (under $\boldsymbol{a}$) of the vectors in the first coordinate basis, *expressed with respect to the second coordinate basis.* For, when the i-th basis vector $\mathbf{u}_i$ is expressed with respect to the first coordinate basis, it has a coordinate column E_i with the number 1 in the i-th position and zeros elsewhere (a *unit column vector*); hence the statement follows by applying Equation (3) to $P^{-1}(AE_i)$. This observation can sometimes shorten the computation of $P^{-1}AP$. For instance, consider the computation of C in Section 3.1, Problem 7. We can regard $\{\mathbf{u} + \mathbf{v}, \mathbf{u} - 2\mathbf{v}\}$ as a *first* coordinate basis to get P^{-1} amd $P^{-1}A$ without computation. Thus

$$P^{-1} = \begin{pmatrix} 1 & 1 \\ 1 & -2 \end{pmatrix}, \quad P^{-1}A = \begin{pmatrix} 1 & 2 \\ 1 & -4 \end{pmatrix}, \quad P = \tfrac{1}{3}\begin{pmatrix} 2 & 1 \\ 1 & -1 \end{pmatrix}, \quad P^{-1}AP = C.$$

(Note that the matrix P here is the inverse of the matrix denoted by P in Problem 7.)

EXAMPLE 1. Suppose $\boldsymbol{a}$ is a perpendicular reflection of real 3-dimensional space across the plane $x - y + z = 0$, where (x, y, z) are Cartesian coordinates, with the usual mutually perpendicular unit vectors $\{\mathbf{i}, \mathbf{j}, \mathbf{k}\}$ as a coordinate basis at some point. The given information about $\boldsymbol{a}$ is readily expressed in terms of a convenient *first* coordinate basis such as

$$\{\mathbf{i} - \mathbf{j} + \mathbf{k}, \quad \mathbf{j} + \mathbf{k}, \quad \mathbf{i} + \mathbf{j}\},$$

where $\mathbf{i} - \mathbf{j} + \mathbf{k}$ is perpendicular to the given plane and the two other vectors are just a particular choice of coordinate basis for the invariant subspace at $\boldsymbol{O}$ consisting of the position vectors to the points of the given plane. Hence $\boldsymbol{a}$ is determined by the vector equations

$$\boldsymbol{a}(\mathbf{i} - \mathbf{j} + \mathbf{k}) = -\mathbf{i} + \mathbf{j} - \mathbf{k}, \quad \boldsymbol{a}(\mathbf{j} + \mathbf{k}) = \mathbf{j} + \mathbf{k}, \quad \boldsymbol{a}(\mathbf{i} + \mathbf{j}) = \mathbf{i} + \mathbf{j}.$$

This gives immediately a representation of $\boldsymbol{a}$, with respect to the *first* coordinate basis, by

$$A = \operatorname{diag}(-1, 1, 1).$$

In this example, the invertible matrix P, whose columns express the *second* coordinate basis $\{\mathbf{i}, \mathbf{j}, \mathbf{k}\}$ in terms of the *first* one, is less easily computed than is its inverse, because it is obvious that

$$P^{-1} = \begin{pmatrix} 1 & 0 & 1 \\ -1 & 1 & 1 \\ 1 & 1 & 0 \end{pmatrix}; \quad \text{hence} \quad P = \tfrac{1}{3}\begin{pmatrix} 1 & -1 & 1 \\ -1 & 1 & 2 \\ 2 & 1 & -1 \end{pmatrix}.$$

Here we also note that the right-hand sides of the vector equations for $\boldsymbol{a}$ give us $P^{-1}A$ directly as

$$P^{-1}A = \begin{pmatrix} -1 & 0 & 1 \\ 1 & 1 & 1 \\ -1 & 1 & 0 \end{pmatrix},$$

which is readily checked against the known A. So, either way, we find that $\boldsymbol{a}$ is represented by

$$B = P^{-1}AP = \frac{1}{3}\begin{pmatrix} 1 & 2 & -2 \\ 2 & 1 & 2 \\ -2 & 2 & 1 \end{pmatrix}$$

with respect to the second coordinate basis $\{\mathbf{i}, \mathbf{j}, \mathbf{k}\}$. This computation of B is actually equivalent to using algebraic elimination on the simultaneous vector equations

$$\begin{aligned} \boldsymbol{a}\mathbf{i} - \boldsymbol{a}\mathbf{j} + \boldsymbol{a}\mathbf{k} &= -\mathbf{i} + \mathbf{j} - \mathbf{k}, \\ \boldsymbol{a}\mathbf{j} + \boldsymbol{a}\mathbf{k} &= \mathbf{j} + \mathbf{k}, \\ \boldsymbol{a}\mathbf{i} + \boldsymbol{a}\mathbf{j} \qquad &= \mathbf{i} + \mathbf{j}, \end{aligned}$$

in order to solve for $\boldsymbol{a}\mathbf{i}$, $\boldsymbol{a}\mathbf{j}$, and $\boldsymbol{a}\mathbf{k}$ as linear combinations of $\mathbf{i}, \mathbf{j}, \mathbf{k}$.

EXAMPLE 2. In Section 2.6, Example 1, we can determine an invertible linear transformation $\boldsymbol{p}$ by the equations $\boldsymbol{p}\mathbf{i} = \mathbf{i}$ and $\boldsymbol{p}\mathbf{j} = (\sqrt{2}/2)(\mathbf{i} + \mathbf{j})$, having the corresponding invertible matrix representation

$$P = \begin{pmatrix} 1 & \sqrt{2}/2 \\ 0 & \sqrt{2}/2 \end{pmatrix}, \quad \text{with} \quad P^{-1} = \begin{pmatrix} 1 & -1 \\ 0 & \sqrt{2} \end{pmatrix}.$$

With these we can again obtain the representation given in that example, for instance, by computing

$$P^{-1}\begin{pmatrix} \cos\phi & -\sin\phi \\ \sin\phi & \cos\phi \end{pmatrix} P.$$

Suppose we have a relation $B = P^{-1}AP$ among three matrices A, B, P, where all the entries are in the scalar field of a vector space $\mathbf{V}$. Let $\{\mathbf{u}_1, \mathbf{u}_2\}$ be a *first* coordinate basis of $\mathbf{V}$ and let $\{\mathbf{v}_1, \mathbf{v}_2\}$ be a *second* basis derived from the first one by use of the invertible matrix P:

$$\mathbf{v}_i = \sum \mathbf{u}_j p_{ji}.$$

Also, let $\boldsymbol{a}$ be the linear transformation of $\mathbf{V}$ determined with respect to $\{\mathbf{u}_1, \mathbf{u}_2\}$ by the matrix A, and let $\boldsymbol{b}$ be the linear transformation determined with respect to $\{\mathbf{v}_1, \mathbf{v}_2\}$ by B. If $\mathbf{u}$ is any vector in $\mathbf{V}$, with coordinate column X with respect to $\{\mathbf{u}_1, \mathbf{u}_2\}$, then $\mathbf{u}$ has a coordinate column $P^{-1}X$ with respect to $\{\mathbf{v}_1, \mathbf{v}_2\}$. Now, consider the images $\boldsymbol{a}\mathbf{u}$ and $\boldsymbol{b}\mathbf{u}$. The coordinate column matrices of these vectors with respect to $\{\mathbf{v}_1, \mathbf{v}_2\}$ are $P^{-1}AX$ and $BP^{-1}X$, respectively. Since we are assuming that $BP^{-1} = P^{-1}A$, we get $\boldsymbol{a}\mathbf{u} = \boldsymbol{b}\mathbf{u}$ for every $\mathbf{u}$. Therefore, $\boldsymbol{a} = \boldsymbol{b}$ and we have that *similar matrices can be regarded as coordinate representations, with respect to two coordinate bases, of a single linear transformation of a suitable vector space.* This is the converse of what we have already shown.

*Thus, if A, B, and P are three given matrices with entries in the scalar field of a given vector space $\mathbf{V}$, then we may state that: *A and B are similar matrices* *related by the equation* $B = P^{-1}AP$, *if and only if A and B represent the same linear transformation* $\boldsymbol{a}$ of $\mathbf{V}$ *with respect to two coordinate bases* $\{\mathbf{u}_1, \mathbf{u}_2\}$ *and* $\{\mathbf{v}_1, \mathbf{v}_2\}$, *respectively, where these bases are connected by the equations*

$$\mathbf{v}_i = \sum_j \mathbf{u}_j p_{ji} \qquad (i = 1, 2).$$

Finally, consider the set $S(\boldsymbol{a}) = \{\boldsymbol{c} \mid \boldsymbol{c} \text{ similar to } \boldsymbol{a}\}$, as defined in Section 3.1, Problem 5. *If we look at the set of matrices which represent all the linear transformations in* $S(\boldsymbol{a})$ *with respect to a fixed basis, then we see that this set is the same as the set of matrices which represent the single linear transformation* $\boldsymbol{a}$ *with respect to all possible bases.* For in each case, we have the same set of *similar* matrices (see Problem 8 below). The simplest and most revealing matrix representations of the linear transformations in $S(\boldsymbol{a})$ are discussed in Chapter 7.

EXAMPLE 3. In Section 2.18 we classified the linear transformations of the plane (real 2-dimensional vector space) into three collections of distinct non-overlapping classes (a′), (b′), (c′). We can now relate these classes to similarity.

(a′) Those linear transformations with the same pair of characteristic numbers s_1, s_2, and for which there is a pair of non-proportional characteristic vectors, are *similar linear transformations* because they are all represented by $\operatorname{diag}(s_1, s_2)$.

(b′) Those linear transformations with the same repeated characteristic number s, and whose characteristic vectors generate only a 1-dimensional subspace, are *similar linear transformations* because they are all represented by $\begin{pmatrix} s & 1 \\ 0 & s \end{pmatrix}$.

(c′) Those linear transformations for which there is no characteristic vector and which have the same characteristic polynomial $x^2 - dx - b$ (d and b real, $d^2 + 4b < 0$) are *similar linear transformations* because they are all represented by $\begin{pmatrix} 0 & b \\ 1 & d \end{pmatrix}$.

This classification is, simultaneously, a classification of all real 2×2 matrices under similarity by real invertible matrices.

EXAMPLE 4. If we consider a complex 2-dimensional vector space (complex numbers as the field of scalars), the method of classification in Example 3 still works except that type (c′) does not exist because every quadratic equation factors with respect to the complex numbers and this guarantees the existence of characteristic numbers for every linear transformation of this vector space.

EXAMPLE 5. If $A = \begin{pmatrix} \cos\phi & -\sin\phi \\ \sin\phi & \cos\phi \end{pmatrix}$, then the characteristic polynomial of A is

$$|xI - A| = x^2 - (2\cos\phi)x + 1.$$

Suppose ϕ is not an integral multiple of π. Then with respect to *real* scalars this polynomial is *irreducible*, that is, it can not be factored non-trivially without using numbers other than real numbers. Hence any linear transformation associated with such an A fits into class (c′) of Example 3, so A is similar to

$$\begin{pmatrix} 0 & -1 \\ 1 & 2\cos\phi \end{pmatrix}.$$

If our field of scalars happens to include the roots of the characteristic equation of A, then A is similar to

$$\operatorname{diag}(e^{i\phi}, e^{-i\phi}).$$

EXAMPLE 6. Suppose a linear transformation $\boldsymbol{a}$ is represented by $A = \operatorname{diag}(s_1, s_2)$. If $p(x)$ is any polynomial with scalar coefficients, then

$$p(A) = \operatorname{diag}\big(p(s_1), p(s_2)\big).$$

Thus the linear transformation $p(\boldsymbol{a})$ has characteristic polynomial $\big(x - p(s_1)\big)\big(x - p(s_2)\big)$, and its characteristic numbers are $p(s_1)$ and $p(s_2)$. But if $\boldsymbol{a}$ is represented by $A = \begin{pmatrix} s & 1 \\ 0 & s \end{pmatrix}$, then

$$p(A) = \begin{pmatrix} p(s) & p'(s) \\ 0 & p(s) \end{pmatrix},$$

where $p'(x) = dp(x)/dx$. The characteristic polynomial of the latter matrix is $\big(x - p(s)\big)^2$.

EXAMPLE 7. If $PB = AP$ for an invertible matrix P, then $|B| = |A|$, and

$$|xI - A| = |xI - PBP^{-1}| = |P(xI - B)P^{-1}| = |xI - B|.$$

Therefore *similar linear transformations have the same characteristic polynomial.* The converse is not true in general, as is shown by the linear transformations represented by sI and $\begin{pmatrix} s & 1 \\ 0 & s \end{pmatrix}$. Each has characteristic polynomial $(x - s)^2$, but they are *not* similar (Problem 2 below).

PROBLEMS

1. If A and B are similar matrices, show that: (a) $|A| = |B|$, (b) $\sum a_{ii} = \sum b_{ii}$, (c) B is similar to a matrix C if and only if A is similar to C. (See Section 6.2, Example 2.)
2. Show that: (a) If $\{s_1, s_2\}$ and $\{t_1, t_2\}$ are two pairs (not ordered) of complex numbers, then $\operatorname{diag}(s_1, s_2)$ and $\operatorname{diag}(t_1, t_2)$ are similar by an invertible P with complex entries if and only if the two pairs consist of the same numbers. (b) No matrix of form $\begin{pmatrix} s & 1 \\ 0 & s \end{pmatrix}$ is similar to $\operatorname{diag}(s_1, s_2)$.
3. Show that there is no real matrix P such that $P^{-1}AP$ is diagonal if
$$A = \begin{pmatrix} -1 & 1 \\ -1 & 0 \end{pmatrix}.$$
4. Produce a *real* invertible matrix P such that $P^{-1}AP = B$ if
$$A = \begin{pmatrix} 0 & 0 & 1 \\ 1 & 0 & 0 \\ 0 & 1 & 0 \end{pmatrix}, \qquad B = \begin{pmatrix} 0 & 1 & 0 \\ 0 & 0 & 1 \\ 1 & 0 & 0 \end{pmatrix},$$
and thus show the similarity of the linear transformations $\boldsymbol{a}$ and $\boldsymbol{b}$ of a real vector space, defined on a coordinate basis $\{\mathbf{u}, \mathbf{v}, \mathbf{w}\}$ by
$$\begin{aligned} \boldsymbol{a}\mathbf{u} &= \mathbf{v}, & \boldsymbol{b}\mathbf{u} &= \mathbf{w}, \\ \boldsymbol{a}\mathbf{v} &= \mathbf{w}, \quad \text{and} & \boldsymbol{b}\mathbf{v} &= \mathbf{u}, \\ \boldsymbol{a}\mathbf{w} &= \mathbf{u}, & \boldsymbol{b}\mathbf{w} &= \mathbf{v}. \end{aligned}$$
5. Find a basis with respect to which $\boldsymbol{b}$ in Problem 4 is represented by A. Show that A is similar to $\operatorname{diag}(1, \omega, \omega^2)$, where ω is an imaginary cube root of 1.
6. If $\{A_1, \ldots, A_n\}$ and $\{B_1, \ldots, B_n\}$ are two sets of square matrices and if A_i is similar to B_i for each i, show that the diagonal-block matrix $\operatorname{diag}(A_1, \ldots, A_n)$ is similar to $\operatorname{diag}(B_1, \ldots, B_n)$.
7. With respect to an x, y, z Cartesian coordinate system in real 3-dimensional space, suppose a linear transformation $\boldsymbol{a}$ has the defining property that the line $x = y = z$ is the perpendicular bisector of the line segment which connects any point to its image point. Find the matrix representation of $\boldsymbol{a}$ with respect to the given coordinate system.
8. Let $\{\mathbf{u}, \mathbf{v}\}$ be an arbitrary basis of a 2-dimensional vector space, and suppose that each entry in the following table is a coordinate basis for which the linear transformation above the entry is represented by the matrix to the left of the entry. Show that the existence of this table is equivalent to the similarity of two linear transformations $\boldsymbol{a}$ and $\boldsymbol{b}$ via an equation $\boldsymbol{pb} = \boldsymbol{ap}$, or the similarity of two matrices A and B via an equation $PB = AP$.

	$\boldsymbol{a}$	$\boldsymbol{b}$
A	$\{\mathbf{u}, \mathbf{v}\}$	$\{\boldsymbol{p}^{-1}\mathbf{u}, \boldsymbol{p}^{-1}\mathbf{v}\}$
B	$\{\boldsymbol{p}\mathbf{u}, \boldsymbol{p}\mathbf{v}\}$	$\{\mathbf{u}, \mathbf{v}\}$

3.4 REAL SYMMETRIC MATRICES

A matrix is called **symmetric** *if and only if it equals its transpose*, that is, if and only if

$$A = A^t.$$

This is consistent with our previous definition (Section 2.17, Example 4) for the 2×2 case, where a symmetric matrix is one that has equal off-diagonal entries. In the 3×3 case a symmetric matrix has the form

$$\begin{pmatrix} a & d & e \\ d & b & f \\ e & f & c \end{pmatrix}.$$

If we use the double subscript notation, $A = (a_{ij})$, then *the symmetry condition* $A = A^t$ *means that* $a_{ij} = a_{ji}$ *for all values of the row index i and column index j.*

EXAMPLE 1. Every diagonal matrix is trivially symmetric. If A is any square matrix, then $A + A^t$ is symmetric, as are also the products AA^t and A^tA. These facts can be verified directly or by use of Section 3.2, Problem 3.

Now, *it may happen that a linear transformation* $\boldsymbol{a}$ *is represented by a symmetric matrix A with respect to some coordinate basis.* Suppose that such an $\boldsymbol{a}$ is a linear transformation of a real 2-dimensional vector space. Then we have seen (Section 2.17, Example 4) that $\boldsymbol{a}$ *has two real characteristic numbers* s_1, s_2, possibly equal. To these numbers there belong characteristic vectors of $\boldsymbol{a}$ and corresponding real characteristic column vectors of the real symmetric matrix A, which we are assuming represents $\boldsymbol{a}$. *We also noted that* $A = sI$ *when* $s_1 = s_2 = s$.

EXAMPLE 2. Whether or not the 2×2 *real* matrix A of the linear transformation $\boldsymbol{a}$ is symmetric, suppose it has two *distinct real* characteristic numbers s_1 and s_2. Let U_1 and U_2 be characteristic column vectors belonging to these numbers, so $AU_i = s_iU_i$ $(i = 1, 2)$. If U_1 and U_2 are proportional, then $U_2 = kU_1$ for some $k \neq 0$. But this implies $AU_2 = kAU_1 = ks_1U_1$, as well as $AU_2 = ks_2U_1$, which is impossible because $s_1 \neq s_2$, $U_1 \neq 0$ and $k \neq 0$. *Hence* $\{U_1, U_2\}$ *is a basis of the vector space of* 2×1 *column vectors.* Moreover, if the characteristic vectors of the linear transformation $\boldsymbol{a}$ (represented by A), which are represented by U_1 and U_2, are $\mathbf{u}_1$ and $\mathbf{u}_2$, then $\{\mathbf{u}_1, \mathbf{u}_2\}$ must be a basis. *Using* $\{\mathbf{u}_1, \mathbf{u}_2\}$ *as a coordinate basis, we have* $\boldsymbol{a}\mathbf{u}_i = s_i\mathbf{u}_i$ $(i = 1, 2)$, *so* $\boldsymbol{a}$ *is represented with respect to this basis by* $\operatorname{diag}(s_1, s_2)$. If A is, in addition, *symmetric*, then the case $s_1 = s_2 = s$ implies A is already diagonal, that is, equal to $\operatorname{diag}(s, s) = sI$ (Section 2.17, Example 4).

**Therefore, if a linear transformation of a real 2-dimensional vector space can be represented by a symmetric matrix with respect to some coordinate basis,* *then it can be represented by a diagonal matrix with respect to some coordinate basis.*

Suppose a *real symmetric matrix* A has two *distinct* characteristic numbers s_1 and s_2. Let U_1 and U_2 be characteristic column vectors belonging to these numbers. From $AU_i = s_iU_i (i = 1, 2)$ we get $U_2^tAU_1 = s_1U_2^tU_1$ and $U_1^tAU_2 = s_2U_1^tU_2$. Since $A = A^t$, the left-hand sides are equal. Therefore

$$(s_1 - s_2)U_2^tU_1 = 0.$$

(A 1×1 matrix is often denoted simply by its entry, as is done in the present case for the 1×1 zero matrix.) This equation implies $U_2^tU_1 = 0$ or, what is the same, $U_1^tU_2 = 0$. If our reference frame is Cartesian, then the equation $U_2^tU_1 = 0$ coincides with the condition for the orthogonality (perpendicularity) of two lines in the direction of non-zero vectors whose coordinate columns are U_1 and U_2, respectively. *This geometric terminology is applied in general to any two real column vectors U and V for which*

$$U^tV = 0,$$

by calling U and V ***orthogonal.***

EXAMPLE 3. *If A is a real 2×2 symmetric matrix, then there exist two orthogonal characteristic column vectors U_1 and U_2 which are not proportional.* If $s_1 \neq s_2$, we have already proved the non-proportionality even more generally in Example 2, although it also follows from their orthogonality. If $s_1 = s_2$, then every non-zero real column matrix is a characteristic column vector of A; so we pick $U_1 \neq O$ and solve $U_1^tV = 0$ for a real non-zero orthogonal column vector which will then serve as U_2. In Section 2.17, Example 1, for instance, it is readily verified that $(1, 1)^t$ is orthogonal to $(1, -1)^t$ and both are characteristic column vectors.

Let U_1 and U_2 be orthogonal characteristic column vectors of a real symmetric 2×2 matrix A. Define a matrix P whose columns are formed from U_1 and U_2, respectively. We can write P in the partitioned form

$$P = (U_1, U_2),$$

where the comma is there merely to separate the symbols. In terms of P, *we can consolidate the equations $AU_i = s_iU_i$ $(i = 1, 2)$ into the single equation*

$$PS = AP, \quad \text{where} \quad S = \text{diag}(s_1, s_2).$$

As we have noted (Section 2.13, Problem 6), a matrix like P is invertible because its columns, considered as vectors, define a basis for the vector space of column vectors. Therefore we have $P^{-1}AP = S$. *This means that the linear transformation represented by A can also be represented by the diagonal matrix S,* which corroborates the result of Example 2, but also gives *an explicit matrix formula* for *a connecting matrix P.*

EXAMPLE 4. We can discover more about the above matrix $P = (U_1, U_2)$ if we compute the symmetric matrix P^tP as follows:

$$P^tP = \begin{pmatrix} U_1^t \\ U_2^t \end{pmatrix} (U_1, U_2) = \operatorname{diag}(U_1^t U_1, U_2^t U_2).$$

Since U_1 and U_2 are not zero, we can define an invertible matrix Q by

$$Q = \operatorname{diag}((U_1^t U_1)^{-1/2}, (U_2^t U_2)^{-1/2}).$$

Then $Q^t = Q$ and $(Q^2P^t)P = I$, which gives the inverse of P. But also, we see that

$$(PQ)^t(PQ) = I,$$

a property we shall consider below, in the case $Q = I$.

If a real non-zero column vector U is multiplied by the real number $(U^tU)^{-1/2}$, then the resulting column vector is said to be ***normalized.*** We can normalize the vectors in any set $\{U_1, U_2\}$ of orthogonal characteristic column vectors of our real symmetric matrix A above. *Let us assume that U_1 and U_2 are already normalized, hence*

$$U_i^t U_j = 0 \quad \text{if } i \neq j, \quad \text{but} = 1 \text{ if } i = j.$$

Such a pair of column vectors is called ***orthonormal.*** When a set $\{U_1, U_2\}$ of characteristic column vectors of A is thus chosen to be an orthonormal pair, then $Q = I$ in Example 4 above, and the matrix

$$P = (U_1, U_2)$$

has the property

$$P^tP = I.$$

Since this implies $P^t = P^{-1}$, we also have $PP^t = I$. *Any real matrix which, like this matrix P, has its transpose as its inverse, is called* ***real orthogonal.***

*Our result is: *Any 2×2 real symmetric matrix A is similar to a real diagonal matrix S, connected by a real orthogonal matrix P whose columns are orthonormal characteristic column vectors of A,*

$$S = \operatorname{diag}(s_1, s_2) = P^{-1}AP.$$

Later we shall see that this is true for *any* real symmetric matrix, in particular, for the 3×3 case (see Section 3.5, Problem 6) *which we shall assume in this chapter.*

EXAMPLE 5. The matrices

$$P = \begin{pmatrix} \cos\phi & -\sin\phi \\ \sin\phi & \cos\phi \end{pmatrix} \quad \text{and} \quad Q = \begin{pmatrix} \cos\phi & \sin\phi \\ \sin\phi & -\cos\phi \end{pmatrix}$$

are real orthogonal (ϕ is a real number). But $|P| = 1$ while $|Q| = -1$. If we note that $Q = P\operatorname{diag}(1, -1)$, we can regard Q as the representation of the successive application of a special reflection and a rotation. When a real orthogonal matrix has determinant 1, it is called a *rotation matrix* or *proper orthogonal matrix;* when the determinant equals -1, the matrix is called *improper orthogonal.*

EXAMPLE 6. Our discussion implies a computational procedure which we illustrate here. We shall find a real orthogonal P and a real diagonal S for two real symmetric matrices.

(a) First, let $A = \begin{pmatrix} 0 & 2 \\ 2 & 0 \end{pmatrix}$. Then $|xI - A| = x^2 - 4$, so $s_1 = 2$, $s_2 = -2$, and $S = \text{diag}(2, -2)$. If we wish to see an orthogonal matrix P for which $S = P^{-1}AP$, we solve $(sI - A)X = O$ first with $s = 2$, then with $s = -2$. The system $(2I - A)X = O$ yields an equation $x_1 - x_2 = 0$, so we choose a normalized solution $U_1 = (1/\sqrt{2})(1, 1)^t$. The system $(-2I - A)X = O$ yields $x_1 + x_2 = 0$, so we choose a normalized solution $U_2 = (1/\sqrt{2})(1, -1)^t$. Then $P = (U_1, U_2)$, for which it is easy to check that $PS = AP$. (The fact that here $P = P^t$, is accidental.)

(b) Second, let

$$A = \begin{pmatrix} 0 & 1 & 1 \\ 1 & -1 & 0 \\ 1 & 0 & 1 \end{pmatrix}.$$

Then $|xI - A| = x^3 - 3x$. For, expansion of $|A|$ by the top row yields

$$0\begin{vmatrix} -1 & 0 \\ 0 & 1 \end{vmatrix} - 1\begin{vmatrix} 1 & 0 \\ 1 & 1 \end{vmatrix} + 1\begin{vmatrix} 1 & -1 \\ 1 & 0 \end{vmatrix} = 0,$$

which is the *constant term* in $|xI - A|$, while the other coefficients come from the computations $-(0 - 1 + 1) = 0$ and

$$\begin{vmatrix} 0 & 1 \\ 1 & -1 \end{vmatrix} + \begin{vmatrix} 0 & 1 \\ 1 & 1 \end{vmatrix} + \begin{vmatrix} -1 & 0 \\ 0 & 1 \end{vmatrix} = -1 - 1 - 1 = -3$$

(see Section 2.17, Example 3). Hence the characteristic numbers are $\{0, \sqrt{3}, -\sqrt{3}\}$, and $S = \text{diag}(0, \sqrt{3}, -\sqrt{3})$. To compute P, we solve, in turn, the equations

$$(0I - A)X = O, \quad (\sqrt{3}\, I - A)X = O, \quad \text{and} \quad (-\sqrt{3}\, I - A)X = O.$$

Because the characteristic numbers are distinct, the characteristic column vectors are *orthogonal. Normalized* solutions can be selected as follows:

$$X_1 = (1/\sqrt{3})(1, 1, -1)^t,$$
$$X_2 = (1/\sqrt{3})(1, (\sqrt{3} - 1)/2, \quad (\sqrt{3} + 1)/2)^t,$$
$$X_3 = (1/\sqrt{3})(1, -(\sqrt{3} + 1)/2, \quad (-\sqrt{3} + 1)/2)^t.$$

Therefore, we take $P = (X_1, X_2, X_3)$.

EXAMPLE 7. We can try to compute *directly* the plane rotation matrix P (see Example 5) which takes a 2×2 real symmetric matrix A into $S = \text{diag}(s_1, s_2)$. Set

$$A = \begin{pmatrix} a & b \\ b & c \end{pmatrix},$$

and consider $PS = AP$, or in more detail,

$$\begin{pmatrix} s_1 \cos\phi & -s_2 \sin\phi \\ s_1 \sin\phi & s_2 \cos\phi \end{pmatrix} = \begin{pmatrix} a\cos\phi + b\sin\phi & -a\sin\phi + b\cos\phi \\ b\cos\phi + c\sin\phi & -b\sin\phi + c\cos\phi \end{pmatrix}.$$

If we equate the entries in the respective first columns and then divide the two left-hand sides and the two right-hand sides of these equations, we get (omitting exceptional cases):

$$\tan\phi = (b + c\tan\phi)/(a + b\tan\phi),$$

or

$$\tan^2\phi + \big((a - c)/b\big)\tan\phi - 1 = 0.$$

Hence

$$(1 - \tan^2\phi)/\tan\phi = (a - c)/b,$$

which implies

$$\tan 2\phi = (2\tan\phi)/(1 - \tan^2\phi) = 2b/(a - c).$$

This is the familiar formula from analytic geometry.

EXAMPLE 8. Can a linear transformation always be represented by a symmetric matrix by choosing a suitable coordinate basis? Consider the special case of a linear transformation which is represented by $A = \begin{pmatrix} 0 & 1 \\ 0 & 0 \end{pmatrix}$, and try to find a real invertible matrix $P = \begin{pmatrix} p & q \\ r & s \end{pmatrix}$ for which $PB = AP$ and $B = \begin{pmatrix} a & b \\ b & c \end{pmatrix} = B^t$. If we pre-multiply $PB = AP$ by

$$P^{-1} = (1/|P|)\begin{pmatrix} s & -q \\ -r & p \end{pmatrix},$$

we get

$$B = (1/|P|)\begin{pmatrix} sr & s^2 \\ -r^2 & -sr \end{pmatrix}.$$

Hence $s^2 = -r^2 = b$, which implies that we cannot find a *real* B. However, if we allow *complex* numbers, then $P = \begin{pmatrix} i & -1 \\ 1 & -i \end{pmatrix}$ changes A into $P^{-1}AP = (-\frac{1}{2})\begin{pmatrix} i & 1 \\ 1 & -i \end{pmatrix}$, where $i^2 = -1$. Note that Section 3.3, Problem 1 may also be applied with $B = P^{-1}AP$. It implies $ac - b^2 = 0$, $a + c = 0$, hence $a^2 + b^2 = 0$.

PROBLEMS

1. If U and V are non-zero column vectors such that $U^tV = 0$, show that they are not proportional. If U, V, W are non-zero and such that $U^tV = U^tW = V^tW = 0$, show that no non-trivial linear combination of them equals the zero column vector.
2. Find the characteristic numbers and characteristic column vectors of $\begin{pmatrix} i & 1 \\ 1 & -i \end{pmatrix}$, where $i^2 = -1$. Do the same for $\begin{pmatrix} 1 & i \\ -i & 1 \end{pmatrix}$.
3. If $A = \begin{pmatrix} 1 & -1 \\ -1 & 1 \end{pmatrix}$, find a real orthogonal matrix P such that P^tAP is diagonal.
4. Show that: (a) If $XAY = XBY$ for all column vectors in $n \times 1$ column vector space, then $A = B$. (b) If an $n \times n$ matrix A is real symmetric and $X^tAX = 0$ for all X, then $A = O$.
5. If a 2×2 matrix $A = (a_{ij})$ has complex entries such that $a_{ij} = \bar{a}_{ji}$, show that the characteristic numbers of A are real.
6. Suppose that A is a square matrix, at least 3×3, with entries from an arbitrary field. If A has at least three distinct characteristic numbers, with corresponding characteristic column vectors $\{U_1, U_2, U_3\}$, show that no non-trivial linear combination of these three vectors equals O.
7. In Example 7, suppose $a = c$. Recall the fact that this implies $a \pm b$ are the values of s_1, s_2, and compare entries in $PS = AP$ to show that $\cos\phi = \pm\sin\phi$ if $b \neq 0$.

3.5 REAL QUADRATIC FORMS

If a, b, c are real numbers and x_1, x_2 are variables, then *a polynomial in* x_1, x_2 *of the form*

$$ax_1^2 + bx_1x_2 + cx_2^2$$

is called a ***real quadratic form.*** If we halve the coefficient b and relabel the two parts, and also relabel the other coefficients, *we can write this quadratic form as*

$$a_{11}x_1^2 + a_{12}x_1x_2 + a_{21}x_2x_1 + a_{22}x_2^2, \quad \text{where} \quad a_{12} = a_{21}.$$

It is easily verified that *this form is the entry in the* 1×1 *matrix*

$$X^tAX = (\textstyle\sum a_{ij}x_ix_j),$$

where $X = (x_1, x_2)^t$ *and* $A = (a_{ij}) = A^t$. *Hence, A is a real symmetric matrix.* We shall usually follow the custom of omitting the parentheses about the entry of a 1×1 matrix.

EXAMPLE 1. Suppose we have the quadratic form $x_1^2 + x_1x_2$. The matrix of this form is the real symmetric matrix $A = \begin{pmatrix} 1 & \frac{1}{2} \\ \frac{1}{2} & 0 \end{pmatrix}$, and

$$X^tAX = x_1^2 + x_1x_2.$$

EXAMPLE 2. A similar analysis applies to quadratic forms in more than two variables. Thus, $-x_2^2 + x_3^2 + 2x_1x_2 + 2x_1x_3$ can be expressed by X^tAX, where $X = (x_1, x_2, x_3)^t$ and

$$A = \begin{pmatrix} 0 & 1 & 1 \\ 1 & -1 & 0 \\ 1 & 0 & 1 \end{pmatrix}.$$

The matrices of these forms are real symmetric. Now, *if A is any 2×2 real symmetric matrix, we know there exists a real orthogonal matrix P such that $P^{-1}AP$ is diagonal.* In anticipation of the proof of this fact when $n > 2$, we write:

$$P^{-1}AP = \operatorname{diag}(s_1, \ldots, s_n), \quad P^tP = I,$$

where the s_i's are the characteristic numbers of A and they are real. In the 2×2 case, for example, one can therefore introduce new variables y_1, y_2 into the form X^tAX by the relation

$$X = PY,$$

where $Y = (y_1, y_2)^t$, to get

$$X^tAX = Y^tP^{-1}APY = \sum s_iy_i^2,$$

where we have used the fact that $P^t = P^{-1}$ and expressed the result in notation that applies to the general $n \times n$ case. As we shall see later, this reduction is true for all real symmetric matrices.

EXAMPLE 3. We have already computed the characteristic numbers of the matrix A that appears in Example 2, as well as three mutually orthogonal characteristic column vectors of A (see Section 3.4, Example 6b). Thus we know that, for a suitable $Y = (y_1, y_2, y_3)^t$,

$$-x_2^2 + x_3^2 + 2x_1x_2 + 2x_1x_3 = \sqrt{3}\, y_2^2 - \sqrt{3}\, y_3^2,$$

and also that the real orthogonal matrix P, for which $X = PY$, equals (X_1, X_2, X_3), where the X_i's are normalized characteristic vectors, as previously calculated.

EXAMPLE 4. In Example 1, the quadratic form has the matrix

$$A = \begin{pmatrix} 1 & \frac{1}{2} \\ \frac{1}{2} & 0 \end{pmatrix},$$

whose characteristic numbers are $(1 \pm \sqrt{2})/2$. Hence

$$X^tAX = ((1 + \sqrt{2})/2)y_1^2 + ((1 - \sqrt{2})/2)y_2^2.$$

We can get P here by applying Section 3.4, Example 7. With $\phi = \pi/8$, we find

$$P = \begin{pmatrix} \cos \pi/8 & -\sin \pi/8 \\ \sin \pi/8 & \cos \pi/8 \end{pmatrix}.$$

If all that is desired is a re-expression of a quadratic form as a "sum of weighted squares," which means a sum without cross-product terms, there is a simple procedure (essentially, completion of squares) which we shall consider later (Section 6.7, Example 6). However, in such a reduction the coefficients of the reduced form usually are *not* the characteristic numbers of A, *nor* is the change of variables effected by a real orthogonal matrix.

EXAMPLE 5.

$$x_1^2 + x_1x_2 = (x_1 + (\tfrac{1}{2})x_2)^2 - (\tfrac{1}{4})x_2^2 = y_1^2 - (\tfrac{1}{4})y_2^2,$$

where $y_1 = x_1 + (\frac{1}{2})x_2$ and $y_2 = x_2$. Compare this with Example 4.

PROBLEMS

1. By finding the characteristic numbers of suitable real symmetric matrices, verify that:
   (a) $7x_1^2 + 6x_2^2 + 5x_3^2 - 4x_1x_2 - 4x_2x_3 = 3y_1^2 + 6y_2^2 + 9y_3^2$.
   (b) $x_1^2 - 2x_2^2 + x_3^2 + 4x_1x_2 - 8x_1x_3 - 4x_2x_3 = -3y_1^2 - 3y_2^2 + 6y_3^2$.
   (c) $2x_1^2 + 2x_2^2 + 3x_3^2 + 4x_1x_2 + 2x_1x_3 + 2x_2x_3 = 2y_1^2 + 5y_2^2$.
2. Find the symmetric matrices and their characteristic numbers for the following quadratic forms:
   (a) $(x_1 - x_2)^2 + (x_1 - x_3)^2 + (x_2 - x_3)^2$.
   (b) $(x_1 + x_2 + x_3)^2$.
   (c) $x_1x_2 + x_1x_3 + x_2x_3$.
3. If the symmetric matrix A of a real quadratic form can be expressed as $A = B^tB$ for some real matrix B, show that the form is never negative, that is, $X^tAX \geq 0$ for every real column matrix X.
4. In Example 4, multiply out $P^{-1}AP$ to verify the given diagonal form. Describe the plane conic section whose coordinate equation is $x^2 + xy = 1$.
5. If A and B are real symmetric matrices such that $X^tAX = X^tBX$ for all X, show that $A = B$.
6. Let U_1 be a normalized real characteristic column vector belonging to the characteristic number s_1 of a real symmetric 3×3 A. Show that s_1 always exists and that $U_1^tX = 0$ can always be solved for an orthonormal pair of real column vectors U_2, U_3. Set $P = (U_1, U_2, U_3)$ and show that A is similar to

$$\begin{pmatrix} s_1 & L \\ O & B \end{pmatrix}.$$

   Because P^tAP is also real symmetric, show that $L = O$ and $B = B^t$. Set $R = \text{diag}(1, Q)$, where Q is a real orthogonal matrix such that $Q^tBQ = \text{diag}(s_2, s_3)$. Show that $(PR)^tA(PR) = \text{diag}(s_1, s_2, s_3)$.

3.6 COLUMN VECTOR SPACE

Suppose $\mathbf{V}$ is a 2-dimensional vector space. The correspondence $\mathbf{w} \leftrightarrow W = (x, y)^t$ between a vector $\mathbf{w}$ in $\mathbf{V}$ and its coordinate column, and the correspondence $\boldsymbol{a} \leftrightarrow A$ between a linear transformation $\boldsymbol{a}$ of $\mathbf{V}$ and the coefficient matrix of its coordinate equations, are the source of a natural *one-to-one mapping of* $\mathbf{V}$ *onto the* 2×1 *column vector space* that pairs $\boldsymbol{a}$ with the linear transformation $W \rightarrow AW$. *Besides being an isomorphism* (see Section 1.5) *of the vector spaces, it also has the property* $\boldsymbol{a}\mathbf{w} \leftrightarrow AW$, wherein W poses as a column vector which is the image of $\mathbf{w}$. The details of this particular isomorphism in connection with a basis change associated with an invertible linear transformation $\boldsymbol{p}$, may be reviewed as follows (all bases in this section are coordinate bases and, in the right-hand list, they and their image pairs are presented also as partitioned matrices):

First coordinate basis

$\{\mathbf{u}, \mathbf{v}\}$	$\leftrightarrow \{U = (1, 0)^t,\ V = (0, 1)^t\},\ (U, V) = I$
$\mathbf{w} = x\mathbf{u} + y\mathbf{v}$	$W = xU + yV = (x, y)^t$
$\left.\begin{aligned}\boldsymbol{a}\mathbf{u} &= a\mathbf{u} + c\mathbf{v}\\ \boldsymbol{a}\mathbf{v} &= b\mathbf{u} + d\mathbf{v}\end{aligned}\right\}$	$(AU, AV) = \begin{pmatrix} a & b \\ c & d \end{pmatrix} = A$
$\boldsymbol{a}\mathbf{w} = \mathbf{w}' = x'\mathbf{u} + y'\mathbf{v}$	$AW = W' = (x', y')^t$
$\left.\begin{aligned}\boldsymbol{p}\mathbf{u} &= e\mathbf{u} + g\mathbf{v}\\ \boldsymbol{p}\mathbf{v} &= f\mathbf{u} + h\mathbf{v}\end{aligned}\right\}$	$(PU, PV) = \begin{pmatrix} e & f \\ g & h \end{pmatrix} = P$

Second coordinate basis

$\{\mathbf{u}_1 = \boldsymbol{p}\mathbf{u}, \mathbf{v}_1 = \boldsymbol{p}\mathbf{v}\}$	$\leftrightarrow \{U_1 = (e, g)^t,\ V_1 = (f, h)^t\},\ (U_1, V_1) = P$
$\mathbf{w} = x_1\mathbf{u}_1 + y_1\mathbf{v}_1$	$W = x_1U_1 + y_1V_1 = PW_1,\ W_1 = (x_1, y_1)^t$
$\left.\begin{aligned}\boldsymbol{a}\mathbf{u}_1 &= a_1\mathbf{u}_1 + c_1\mathbf{v}_1\\ \boldsymbol{a}\mathbf{v}_1 &= b_1\mathbf{u}_1 + d_1\mathbf{v}_1\end{aligned}\right\}$	$(AU_1, AV_1) = AP = PA_1,$ $A_1 = \begin{pmatrix} a_1 & b_1 \\ c_1 & d_1 \end{pmatrix} = P^{-1}AP$
$\boldsymbol{a}\mathbf{w} = \mathbf{w}' = x_1'\mathbf{u}_1 + y_1'\mathbf{v}_1$	$APW_1 = PA_1W_1 = PW_1',\ W_1' = (x_1', y_1')^t,$ $A_1W_1 = (P^{-1}AP)W_1 = W_1'$

So when the coordinate basis of a column vector space is changed from the columns of I to those of P, then the column vector W (which coincides as a matrix with its first coordinate column) has a second coordinate column W_1 such that $W = PW_1$, and the linear transformation of the column vector space described by $W \rightarrow AW$ is the same as the one described by $W_1 \rightarrow P^{-1}APW_1$. What happens if $\mathbf{V}$ itself is a column vector space and $\{\mathbf{u}, \mathbf{v}\}$ is an arbitrary basis of $\mathbf{V}$, say

$$\{\mathbf{u} = X = (k, m)^t, \quad \mathbf{v} = Y = (l, n)^t\}\ ?$$

If we set $B = (X, Y)$ and pre-multiply every column vector that appears in the right-hand list (those that double as coordinate columns with respect to $\{\mathbf{u}, \mathbf{v}\}$) by the matrix B, then we get the following *matrix statements* of the first, third, fifth, sixth, and eighth expressions in the left-hand list, namely:

$(X, Y) = B \qquad (\mathbf{u} = X, \mathbf{v} = Y)$
$(\boldsymbol{a}X, \boldsymbol{a}Y) = BA$ (If we abbreviate the left-hand side by $\boldsymbol{a}(B)$, then $A = B^{-1}\boldsymbol{a}(B)$.)
$(\boldsymbol{p}X, \boldsymbol{p}Y) = BP$ (Hence, $P = B^{-1}\boldsymbol{p}(B)$.)

$(X_1, Y_1) = BP = B_1$

$(\boldsymbol{a}X_1, \boldsymbol{a}Y_1) = BAP = BPA_1, \ A_1 = P^{-1}AP$ (Hence, $\boldsymbol{a}(B_1) = B_1A_1$ and $A_1 = \boldsymbol{p}(B)^{-1}BAB^{-1}\boldsymbol{p}(B) = \boldsymbol{p}(B)^{-1}\boldsymbol{a}(B)B^{-1}\boldsymbol{p}(B)$.)

EXAMPLE. Let us use the above matrix algebra to answer the following problem involving column vectors. *Suppose* $\boldsymbol{a}$ *is a linear transformation of column vector space, determined by* $X \to X'$, $Y \to Y'$, that is

$$\boldsymbol{a}X = X',$$

$$\boldsymbol{a}Y = Y',$$

where $\{X, Y\}$ is a coordinate basis and $\{X', Y'\}$ is a set of any two prescribed column vectors. Then $B = (X, Y)$ and $\boldsymbol{a}(B) = (X', Y')$ in the above list. *We wish to find the matrix representations of* $\boldsymbol{a}$ *with respect to:* (a) $\{X, Y\}$ *as a coordinate basis;* (b) *an arbitrary second basis* $\{X_1, Y_1\}$; (c) $\{U, V\}$ *as a coordinate basis*, where $(U, V) = I$; and (d) $\{X', Y'\}$ as a coordinate basis *if* (X', Y') *happens to be invertible*. This can be done directly by expressing each of the vectors X, Y, X', Y' as linear combinations of the desired basis vectors and substituting in the two vector equations which determine $\boldsymbol{a}$, or by consulting the list. The results are:

(a) $A = (X, Y)^{-1}(X', Y')$, by the second line of the list.

(b) $A_1 = P^{-1}AP = (X_1, Y_1)^{-1}(X', Y')(X, Y)^{-1}(X_1, Y_1)$, by the last line of the list. $P = (X, Y)^{-1}(X_1, Y_1)$ in this case, by the third line of the list.

(c) $BAB^{-1} = (X', Y')(X, Y)^{-1}$, since $B^{-1} = P$ in this case (see Problem 3 below).

(d) In this case, $(X', Y') = (X_1, Y_1)$, therefore $P = (X, Y)^{-1}(X', Y') = A$, so $P^{-1}AP = A$ again (see Section 3.2, Example 3).

Hereafter, we shall usually refer to the columns of the $n \times n$ identity I as $E_1, \ldots, E_n$, respectively, when they are considered as column vectors. Thus in (c) above, we found the representation of $\boldsymbol{a}$ with respect to $\{E_1, E_2\}$. The number of rows in E_i will be clear from context. E_i is called a *unit column vector* (Section 2.6, Example 3, and Section 3.3).

PROBLEMS

1. Apply the above Example to the Problems 1, 2 in Section 2.6.
2. If $\boldsymbol{a}(2, 1)^t = (1, 2)^t$ and $\boldsymbol{a}(1, 2)^t = (0, 0)^t$, work out parts (a) and (c) of the Example above.
3. If $(E_1, E_2) = I$, express each of the equations (in the Example) $\boldsymbol{a}X = X'$, $\boldsymbol{a}Y = Y'$, in terms of E_1 and E_2, compare coefficients, and thus find the matrix of $\boldsymbol{a}$ with respect to $\{E_1, E_2\}$. Compare with the Example, part (c). Apply this to Problem 2.

4. In part (b) of the Example, compute $P^{-1}A$ from the fact that its columns must be the coordinate columns of X', Y' with respect to the new basis, that is, $(X', Y') = (X_1, Y_1)P^{-1}A$.

3.7 FACTOR SPACE

In Section 2.18 and also in Section 3.3, Examples 3, 6, 7, and Problem 2, we considered a type of linear transformation $\boldsymbol{a}$ of the plane which can be represented by a matrix of the form

$$A = \begin{pmatrix} s & 1 \\ 0 & s \end{pmatrix}.$$

We saw that the real 2-dimensional vector space $\mathbf{V}$ on which $\boldsymbol{a}$ acts does not decompose into a non-trivial direct sum of *invariant* subspaces, but $\mathbf{V}$ does have a 1-dimensional invariant subspace whose non-zero vectors all belong to the characteristic number s. The behavior of $\boldsymbol{a}$ can be used to explain the idea of a *factor space*, which we now do in a simple geometric way for real 2- and 3-dimensional vector spaces. Let us assume $s \neq 0$.

1. *Parallel lines.* First, we observe a property of lines in the plane. In Figure 39 let l_0, l, l' be parallel lines and let $\boldsymbol{O}$ be a point on l_0 at which we take our vector space $\mathbf{V}$ of position vectors. It is easily verified that no matter how we choose a position vector $\mathbf{u}$ to a point on the line l and a position vector $\mathbf{u}'$ to a point on the line l', the *position vector* $\mathbf{u}''$ (which is the sum $\mathbf{u} + \mathbf{u}'$) *always ends on the same line* l'', *which is parallel to* l_0. *Hence the line* l'' *does not depend on which pair* $\mathbf{u}$, $\mathbf{u}'$ *is chosen for the construction of* $\mathbf{u}'' = \mathbf{u} + \mathbf{u}'$, *provided* $\mathbf{u}$ *ends on* l *and* $\mathbf{u}'$ *on* l'.

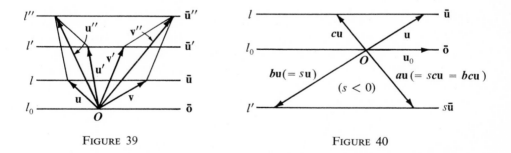

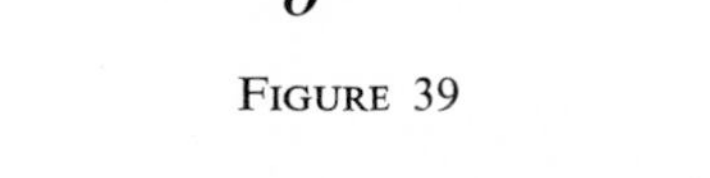

FIGURE 39

FIGURE 40

EXAMPLE 1. In Figure 40, let $\{\mathbf{u}_0, \mathbf{v}_0\}$ be a coordinate basis at $\boldsymbol{O}$ ($\mathbf{v}_0$ not shown). Let $\mathbf{u}$ be a constant position vector to some point on the line l. Then a vector equation for l is $\mathbf{w} = \mathbf{u} + t\mathbf{u}_0$, where each real value of the parameter t determines a unique position vector $\mathbf{w}$ to l. Now suppose $\mathbf{u}$ is a scalar multiple of the second basis vector $\mathbf{v}_0$, say $\mathbf{u} = r\mathbf{v}_0$. Then each line parallel to l_0 corresponds to a unique value of the scalar r. Thus, l' has an equation $\mathbf{w} = \mathbf{u}' + t'\mathbf{u}_0$, where $\mathbf{u}' = r'\mathbf{v}_0$. The property illustrated in Figure 39 can also be verified by inspection of the sum

$$(r\mathbf{v}_0 + t\mathbf{u}_0) + (r'\mathbf{v}_0 + t'\mathbf{u}_0).$$

2. *Effect of* $\boldsymbol{a}$. Second, we observe that the matrix

$$A = \begin{pmatrix} s & 1 \\ 0 & s \end{pmatrix} \quad (s \neq 0) \tag{4}$$

is a product of two commutative matrices, one of which represents a similitude $\boldsymbol{b}$ (possibly negative) of magnitude s and the other a shear $\boldsymbol{c}$ of magnitude $1/s$, that is,

$$\boldsymbol{a} \leftrightarrow A = BC = CB, \quad \text{where} \quad \boldsymbol{b} \leftrightarrow B = sI, \quad \boldsymbol{c} \leftrightarrow C = \begin{pmatrix} 1 & 1/s \\ 0 & 1 \end{pmatrix},$$

all taken with respect to the same coordinate basis at $\boldsymbol{O}$. Hence the linear transformation $\boldsymbol{a}$ can be factored as follows:

$$\boldsymbol{a} = \boldsymbol{bc} = \boldsymbol{cb}.$$

Let l_0 be the fixed line through $\boldsymbol{O}$ parallel to which the shear $\boldsymbol{c}$ occurs; that is, $\boldsymbol{c}$ has a characteristic vector $\mathbf{u}_0$ in the direction of l_0. Let $\{\mathbf{u}_0, \mathbf{v}_0\}$ be the coordinate basis at $\boldsymbol{O}$ with respect to which we are taking A, B, and C as representations of $\boldsymbol{a}$, $\boldsymbol{b}$, and $\boldsymbol{c}$. Thus

$$\begin{aligned} \boldsymbol{a}\mathbf{u}_0 &= s\mathbf{u}_0, & \boldsymbol{b}\mathbf{u}_0 &= s\mathbf{u}_0, & \boldsymbol{c}\mathbf{u}_0 &= \mathbf{u}_0, \\ \boldsymbol{a}\mathbf{v}_0 &= \mathbf{u}_0 + s\mathbf{v}_0, & \boldsymbol{b}\mathbf{v}_0 &= s\mathbf{v}_0, & \boldsymbol{c}\mathbf{v}_0 &= (1/s)\mathbf{u}_0 + \mathbf{v}_0. \end{aligned}$$

Then we can illustrate the effect of $\boldsymbol{a}$ by Figure 40, where $s < 0$. This figure shows how $\boldsymbol{a}$ *permutes the lines in the family of lines parallel to the invariant line* l_0. Every vector $\mathbf{u}$ which ends on l has an image which ends on l', and l' is determined by $\boldsymbol{b}$ alone.

EXAMPLE 2. We can find a vector equation for the image of the line l under our linear transformation $\boldsymbol{a}$ by applying $\boldsymbol{a}$ to both sides of the vector equation $\mathbf{w} = \mathbf{u} + t\mathbf{u}_0$. We get

$$\boldsymbol{a}\mathbf{w} = \boldsymbol{a}\mathbf{u} + t\boldsymbol{a}\mathbf{u}_0 = \boldsymbol{a}\mathbf{u} + (st)\mathbf{u}_0.$$

Since $\mathbf{u}$ is constant in the original equation (equation of the counterimage), so is $\boldsymbol{a}\mathbf{u}$ in the equation of the image. Hence $\boldsymbol{a}\mathbf{w}$ is a variable position vector to a line parallel to l_0.

3. *Cosets and factor space.* Observations 1. and 2. can be fitted together by creating a certain vector space from this family of parallel lines. First, whether or not l_0 is invariant under $\boldsymbol{a}$, *for each* $\mathbf{u}$ *we define a certain subset* $\mathbf{u} + [\mathbf{u}_0]$ of $\mathbf{V}$

by the formula

$$\mathbf{u} + [\mathbf{u}_0] = \{\mathbf{w} \mid \mathbf{w} = \mathbf{u} + t\mathbf{u}_0, \quad t \text{ a scalar}\};$$

that is, $\mathbf{u} + [\mathbf{u}_0]$ *denotes the set of all position vectors to the points on the line* l. The expression $\mathbf{u} + t\mathbf{u}_0$ is a parametrized form of $\mathbf{u} + [\mathbf{u}_0]$, hence the + sign.

Unless $l = l_0$, the set denoted by $\mathbf{u} + [\mathbf{u}_0]$ is not a subspace. $\mathbf{u} + [\mathbf{u}_0]$ *is called a* ***coset of the subspace*** $[\mathbf{u}_0]$, *and* $\mathbf{u}$ *is called a* ***representative of the coset.*** These terms are introduced here so that we can practice working with them in a simple case, and also get some facts that generalize readily for later applications to any finite-dimensional vector space.

When $[\mathbf{u}_0]$ *is fixed or clearly understood in a discussion, it is convenient to denote the coset* $\mathbf{u} + [\mathbf{u}_0]$ *by* $\bar{\mathbf{u}}$. Thus, in our case, the cosets corresponding to the lines l and l' in Figure 40 are:

$$\bar{\mathbf{u}} = \mathbf{u} + [\mathbf{u}_0] = \textit{the coset of } [\mathbf{u}_0] \textit{ with representative } \mathbf{u},$$

$$\bar{\mathbf{u}}' = \mathbf{u}' + [\mathbf{u}_0] = \textit{the coset of } [\mathbf{u}_0] \textit{ with representative } \mathbf{u}'.$$

Also in this case, a special set of representatives (one representative for each coset) consists of all the vectors in $[\mathbf{v}_0]$. The subspace $[\mathbf{u}_0]$ of position vectors to points of l_0 is the particular coset $\bar{\mathbf{o}}$,

$$\bar{\mathbf{o}} = \mathbf{o} + [\mathbf{u}_0] = [\mathbf{u}_0].$$

Now, from Figure 39 we see that:

(a) $\bar{\mathbf{u}} = \bar{\mathbf{v}}$ *if and only if* $\mathbf{u}$ *and* $\mathbf{v}$ *reach to the same line.* We express this in terms of cosets by saying that any vector in a given coset and only such a vector can serve as representative of that coset. Every vector is in just *one* coset, and each coset is *uniquely* determined by any one of its constituent vectors. *Equality of cosets* is therefore defined as follows:

$$\bar{\mathbf{u}} = \bar{\mathbf{v}} \quad \text{if and only if } \mathbf{u} - \mathbf{v} \text{ is in } [\mathbf{u}_0].$$

(b) $\bar{\mathbf{u}}'' = \overline{\mathbf{u} + \mathbf{u}'} = \overline{\mathbf{v} + \mathbf{v}'}$ *for any choice of the pair* $\mathbf{u}$, $\mathbf{v}$ *from* $\bar{\mathbf{u}}$ *and the pair* $\mathbf{u}'$, $\mathbf{v}'$ *from* $\bar{\mathbf{u}}'$. That is, the coset $\bar{\mathbf{u}}''$ is determined by the cosets $\bar{\mathbf{u}}$ and $\bar{\mathbf{u}}'$ *independently of the choice of representatives* $\mathbf{u}''$, $\mathbf{u}$, and $\mathbf{u}'$. Hence we define a ***sum of cosets*** by

$$\bar{\mathbf{u}} + \bar{\mathbf{u}}' = \bar{\mathbf{u}}''.$$

(c) *For any scalar* t, *the line to which* $t\mathbf{u}$ *reaches is the same for every* $\mathbf{u}$ *in the coset* $\bar{\mathbf{u}}$. So we define a ***scalar multiple of the coset*** $\bar{\mathbf{u}}$ by

$$t\bar{\mathbf{u}} = \overline{t\mathbf{u}}.$$

It can be verified that with respect to addition and scalar multiple defined as above, then ***this set of cosets is a vector space,*** *with each coset a "vector."* This vector space is called the ***factor space of*** $\mathbf{V}$ ***modulo*** $[\mathbf{u}_0]$ and is denoted by

$$\mathbf{V}/[\mathbf{u}_0].$$

In our case, $\mathbf{V}/[\mathbf{u}_0]$ is 1-dimensional and $\{\bar{\mathbf{v}}_0\}$ is a basis. We note that $\mathbf{V} = [\mathbf{u}_0] \dotplus [\mathbf{v}_0]$ and that $[\mathbf{v}_0]$ is isomorphic to $\mathbf{V}/[\mathbf{u}_0]$ (see Problem 11 below).

EXAMPLE 3. From the geometry of the 2-dimensional case, it is clear that we can always find (as above) a 1-dimensional subspace whose vectors can serve as representatives for the distinct cosets of the given subspace $[\mathbf{u}_0]$. Just take any line through $\boldsymbol{O}$, not coincident with l_0, and use the position vectors to it. Now, if $\mathbf{w}_0$ is a non-zero position vector to a point of such a line, then we have the direct sum $\mathbf{V} = [\mathbf{u}_0] \dotplus [\mathbf{w}_0]$. Unfortunately, our linear transformation $\boldsymbol{a}$ will *not* map $[\mathbf{w}_0]$ into itself, which is the reason we look at the factor space.

4. *Factor linear transformations.* Finally, we consider again the role of $\boldsymbol{a}$. *Denote by* $\bar{\boldsymbol{a}}$ *the linear transformation* ***of the factor space*** $\mathrm{V}/[\mathbf{u}_0]$ *defined* ("*induced*") *by the equation*

$$\bar{\boldsymbol{a}}\bar{\mathbf{u}} = \overline{\boldsymbol{a}\mathbf{u}},$$

that is, by

$$\bar{\mathbf{u}} \rightarrow \bar{\boldsymbol{a}}\bar{\mathbf{u}} = \boldsymbol{a}\mathbf{u} + [\mathbf{u}_0].$$

$\bar{\boldsymbol{a}}$ *is a mapping because* $[\mathbf{u}_0]$ *is invariant under* $\boldsymbol{a}$. *It is a linear transformation* (as is clear geometrically in our case) *because*:

$$\begin{aligned} \bar{\boldsymbol{a}}s\bar{\mathbf{u}} &= \bar{\boldsymbol{a}}(\overline{s\mathbf{u}}) = \overline{\boldsymbol{a}s\mathbf{u}} = \overline{s\boldsymbol{a}\mathbf{u}} = s\overline{\boldsymbol{a}\mathbf{u}} = s\bar{\boldsymbol{a}}\bar{\mathbf{u}}, \\ \bar{\boldsymbol{a}}(\bar{\mathbf{u}} + \bar{\mathbf{u}}') &= \bar{\boldsymbol{a}}(\overline{\mathbf{u} + \mathbf{u}'}) = \overline{\boldsymbol{a}(\mathbf{u} + \mathbf{u}')} \\ &= \overline{\boldsymbol{a}\mathbf{u} + \boldsymbol{a}\mathbf{u}'} = \overline{\boldsymbol{a}\mathbf{u}} + \overline{\boldsymbol{a}\mathbf{u}'} = \bar{\boldsymbol{a}}\bar{\mathbf{u}} + \bar{\boldsymbol{a}}\bar{\mathbf{u}}'. \end{aligned}$$

Thus, in Example 2, the effect of $\boldsymbol{a}$ on l is to map the coset $\bar{\mathbf{u}}$ onto the coset $\overline{\boldsymbol{a}\mathbf{u}}$.

Now, with $\boldsymbol{a} = \boldsymbol{bc}$, as factored in Observation 2, we find that

$$\bar{\boldsymbol{a}}\bar{\mathbf{u}} = \bar{\boldsymbol{b}}\bar{\mathbf{u}} = \overline{s\mathbf{u}} = s\bar{\mathbf{u}},$$

that is, $\boldsymbol{a}$ *induces the* (possibly negative) *similitude*

$$\bar{\boldsymbol{a}}\bar{\mathbf{u}} = s\bar{\mathbf{u}},$$

in the factor space $\mathrm{V}/[\mathbf{u}_0]$. (In fact, $\bar{\boldsymbol{a}} = \bar{\boldsymbol{b}} = s\bar{\boldsymbol{i}}$, and $\bar{\boldsymbol{c}} = \bar{\boldsymbol{i}}$.) This is a quite special case of a linear transformation induced in a factor space of a vector space, but it illustrates the general idea. *We call the induced linear transformation* $\bar{\boldsymbol{a}}$ *a* ***factor linear transformation.*** With respect to $\{\bar{\mathbf{v}}_0\}$ as a coordinate basis of $\mathrm{V}/[\mathbf{u}_0]$, we see that

$$\bar{\boldsymbol{a}} \leftrightarrow (s), \quad \bar{\boldsymbol{b}} \leftrightarrow (s), \quad \bar{\boldsymbol{c}} \leftrightarrow (1).$$

Although $V = [\mathbf{u}_0] \dotplus [\mathbf{v}_0]$ in our 2-dimensional case, still our linear transformation $\boldsymbol{a}$ does not induce (by restriction of its domain) a linear transformation of $[\mathbf{v}_0]$, but it does induce (by application to representatives of cosets) a linear transformation of the factor space $[\bar{\mathbf{v}}_0]$.

EXAMPLE 4. Let

$$A = \begin{pmatrix} s & 1 & 0 \\ 0 & s & 1 \\ 0 & 0 & s \end{pmatrix} \quad (s \neq 0) \tag{5}$$

represent a linear transformation $\boldsymbol{a}$ of real 3-dimensional space. This matrix A is the 3-dimensional analogue of the matrix in Equation (4) above, and $A = BC = CB$ with

$$B = sI \quad \text{and} \quad C = \begin{pmatrix} 1 & 1/s & 0 \\ 0 & 1 & 1/s \\ 0 & 0 & 1 \end{pmatrix}.$$

Using $(x, y, z)^t$ to denote a coordinate column, we see that the x, y-plane is an invariant plane and that planes parallel to the x, y-plane behave like the lines parallel to l_0 in our 2-dimensional case above.
Let $\{\mathbf{u}_0, \mathbf{v}_0, \mathbf{w}_0\}$ be the coordinate basis to which the matrix A in Equation (5) is referred. Then a coset $\bar{\mathbf{u}}$ of the invariant 2-dimensional subspace $[\mathbf{u}_0, \mathbf{v}_0]$ has the following form, because a representative $\mathbf{u}$ can be replaced by a suitable vector $z\mathbf{w}_0$ from $[\mathbf{w}_0]$ (see Figure 41):

$$\bar{\mathbf{u}} = \mathbf{u} + [\mathbf{u}_0, \mathbf{v}_0] = \{\mathbf{w} \mid \mathbf{w} = \mathbf{u} + x\mathbf{u}_0 + y\mathbf{v}_0\} = \overline{z\mathbf{w}_0} = z\bar{\mathbf{w}}_0,$$

where x and y vary over the real numbers and z is determined by $\mathbf{u}$. The factor space is again 1-dimensional, and the factor linear transformation is given by $\bar{\boldsymbol{a}}\bar{\mathbf{u}} = s\bar{\mathbf{u}}$, so

$$\bar{\boldsymbol{a}} \leftrightarrow (s).$$

There is another possibility here, because the x-axis is an *invariant line*. With respect to this line, it is possible to create a 2-dimensional factor space rather than the 1-dimensional kinds so far shown. Each coset $\bar{\mathbf{u}}$ has the form:

$$\bar{\mathbf{u}} = \mathbf{u} + [\mathbf{u}_0] = \overline{y\mathbf{v}_0 + z\mathbf{w}_0} = y\bar{\mathbf{v}}_0 + z\bar{\mathbf{w}}_0,$$

where y and z are determined by the representative $\mathbf{u}$. This coset corresponds to a line parallel to $\mathbf{u}_0$. See Figure 42. If we select $\{\bar{\mathbf{v}}_0, \bar{\mathbf{w}}_0\}$ as a coordinate basis for the factor space modulo $[\mathbf{u}_0]$, then

$$\bar{\boldsymbol{a}}\bar{\mathbf{v}}_0 = s\bar{\mathbf{v}}_0,$$
$$\bar{\boldsymbol{a}}\bar{\mathbf{w}}_0 = \bar{\mathbf{v}}_0 + s\bar{\mathbf{w}}_0.$$

Hence the *factor linear transformation* $\bar{\boldsymbol{a}}$ *is represented by the matrix in Equation* (4),

$$\bar{\boldsymbol{a}} \leftrightarrow \begin{pmatrix} s & 1 \\ 0 & s \end{pmatrix}.$$

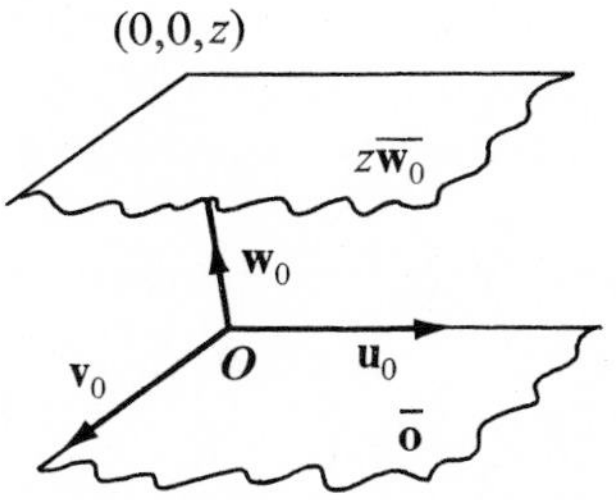

FIGURE 41

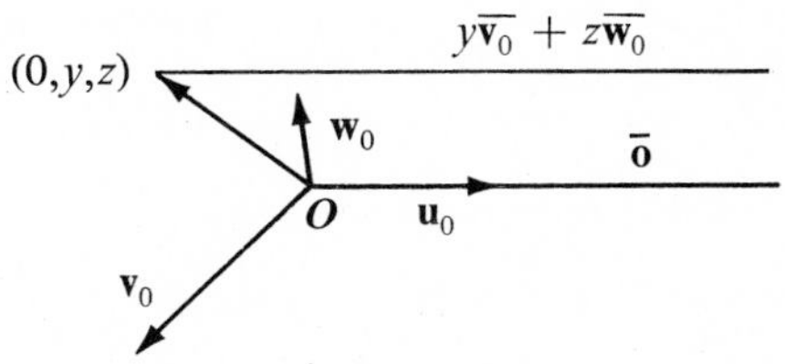

FIGURE 42

Although $\mathbf{V} = [\mathbf{u}_0] \dotplus [\mathbf{v}_0, \mathbf{w}_0]$, still our linear transformation $\boldsymbol{a}$ does not induce a linear transformation of $[\mathbf{v}_0, \mathbf{w}_0]$. It does, however, induce a linear transformation of the factor space $[\bar{\mathbf{v}}_0, \bar{\mathbf{w}}_0]$.

EXAMPLE 5. Neither of the matrices A in Equations (4) and (5) is similar to a diagonal matrix, because the latter would have to be a scalar matrix sI. Could the 3×3 matrix A in (5) be similar to diag(B, s) for some 2×2 matrix B? If it were, then diag(B, s) would be similar to sI (impossible) *or* to

$$A_0 = \operatorname{diag}\left(\begin{pmatrix} s & 1 \\ 0 & s \end{pmatrix}, \ s\right).$$

But $(A_0 - sI)^2 = O$ whereas $(A - sI)^2 \neq O$; a contradiction.

PROBLEMS

1. Prove that $\mathbf{u}''$ and $\mathbf{v}''$ reach to the same line in Figure 39.
2. (a) Find the characteristic numbers and characteristic column vectors of the matrices A, B, C in Observation 2.

   (b) Show that the only matrices that commute with the matrix C in Observation 2 have the form $\begin{pmatrix} a & b \\ 0 & a \end{pmatrix}$.
3. In each of the following cases, regard the set of position vectors to each of the six given loci as a coset of a suitable subspace. Describe each coset in terms of a representative and a basis of the subspace, using coordinate columns.

   (a) In real 2-dimensional space: 1. $x = 1$,
   2. $x + y = 2$,
   3. $2x - 3y = 1$.

   (b) In real 3-dimensional space: 1. $x = 1$,
   2. $x + y + z = 1$,
   3. $x = y = z - 1$.
4. Let $\{X, Y, Z\}$ be a coordinate basis of a 3-dimensional column vector space $\mathbf{V}$. Show that (a) $\mathbf{V}/[X, Z] = [\bar{Y}]$, (b) $\mathbf{V}/[Y] = [\bar{X}, \bar{Z}]$.
5. (a) In Problem 4(a), determine $\boldsymbol{a}$ by: $\boldsymbol{a}X = Z$, $\boldsymbol{a}Y = X$, $\boldsymbol{a}Z = Z$, and find a matrix representation of the factor transformation $\bar{\boldsymbol{a}}$. (b) In Problem 4(b) determine $\boldsymbol{a}$ by: $\boldsymbol{a}X = Y + Z$, $\boldsymbol{a}Y = Y$, $\boldsymbol{a}Z = X + Y$, and find a matrix representation of $\bar{\boldsymbol{a}}$.
6. If $\mathbf{V}_0$ is any subspace of a real 2- or 3-dimensional vector space, show that there is another subspace $\mathbf{V}_1$ such that the vectors in $\mathbf{V}_1$ can serve as representatives for the cosets modulo $\mathbf{V}_0$. What is $\mathbf{V}/[\mathbf{o}]$?
7. Show that the linear transformation $\boldsymbol{a}$ in Observation 2 can be written $\boldsymbol{a} = s\boldsymbol{i} + \boldsymbol{n}$ where $\boldsymbol{n}$ is represented by $\begin{pmatrix} 0 & 1 \\ 0 & 0 \end{pmatrix}$ with respect to the given coordinate basis $\{\mathbf{u}_0, \mathbf{v}_0\}$. Use this to show $\bar{\boldsymbol{a}}\bar{\mathbf{u}} = s\bar{\mathbf{u}}$ for every $\bar{\mathbf{u}}$ in $\mathbf{V}/[\mathbf{u}_0]$.
8. In Example 4, assume $s = 0$ and describe the factor linear transformations in both cases.

9. In Example 4, show that the linear transformation $\boldsymbol{a}$ induces a linear transformation in the x, y-plane which is represented by the matrix in Equation (4) with respect to a suitable coordinate basis.

10. In Example 5, show that B has characteristic numbers s, s, and complete the proof that diag(B, s) is similar to sI or A_0.

11. In Observation 3, show that $[\mathbf{v}_0]$ is isomorphic to $\mathbf{V}/[\mathbf{u}_0]$ by virtue of the correspondence $y\mathbf{v}_0 \leftrightarrow y\mathbf{v}_0 + [\mathbf{u}_0]$.

4

Vector Spaces

4.1 A MORE GENERAL CONTEXT

On our way to a more detailed analysis of linear transformations, we gather more facts about general finite-dimensional vector spaces. We have noticed that the interpretation of a linear system as the coordinate equations of a linear transformation of real 2- or 3-dimensional vector space can be abstracted and extended to vector spaces with unrestricted fields of scalars. We prepare to take advantage of what is suggested by the simpler context. Except in the preliminary discussion of bases (Sections 4.4–4.7), we shall deal only with the finite-dimensional case, and continue the simultaneous development of matrix algebra along with the algebra of vectors and linear transformations, thus collecting consequences basic in applications.

PROBLEMS

1. Which of the following ideas required finite-dimensionality: linear combination, isomorphism, invertibility, similarity, coset, invariance, characteristic number?
2. Extend the definition of the product AU in Section 2.4, Equation (11), to a $p \times q$ A and a $q \times 1$ U. Define U^tA^t so that it will equal $(AU)^t$.

4.2 SOLVING LINEAR EQUATIONS

Let us recall a procedure for solving systems of linear equations, and at the same time provide an illustration for subsequent discussions. Consider the following 3×4 system with easy coefficients, and assume that we are working in some number system which is a field that contains the rational numbers:

$$\begin{aligned} 2x - 2y - 2z - 3w &= 0, \\ x - y - 3z - 2w &= 1, \\ 4x - 4y - 5w &= -2. \end{aligned}$$

Here is a particular sequence of typical steps applied, in turn, to successively modified systems:

(a) Interchange the first two equations (we do not show the result of this step).
(b) Add $(-2) \times$ (first equation) to the second equation, and then add $(-4) \times$ (first equation) to the third equation:

$$\begin{aligned} x - y - 3z - 2w &= 1, \\ 4z + w &= -2, \\ 12z + 3w &= -6. \end{aligned}$$

(c) Add $(-3) \times$ (second equation) to the third equation:

$$\begin{aligned} x - y - 3z - 2w &= 1, \\ 4z + w &= -2, \\ 0 &= 0. \end{aligned}$$

(d) Multiply the second equation by $\frac{1}{4}$, and express x and z in terms of y and w:

$$\begin{aligned} x &= -\tfrac{1}{2} + y + (\tfrac{5}{4})w, \\ z &= -\tfrac{1}{2} - (\tfrac{1}{4})w. \end{aligned}$$

(e) The latter system is ***equivalent*** to the initial system (*it has the same solutions*). *We can now present what is called the* **general solution**, *namely, a 4-tuple vector (x, y, z, w) whose entries are given by the formula*

$$\begin{aligned} (x, y, z, w) &= (-\tfrac{1}{2} + y + 5w/4, y, -\tfrac{1}{2} - w/4, w) \\ &= (-\tfrac{1}{2}, 0, -\tfrac{1}{2}, 0) + y(1, 1, 0, 0) + w(\tfrac{5}{4}, 0, -\tfrac{1}{4}, 1). \end{aligned}$$

Every particular solution corresponds to a pair of values of y and w, and vice versa. Here, y and w are treated as independent variables, usually called ***parameters,*** in the given field. There are many variations possible in the final form of such a *parametric description of the original implicit system of equations*, for, the passage from one equivalent system to another can be accomplished in many ways.

To express this general solution in a parametric form appropriate to matrix algebra, we use row vectors or column vectors. *We shall generally use column vectors to represent the solutions.* Thus, *let t_1, t_2 be parameters varying independently over the given field, and define column vectors U, U_1, U_2, and C by*

$$U = (x, y, z, w)^t, \quad U_1 = (1, 1, 0, 0)^t, \quad U_2 = (\tfrac{5}{4}, 0, -\tfrac{1}{4}, 1)^t, \quad C = (-\tfrac{1}{2}, 0, -\tfrac{1}{2}, 0)^t.$$

Then the general solution can be written as the following general linear combination or, *parametric form:*

$$U = C + t_1 U_1 + t_2 U_2. \tag{1}$$

To complete a matrix description of this linear system, we introduce a 3×4 *matrix of coefficients:*

$$A = \begin{pmatrix} 2 & -2 & -2 & -3 \\ 1 & -1 & -3 & -2 \\ 4 & -4 & 0 & -5 \end{pmatrix},$$

and the column vector $U' = (0, 1, -2)^t$. Now, by a natural extension of the meaning of AU when A is square, the original system of equations is written *in the matrix form:*

$$AU = U'. \tag{2}$$

Our work shows that:

(1) $AC = U'$, that is, *C is a particular solution of the* ***non-homogeneous*** $(U' \neq O)$ *system* $AU = U'$.

(2) $A(s_1U_1 + s_2U_2) = O$ for every pair of values s_1,s_2 of the parameters t_1,t_2, that is, every linear combination of U_1 and U_2 is a solution of the ***homogeneous*** *system* $AU = O$.

EXAMPLE. Although y,w occurred as the parameters t_1,t_2 in our solution, it is possible to solve the equations in such a way that any 5 of the 6 possible pairs, *except* the pair z,w, occur as parameters. The general situation will be clarified later.

PROBLEMS

1. Write each of the following systems as a matrix equation like Equation (2), displaying A and U'. Then express in *parametric form* (such as in Equation (1), where there happen to be two parameters) the general solution for each.
   (a) $3x + y = 1$, (b) $2x + 4y - 3z = 8$, $x + 4y - z = 3$, (c) $2x - 2y - 2z = 3$, $x - y - 3z - 2w = 1$.

2. If $A = \begin{pmatrix} 1 & 0 \\ 2 & 1 \\ -1 & 3 \end{pmatrix}$, find the general solution in parametric form for each of the following *homogeneous* systems:
   (a) $A(x, y)^t = (0, 0, 0)^t$, (b) $(x, y, z)A = (0, 0)$,
   (c) $A[A^t(x, y, z)^t] = (0, 0, 0)^t$, (d) $A^t[A(x, y)^t] = (0, 0)^t$.

3. If X and Y are $n \times 1$ column matrices, express each of the following matrix systems as a *single matrix equation:*
   (a) $AX = E$, $DY = F$, (b) $AX = E$, $CX = F$, (c) $AX + BY = E$, $CX + DY = F$.

4. Let A be a $p \times q$ matrix with $1 < p < q$. Let U be an unknown $q \times 1$ column matrix. Show that the homogeneous linear system $AU = O$ is equivalent to one in which $p - 1$ of the modified equations involve $q - 1$ unknowns. Then, by mathematical induction, prove that $AU = O$ has a *non-zero solution*, $U \neq O$.

5. Verify the statement in the Example.

4.3 GENERAL SOLUTION AND THE COSET OF SOLUTIONS

In the system worked out in Section 4.2, we regarded the solutions of $AU = U'$ as vectors in a column vector space whose scalar field contains the rational numbers (for instance, the field of rational numbers itself). The corresponding homogeneous system $AU = O$ had as solutions every vector in a certain *subspace* of this column vector space, namely the subspace $[U_1, U_2]$ generated by $\{U_1, U_2\}$. If we recall the meaning of coset (Section 3.7), we see that our *general solution* (1) *of* $AU = U'$ *determines a coset of the subspace* $[U_1, U_2]$, *namely* $\bar{C}$, *where* C *is a particular solution of* $AU = U'$ *and*

$$\bar{C} = C + [U_1, U_2].$$

The particular solution C *serves as a representative of the coset which consists of all the particular solutions of* $AU = U'$.

EXAMPLE 1. We may replace C in $\bar{C}$ by any vector $C + U$, where U is in $[U_1, U_2]$, and still express the same coset; that is, $\bar{C} = \overline{C + U}$. *This corresponds to the fact that any vector in a given coset* (*and only such a vector*) *can serve to represent the coset* (Section 3.7). If U' is changed to a *different* column vector, say to U'', and *if there exist solutions* of $AU = U''$, then they constitute a coset of $[U_1, U_2]$ disjoint from (nothing in common with) the coset associated with $AU = U'$.

EXAMPLE 2. Consider a system with one equation, say $x + y + z = 1$, in a real 3-dimensional vector space. A short calculation shows that we can take $U_1 = (1, -1, 0)^t$ and $U_2 = (1, 0, -1)^t$ as solutions of $AU = O$, where $A = (1, 1, 1)$ and $U = (x, y, z)^t$. Also, we can take $C = (1, 0, 0)^t$ as a solution of $AU = U'$, where $U' = (1)$. Now regard the column vectors as coordinate columns. Then the coset $C + [U_1, U_2]$, which corresponds to the general solution, has geometric meaning as the description of a plane, that is, C is the coordinate column of a position vector to a fixed point on the plane, and $[U_1, U_2]$ is the set of coordinate columns of position vectors to points on a parallel plane through the origin $\boldsymbol{O}$. (See Figure 43, where $\mathbf{u}_i \leftrightarrow U_i$ and $\mathbf{c} \leftrightarrow C$.) *The corresponding parametric equations of the plane are, therefore, in a column vector form,* $U = C + t_1U_1 + t_2U_2$.

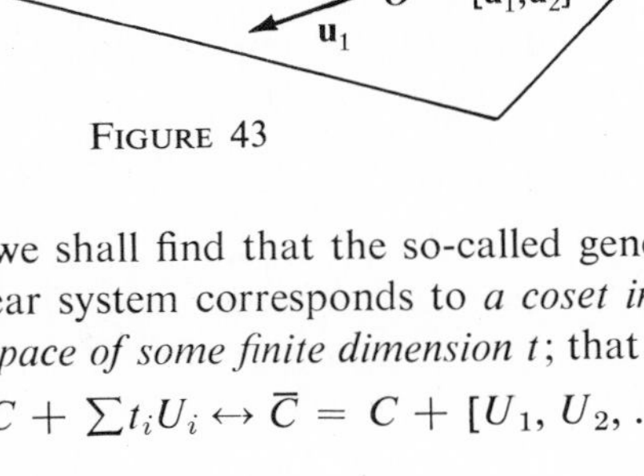

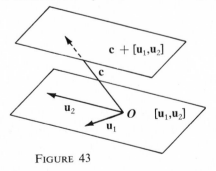

FIGURE 43

More generally, we shall find that the so-called general solution (or, parametric form) of a linear system corresponds to *a coset in a factor space formed modulo a suitable subspace of some finite dimension* t; that is,

$$U = C + \textstyle\sum t_iU_i \leftrightarrow \bar{C} = C + [U_1, U_2, \ldots, U_t]. \tag{3}$$

But a complete understanding of linear systems of equations probably comes best and most illuminating by way of their interpretation as mappings, and we shall take this up in Chapter 6. Meanwhile, we investigate the properties of vector spaces in more detail.

PROBLEMS

1. In real 3-dimensional space, consider the following loci and express them as cosets of appropriate subspaces.
   (a) The line through $\boldsymbol{O}$ and the point $(1, -1, 1)$.
   (b) The line through the points $(1, 1, 1)$, $(2, 1, 0)$.
   (c) The plane through the points $\boldsymbol{O}$, $(1, 1, 1)$, $(1, -1, 0)$.
   (d) The plane through the points $(1, 0, 0)$, $(0, 1, 0)$, $(1, 0, 1)$.
2. For each coset in Problem 1, write the corresponding parametric form and find a linear equation (or system) whose general solution corresponds to the given coset, by eliminating parameters.
3. What geometric interpretations can you make of the following parametric expressions:
   (a) $t_1(1, 1, 1)^t + t_2(2, 2, 2)^t$, (b) $t_1(1, 2, 1)^t + t_2(1, 1, 1)^t + t_3(0, 1, 0)^t$?
4. Show how the general solution of Equation (2) as expressed by Equation (3), changes as U' changes. By suitably varying U', can you cause $\overline{C}$ to vary over the *whole* factor space?

4.4 VECTOR SPACES AND BASES

By a *vector space* we mean a set of objects (called *vectors*) together with a field of numbers (called *scalars*), for which there exists a pair of operations (called *vector addition* and *scalar multiple*) obeying the Rules (I–IV) of Section 1.6.

We shall ultimately assume that Rule (V) holds too, namely, that our vector spaces are finite-dimensional. Meanwhile we state without proof: *Rules* (I)–(IV) *imply that there exists in any given vector space* V *at least one subset* M *such that* ***each vector in* V *is exactly one linear combination of vectors in*** M. *We therefore define a* ***basis*** *of* V *to be a subset* M *of* V *having the latter property.* If M is a finite set, then M is our familiar finite basis of Rule (V). For a while we shall use the term "basis" in the more general sense.

When we say that a vector equals "exactly one" linear combination of a set of vectors, we discount zero multiples and the order in which the summands appear. If a set consists of distinct vectors (hence, it is a *subset* of V), then each of its vectors occurs in at most one summand of any linear combination.

EXAMPLE 1. The set of real polynomials $\{\sum a_i x^i\}$ is a vector space, as we have seen. But it is *not* finite-dimensional. For although every polynomial is a unique linear combination of vectors in the basis $M = \{1, x, x^2, \ldots\}$, yet no finite set of polynomials will serve as basis because the degrees of the non-constant polynomials in such a set are bounded. That M is a basis follows from the fact that a non-zero real polynomial has a finite number of *zeros* (roots of the $\sum a_i x^i = 0$).

EXAMPLE 2. One can conceive of infinitely long row (or column) matrices to which the natural extension of addition and scalar multiple is easily fitted. Thus a vector space is created which is not finite-dimensional, but for which a basis does exist, namely the set of distinct row matrices of the form $(0, \ldots, 0, 1, 0, \ldots)$, which have zero entries except for a 1 in one position.

EXAMPLE 3. The complex numbers $a + bi$ (a, b real), may be regarded as a finite-dimensional vector space over the real scalars. As a basis, one may choose any two complex numbers neither of which is a scalar (real) multiple of the other. Of course, the simplest basis is $\{1, i\}$. This vector space is 2-dimensional. (See Section 2.6, Example 2; Section 2.18, Problem 3.)

EXAMPLE 4. For a pair of fixed positive integers p and q, *the collection of all $p \times q$ matrices with entries from a given field* is a finite-dimensional vector space in which the matrices are considered as vectors to be added and multiplied by scalars according to the rules of matrix algebra. The simplest basis consists of those matrices which have zeros in every position except for one position in which the entry equals 1. This is a basis with pq vectors in it (see Problem 1 below).

EXAMPLE 5. Consider all real polynomials of degree at most 2 (in fact, a similar example exists for any positive integral bound), including all constant polynomials. Besides the obvious basis $\{1, x, x^2\}$, any three polynomials $\{l(x), m(x), n(x)\}$ for which no non-trivial linear combination is identically 0 is a basis. Thus, the set $\{1, x + a, (x + a)^2\}$ is a basis for every choice of the constant a.

EXAMPLE 6. Consider the set of real power series $\{\sum^{\infty} a_i x^i\}$ each of which has an interval of convergence at least equal to 1. In elementary calculus one finds that the sum of two such series, as well as any scalar multiple of such a series, has an interval of convergence at least equal to 1. Hence they constitute a vector space with real scalars.

To take care of singular consequences which may ensue from certain choices of the scalar field, it is desirable to use the concept of an *indeterminate* (or *transcendental quantity*). An indeterminate commonly symbolized by x is used in place of the familiar variable in polynomials. Polynomial expressions in x, with coefficients in the given field, are manipulated as though x were a variable insofar as addition, scalar multiple, and product are concerned, except that *two polynomials in the indeterminate x are equal if and only if like powers of x have* *equal coefficients* (see Example 7 below). With regard to the latter property, the quantity x stands in relation to the given field the way any familiar transcendental number, such as π, stands in relation to the rational numbers. By forming quotients $f(x)/g(x)$, where $g(x) \neq 0$, a new field, containing the given scalar field, is constructed consisting of these quotients, provided equality is defined by:

$$f(x)/g(x) = h(x)/k(x) \quad \text{if and only if} \quad f(x)k(x) = g(x)h(x).$$

This brief sketch will suffice here, since the distinction will seldom concern us. Hereafter, *when we use the unqualified term "polynomial in x," we mean a polynomial in the indeterminate x.*

EXAMPLE 7. If x is a variable scalar from the field of "integers modulo 2," then each of the polynomials in the set $\{x, x^2, x^3, \ldots\}$ defines the same *function*, because $0^n = 0$ and $1^n = 1$. But if x is an indeterminate, then the same set consists of *distinct objects;* in fact, together with 1 it is a basis of the infinite-dimensional space of polynomials in x with coefficients from the field of integers modulo 2.

PROBLEMS

1. Let E_{ij} denote a $p \times p$ matrix which has zero entries except for the number 1 in the i, j-position (see Example 4). Let A be a $p \times p$ matrix. Show that: (a) $A = \sum a_{ij}E_{ij}$, (b) $I = \sum E_{ii}$, (c) $E_{ij}E_{jl} = E_{il}$, (d) $E_{ij}E_{kl} = O$ if $j \neq k$.
2. Referring to Problem 1, compute: (a) $E_{ij}A$, (b) AE_{kl}, (c) $E_{ij}AE_{kl}$, (d) $AE_{ij}A$.
3. Show that the only kind of $p \times p$ matrix that will commute with every $p \times p$ matrix (entries in a field) is of the form sI, that is, it is a *scalar matrix*.
4. Regard the set of all 2×2 matrices, with complex numbers as entries, as a vector space over the reals. Find a basis consisting of 8 matrices.
5. How many invertible 2×2 matrices are there, if the entries are from the field of integers modulo p?
6. In Example 6, show that no finite basis exists.

4.5 LINEAR DEPENDENCE

We recall that if M is any set of vectors from $\mathbf{V}$, then by the definition of [M],

$$\begin{aligned}[\mathrm{M}] &= \textit{the subspace generated by } \mathrm{M} \\ &= \{\textit{all linear combination of vectors in } \mathrm{M}\}.\end{aligned}$$

When M is empty, we define [M] to be the zero vector space $\{\mathbf{o}\}$. Note that [[M]] = [M] (see Problem 6 below). We call M a *generating set* for [M].

EXAMPLE 1. In the vector space of polynomials in an indeterminate x, let

$$\mathrm{M} = \{x^{2n} \mid n = \text{a non-negative integer}\}.$$

Then [M] is the subspace consisting of all polynomials of even degree and the constant polynomials.

Now, consider any subset M of $\mathbf{V}$. Then M *is called* ***linearly dependent*** *if and only if there is some finite subset* $\{\mathbf{v}_1, \ldots, \mathbf{v}_t\}$ *of* M *such that a* ***non-trivial*** *linear combination of these t vectors equals* $\mathbf{o}$; *that is,* M *is linearly dependent if and only if there exists a subset* $\{\mathbf{v}_1, \ldots, \mathbf{v}_t\}$ *of* M *and scalars* $a_1, \ldots, a_t$ ***not all zero*** *such that*

$$a_1\mathbf{v}_1 + \cdots + a_t\mathbf{v}_t = \mathbf{o}.$$

Any such expression of the zero vector as a ***non-trivial*** *linear combination of a subset of* M *is called a* ***linear dependence*** *in* M. *If no such subset* $\{\mathbf{v}_1, \ldots, \mathbf{v}_t\}$ *of* M *exists, then* M *is called* ***linearly independent.*** The empty set will be called linearly independent. *We make the same definitions if* M *is any set of vectors from* $\mathbf{V}$.

EXAMPLE 2. The bases given in Section 4.4, Examples 2, 3, 4, are linearly independent subsets; in fact, *the linear independence of any basis* is an easy consequence of the definition of basis. Note that although the condition for linear independence of *two* vectors is equivalent to neither one being a scalar multiple of the other, the pairwise linear independence of three or more vectors does not imply their linear independence (see also Problem 3 below).

Theorem 1. Let M be a subset of a vector space $\mathbf{V}$. Then M is a basis of $\mathbf{V}$ if and only if (a) $\mathbf{V} = [\mathrm{M}]$ and (b) M is linearly independent.

Proof: Suppose M *is a basis.* Then $\mathbf{V} = [\mathrm{M}]$ because a basis of $\mathbf{V}$ generates $\mathbf{V}$. If M were linearly dependent, then $\mathbf{o}$ would have more than one expression as a linear combination of vectors in M, which would contradict the uniqueness of such a linear combination. *Conversely, suppose* (a) *and* (b) *hold.* From the definition of [M] and the fact that $\mathbf{V} = [\mathrm{M}]$, it follows that every vector in $\mathbf{V}$ is a linear combination of vectors in M. Now, suppose some vector $\mathbf{u}$ in $\mathbf{V}$ equals a linear combination of a subset $\{\mathbf{u}_1, \ldots, \mathbf{u}_p\}$ of M, and also equals another linear combination of a (possibly the same) subset $\{\mathbf{v}_1, \ldots, \mathbf{v}_q\}$ of M. Let $\{\mathbf{w}_1, \ldots, \mathbf{w}_r\}$ consist of all the distinct vectors in $\{\mathbf{u}_1, \ldots, \mathbf{u}_p, \mathbf{v}_1, \ldots, \mathbf{v}_q\}$. Then each of the two assumed linear combinations can be regarded as a linear combination of $\{\mathbf{w}_1, \ldots, \mathbf{w}_r\}$, provided we insert suitable zero multiples where necessary, so

$$\mathbf{u} = \sum a_i\mathbf{w}_i = \sum b_i\mathbf{w}_i.$$

Unless $a_i = b_i$ for every i, this implies a linear dependence in M, namely,

$$\sum (a_i - b_i)\mathbf{w}_i = \mathbf{o},$$

which is in contradiction to (b). Hence the linear combinations are the same, that is, each of them equals $\sum a_i\mathbf{w}_i$. q.e.d.

Corollary. Let M be a subset of a vector space. Then M is a basis of [M] if and only if M is linearly independent.

Proof: Since in this case the vector space **V** of Theorem 1 can be taken equal to [M], condition (a) is superfluous. q.e.d.

EXAMPLE 3. *A subset* M *of* **V** *is linearly dependent if and only if there is some vector* **v** *in* M *such that* **v** *is in* [M − **v**]. (Here, M − **v** *means the subset* M − {**v**} *of* M *obtained by deleting* **v**.) If M − **v** is the empty set, then use the fact that [M − **v**] = {**o**} by definition.

EXAMPLE 4. When the subset M is finite, there is a useful refinement of the result in Example 3. *A finite subset* M *of non-zero vectors of* **V** *is linearly dependent if and only if in any given list of these vectors some vector* (after the first) *is a linear combination of its predecessors in the list.* For, suppose

$$\mathbf{v}_k = \sum_{i=1}^{k-1} a_i\mathbf{v}_i \qquad (k > 1).$$

Then after adding $-\mathbf{v}_k$ to both sides, we have a linear dependence in M. Converse, if M is linearly dependent, then there exists a linear dependence $\sum_{i=1}^{k} a_i\mathbf{v}_i = \mathbf{o}$ with $a_k \neq 0$ and $k > 1$. This implies that $\mathbf{v}_k$ is linearly dependent on its predecessors in the listing of the $\mathbf{v}_i$'s, namely,

$$\mathbf{v}_k = (-1/a_k)\sum_{i=1}^{k-1} a_i\mathbf{v}_i.$$

If a subset of **V** contains the zero vector, then the subset is clearly linearly dependent. Also, M can be any finite set of non-zero vectors from **V**.

EXAMPLE 5. *Every subset of a linearly independent set is itself linearly independent.* For, a linear dependence in a subset is also a linear dependence in the whole set.

EXAMPLE 6. Let M be any subset of **V**. *The following statements are equivalent:*

(a) M *is a basis of* **V**.
(b) M *is a* ***maximal linearly independent subset*** *of* **V** (that is, M is linearly independent, and if **v** is any vector in **V** that is not in M, then **v** is in [M]).
(c) M *is a* ***minimal generating set*** *for* **V** (that is, **V** = [M], but **V** ≠ [M − **v**] for any choice of **v** in M).

To describe the fact that **v** is in [M], the phrase "**v** is linearly dependent on M" is often used. In particular, **v** is linearly dependent on the empty set if and only if **v** = **o**.

PROBLEMS

1. Let $\sum a_i \mathbf{v}_i = \mathbf{o}$ be a linear dependence in a subset M of **V**, and suppose $a_k \neq 0$. Show that [M] = [M − $\mathbf{v}_k$]. If **w** is linearly dependent on M, show that [M] = [M, **w**], where the right-hand side means the subspace generated by M and **w** together.
2. Find a linear dependence in each of the following sets:
   (a) the 3-tuple vectors $\{(1, 3, 2), (3, 7, 4), (0, 1, 1)\}$,
   (b) the columns of the matrix A in Section 4.2,
   (c) the polynomials $\{2 + x, x^2, 1 - 2x^2, (1 - x)^2\}$,
   (d) the matrices
   $$\left\{\begin{pmatrix} 1 & 1 \\ -1 & 1 \end{pmatrix}, \begin{pmatrix} 1 & -1 \\ 1 & 1 \end{pmatrix}, \begin{pmatrix} 0 & 1 \\ 1 & 0 \end{pmatrix}, \begin{pmatrix} 1 & 1 \\ 0 & 0 \end{pmatrix}, \begin{pmatrix} 0 & 0 \\ 1 & 1 \end{pmatrix}\right\},$$
   (e) the matrices $\{I, A, A^2\}$ where $A = \text{diag}(a, b)$, a and b constant.
3. Give an example of four linearly *dependent* vectors such that every subset of three is linearly *independent.*
4. Show that a set of vectors $\{\mathbf{u}_1, \ldots, \mathbf{u}_t\}$ is linearly dependent if and only if the set $\{\mathbf{u}_1, \mathbf{u}_1 + \mathbf{u}_2, \ldots, \mathbf{u}_1 + \cdots + \mathbf{u}_t\}$ is linearly dependent.
5. If **V** = [M] and N is a subset of **V** such that [N] contains M, show that **V** = [N].
6. Let M and N be subsets of **V**. Show that:
   (a) [M] contains N if and only if [M] contains [N],
   (b) [[M]] = [M],
   (c) [M, N] = [[M], N] = [M, [N]], where [M, N] means the subspace generated by the elements of M and N together.
7. Complete Example 6.

4.6 FINITELY GENERATED VECTOR SPACES

If M *is a finite subset of the vector space* **V**, *then* [M] *is called a* ***finitely generated subspace*** *of* **V**. In particular, if (for such an M) **V** = [M], then **V** is a *finitely generated vector space.* In general, every subspace for which there exists a finite generating set is called *finitely generated.* A finitely generated vector space turns out to be finite-dimensional.

Theorem 2. Every finitely generated vector space has a *finite* basis and such a basis can be chosen from any given generating set, finite or infinite.

Proof: Let **V** be a finitely generated vector space. By definition, there exists a finite subset M = $\{\mathbf{v}_1, \ldots, \mathbf{v}_t\}$ of **V** such that **V** = [M]. Now, we may assume that the zero vector has been deleted from M, since its removal will still leave a generating set for **V**. Therefore, if M is not already a basis, we can apply Section 4.5, Example 4 to systematically produce a basis of **V** from M as follows. Suppose M is linearly dependent. Reading from left to right in our list $\mathbf{v}_1, \ldots, \mathbf{v}_t$, there is a first vector which is dependent on its predecessors. Delete this vector, because the remaining set also generates $\mathbf{V}$ (Section 4.5, Problem 1). Repeat this search and deletion until there remains a *linearly independent set, say* $M' = \{\mathbf{v}_{i_1}, \ldots, \mathbf{v}_{i_n}\}$, *where* $i_1 = 1$ *and* $\mathbf{V} = [M']$. Hence M' is a basis of $\mathbf{V}$. Now, for this same vector space $\mathbf{V}$, let N be an *infinite generating set* (assuming $\mathbf{V}$ is infinite). Since $\mathbf{V} = [N]$, each vector of M is a linear combination of vectors in N. Because M is finite, this means that there is a *finite subset* N_0 *of* N such that $[N_0]$ contains M. Hence $\mathbf{V} = [N_0]$ and we can do to N_0 what we did to M.

q.e.d.

Thus, *a vector space is finitely generated if and only if it is finite-dimensional.* Note that these results apply to subspaces, since they are vector spaces.

Corollary. If M is any finite subset of a vector space, then M contains a basis of [M].

Proof: Set $\mathbf{V} = [M]$ and apply Theorem 2. q.e.d.

EXAMPLE. In the vector space of polynomials, as in all vector spaces, any finite subset generates a finite-dimensional subspace. Thus, if $M = \{2x, x + x^3, x^3\}$, then [M] is a finitely generated subspace, and from the set M we can select the following bases: $\{2x, x + x^3\}$, $\{2x, x^3\}$, $\{x + x^3, x^3\}$. (Of course, $\{x, x^3\}$ is a very simple basis, but is not a subset of M.)

PROBLEMS

1. In the vector space of real 2×2 matrices, select a basis of each of the following subspaces by deleting vectors from the given generating sets:

   (a) $\left[\begin{pmatrix} 1 & 0 \\ 0 & 1 \end{pmatrix}, \begin{pmatrix} 1 & 1 \\ 0 & 1 \end{pmatrix}, \begin{pmatrix} 0 & 1 \\ 0 & 0 \end{pmatrix}\right]$,

   (b) $[I, A, A^2, \ldots]$, with $A = \begin{pmatrix} 1 & 1 \\ 0 & 1 \end{pmatrix}$.
2. In Section 4.5, Problem 2, select from each of the given sets a basis of the vector space it generates. In how many ways can each be selected?
3. Show that in a finitely generated vector space, any non-zero vector is part of a basis.
4. Suppose that no *proper* non-zero subspace $\mathbf{W}$ of a given vector space $\mathbf{V}$ (*proper* means $\mathbf{W} \neq \mathbf{V}$) is finitely generated. Show that $\mathbf{V}$ is not finitely generated. Suppose, on the other hand, that every proper subspace is finitely generated; is $\mathbf{V}$ finitely generated?

4.7 UNIQUENESS OF DIMENSION

We know that a finite-dimensional vector space is the same thing as a finitely generated vector space. We now show that the number of vectors in any basis of a finite-dimensional vector space is always finite and is independent of the choice of basis.

Theorem 3. Suppose a vector space $\mathbf{V}$ has a finite basis $M = \{\mathbf{u}_1, \ldots, \mathbf{u}_n\}$. Then every basis is finite and each one has exactly n vectors.

Proof: Let N be any basis of $\mathbf{V}$. If N is also finite, list all the vectors in N in some finite sequence, say $\mathbf{v}_1, \mathbf{v}_2, \ldots, \mathbf{v}_t$. If N is infinite, then "select" from N an infinite sequence $\mathbf{v}_1, \mathbf{v}_2, \ldots$. Since $\mathbf{V} = [M]$, we certainly have

$$\mathbf{V} = [\mathbf{v}_1, \mathbf{u}_1, \ldots, \mathbf{u}_n].$$

But the generating set $\{\mathbf{v}_1, \mathbf{u}_1, \ldots, \mathbf{u}_n\}$ is linearly dependent because M is a basis. Hence some $\mathbf{u}_k$ is linearly dependent on the vectors preceding it in the list $\mathbf{v}_1, \mathbf{u}_1, \ldots, \mathbf{u}_n$. Delete one such vector and denote the remaining set by $\{\mathbf{v}_1, \mathbf{u}_{i_1}, \ldots, \mathbf{u}_{i_{n-1}}\}$. The latter set of n vectors still generates $\mathbf{V}$. We now insert $\mathbf{v}_2$ after $\mathbf{v}_1$ and have $n + 1$ generators, that is,

$$\mathbf{V} = [\mathbf{v}_1, \mathbf{v}_2, \mathbf{u}_{i_1}, \ldots, \mathbf{u}_{i_{n-1}}].$$

But the generating set $\{\mathbf{v}_1, \mathbf{v}_2, \mathbf{u}_{i_1}, \ldots, \mathbf{u}_{i_{n-1}}\}$ is linearly dependent, hence we can delete from it some vector that is in the subset $M - \mathbf{u}_k$, still maintaining a generating set. As we continue this process, we never can delete a vector that was inserted, because the $\mathbf{v}_i$'s are linearly independent. When the sequence $\mathbf{v}_1, \mathbf{v}_2, \ldots$ has at least as many vectors as M, we finally reach the stage $\mathbf{V} = [\mathbf{v}_1, \ldots, \mathbf{v}_n]$; but then any vector $\mathbf{v}_i$ $(i > n)$ in our sequence (if there is one) is linearly dependent on $\{\mathbf{v}_1, \ldots, \mathbf{v}_n\}$, which contradicts the linear independence of N. Hence, *the number of vectors in* N *is finite and not more than n.* We reverse the roles of M and N because N is now known to be finite. Thus we find that $t = n$.

q.e.d.

The integer n above is called the ***dimension*** *of* $\mathbf{V}$ *and is denoted by* dim $\mathbf{V}$. *When a finite-dimensional space has dimension n, then we have called it* ***n-dimensional.*** To the zero space $\{\mathbf{o}\}$ we have assigned the dimension zero, and as its basis, the empty set. We note without proof that the existence of a basis of *any* vector space (see Section 4.4) always leads to a unique dimension, which is the "cardinal number" of the basis.

EXAMPLE 1. The above proof of Theorem 3 shows that *when* $\mathbf{V}$ *is n-dimensional, every subset of* $\mathbf{V}$ *having more than n vectors must be linearly dependent.* Not only is a basis a maximal linearly independent subset with n vectors, but *every maximal linearly independent subset has n vectors.* In fact, by Section 4.5, Example 6, we already know that *any maximal linearly independent subset, and any minimal generating set, is a basis.* Hence, in an n-dimensional vector space $\mathbf{V}$: (a) Any n linearly independent vectors constitute a basis. (b) Any n vectors that generate $\mathbf{V}$ constitute a basis. (See Problem 3 below.)

EXAMPLE 2. *If* $N = \{\mathbf{v}_1, \ldots, \mathbf{v}_t\}$ *is any finite set of linearly independent vectors in a finite-dimensional vector space* $\mathbf{V}$, *then* N *can be enlarged to a basis of* $\mathbf{V}$. For, if $M = \{\mathbf{u}_1, \ldots, \mathbf{u}_n\}$ is a basis, we must have $t \leq n$

(Example 1) and we can conduct the replacement of the $\mathbf{u}_k$'s by the $\mathbf{v}_k$'s as in the proof of Theorem 3. For instance, if we wish to include the 3-tuple vector (1, 1, 0) in a basis of a vector space of 3-tuples, then we can use the list (1, 1, 0), (1, 0, 0), (0, 1, 0), (0, 0, 1) and delete a suitable vector from the last three. By Example 1, *any* enlargement of N to a set of n linearly independent vectors, yields a basis. In theory, we can list $\mathbf{v}_1, \ldots, \mathbf{v}_t, \mathbf{u}_1, \ldots, \mathbf{u}_n$ and eliminate t of the $\mathbf{u}_k$'s, leaving a basis of **V** which includes N. (Actually, any finite generating set for **V** containing N can be used, with N listed first.) In practice, Section 4.5, Example 4 may be applied to conduct the elimination, starting with $\mathbf{v}_1, \ldots, \mathbf{v}_t, \mathbf{u}_1$ to test whether $\mathbf{u}_1$ should be eliminated (see Section 4.9, Problem 5 below).

EXAMPLE 3. Now, we can show that *if* $\mathbf{V}_0$ *is a subspace of a finite-dimensional space* **V**, *then* $\mathbf{V}_0$ *is also finite-dimensional.* For in **V**, and therefore in $\mathbf{V}_0$, there cannot be a set of more than n linearly independent vectors, where $n = \dim \mathbf{V}$. If $\mathbf{V}_0 \neq \{\mathbf{o}\}$, there exist linearly independent subsets with at least one vector, but none with more than n. Hence, there exists in $\mathbf{V}_0$ a maximal linearly independent set of not more than n vectors, which is (see Example 1), therefore, a finite basis of $\mathbf{V}_0$. Also, we note that *if* $\mathbf{V}_0$ *is not equal to* **V**, *then* $\dim \mathbf{V}_0 < \dim \mathbf{V}$, because no basis of $\mathbf{V}_0$ will generate **V** and hence no basis of $\mathbf{V}_0$ is a maximally linearly independent subset of **V**.

From now on our vector spaces will be finite-dimensional vector spaces. We shall use the terms "vector space" and "basis" hereafter with the understanding that the vector space is finite-dimensional and that the basis is finite.

PROBLEMS

1. Complete each of the following subsets to a basis of the corresponding vector space of which it is a subset:

   (a) $\{(1, 1, 0), (1, 0, 1)\}$ in 3-tuple vector space,

   (b) $\left\{\begin{pmatrix} 1 & 3 & 1 \\ 2 & 0 & 0 \end{pmatrix}, \begin{pmatrix} 1 & 0 & 0 \\ 0 & 0 & 1 \end{pmatrix}, \begin{pmatrix} 0 & 0 & 1 \\ 0 & 1 & 0 \end{pmatrix}\right\}$ in the vector space of 2×3 matrices,

   (c) $\{(1, 1, 1, 1)^t, (1, 0, 0, 0)^t\}$ in 4×1 column vector space.

2. If $m > n$ and $\{U_1, \ldots, U_m\}$ are $n \times 1$ column vectors, show that $\sum a_i U_i = O$ non-trivially and express this fact in a single matrix equation.

3. If **V** is n-dimensional and M is a subset of n vectors in **V**, show that M is a basis if and only if M is linearly independent *or* if and only if $\mathbf{V} = [\mathrm{M}]$.

4. If **V** is n-dimensional, show that it has a proper subspace of every dimension $0, 1, \ldots, n - 1$. In 3-tuple vector space with scalar field equal to the integers modulo p, how many subspaces of dimension 1 are there? Of dimension 2?

5. If $\mathbf{V}_0$ is a t-dimensional subspace of an n-dimensional **V**, show that $\mathbf{V}_0$ contains subspaces of dimensions $0, 1, \ldots, t - 1$ and is contained in subspaces of **V** of dimensions $t + 1, \ldots, n$.

6. If two subspaces of $\mathbf{V}$ together contain all the vectors of $\mathbf{V}$, show that one of these subspaces equals $\mathbf{V}$.
7. If $\mathbf{V}_1$ and $\mathbf{V}_2$ are finite-dimensional subspaces of $\mathbf{V}$, show that their ***intersection*** $\mathbf{V}_1 \cap \mathbf{V}_2 = \{\mathbf{v} \mid \mathbf{v} \text{ is in } \mathbf{V}_1 \textit{ and } \mathbf{V}_2\}$ = (subspace of common vectors) is also finite-dimensional. Is this true if only one of the $\mathbf{V}_i$'s is finite-dimensional?

4.8 DIRECT SUMS AND FACTOR SPACES

We shall need some facts about the dimensions of subspaces and factor spaces of a vector space $\mathbf{V}$. *If* M_1 *and* M_2 *are subsets of* $\mathbf{V}$, *let us denote by* $[\mathrm{M}_1, \mathrm{M}_2]$ *the subspace generated by the totality of vectors in* M_1 *and* M_2, *that is, generated by the* ***union***

$$\mathrm{M}_1 \cup \mathrm{M}_2 = \{\mathbf{v} \mid \mathbf{v} \text{ is in } \mathrm{M}_1 \textit{ or } \mathrm{M}_2\}.$$

Note that $[\mathrm{M}_1, \mathrm{M}_2] = [\mathrm{M}_1 \cup \mathrm{M}_2] = [[\mathrm{M}_1], [\mathrm{M}_2]]$.

(a) *Direct sums.* In a generalization of what we considered in Section 2.14, let $\mathbf{V}_1$ and $\mathbf{V}_2$ be given subspaces of a vector space $\mathbf{V}$ and suppose that the subspace $\mathbf{V}_0 = [\mathbf{V}_1, \mathbf{V}_2]$ has the property that every vector $\mathbf{v}_0$ in $\mathbf{V}_0$ is expressible in *exactly one way* as a sum $\mathbf{v}_0 = \mathbf{v}_1 + \mathbf{v}_2$ with $\mathbf{v}_1$ in $\mathbf{V}_1$ and $\mathbf{v}_2$ in $\mathbf{V}_2$. *In this case, we say that* $\mathbf{V}_0$ *is the* ***direct sum*** *of the subspaces* $\mathbf{V}_1$ *and* $\mathbf{V}_2$, *and denote this fact by*

$$\mathbf{V}_0 = \mathbf{V}_1 \dotplus \mathbf{V}_2.$$

The idea of direct sum extends to any finite number of summands and, when the summands are non-zero, it is a generalization of the idea of a basis.

EXAMPLE 1. The phrase "exactly one way" can be replaced by "$\mathbf{o} = \mathbf{v}_1 + \mathbf{v}_2$ if and only if $\mathbf{v}_1 = \mathbf{v}_2 = \mathbf{o}$"; or by the *intersection condition* "$\mathbf{V}_1 \cap \mathbf{V}_2 = \{\mathbf{o}\}$" (whose extension to more than two summands is more complicated to state, see Problem 5 below). Thus, if $\{\mathbf{w}_1, \ldots, \mathbf{w}_n\}$ is a basis of an n-dimensional $\mathbf{V}$, and we divide this basis into two disjoint subsets $\mathrm{M}_1 = \{\mathbf{w}_1, \ldots, \mathbf{w}_s\}$ and $\mathrm{M}_2 = \{\mathbf{w}_{s+1}, \ldots, \mathbf{w}_n\}$, then $\mathbf{V} = [\mathrm{M}_1] \dotplus [\mathrm{M}_2]$. For, if

$$\mathbf{o} = \sum_1^s a_i\mathbf{w}_i + \sum_{s+1}^n a_i\mathbf{w}_i,$$

then all the a_i's equal zero.

Theorem 4. Suppose $\mathbf{V} = [\mathbf{V}_1, \mathbf{V}_2]$ where $\mathbf{V}_1$ and $\mathbf{V}_2$ are subspaces. Then $\mathbf{V} = \mathbf{V}_1 \dotplus \mathbf{V}_2$ if and only if $\dim \mathbf{V} = \dim \mathbf{V}_1 + \dim \mathbf{V}_2$.

Proof: Suppose $\mathbf{V} = \mathbf{V}_1 \dotplus \mathbf{V}_2$. Let $\mathrm{M}_1 = \{\mathbf{u}_1, \ldots, \mathbf{u}_p\}$ be a basis of $\mathbf{V}_1$ and $\mathrm{M}_2 = \{\mathbf{v}_1, \ldots, \mathbf{v}_q\}$ be a basis of $\mathbf{V}_2$. Then $\mathbf{V} = [\mathrm{M}_1, \mathrm{M}_2] = [\mathbf{u}_1, \ldots, \mathbf{u}_p, \mathbf{v}_1, \ldots, \mathbf{v}_q]$. If $\mathbf{o} = \sum a_i\mathbf{u}_i + \sum b_i\mathbf{v}_i$ is a linear dependence, then $\mathbf{o}$ is *not* uniquely represented in the direct sum, which is a contradiction. Hence, the set $\mathbf{M}_1 \cup \mathbf{M}_2$ is a linearly independent generating set of $\mathbf{V}$, therefore, a basis. Consequently $p + q = \dim \mathbf{V}$. *On the other hand, suppose* $\dim \mathbf{V}_1 + \dim \mathbf{V}_2 = \dim \mathbf{V}$, that is, $p + q = \dim \mathbf{V}$. If $\mathbf{V} \neq \mathbf{V}_1 \dotplus \mathbf{V}_2$, then $\mathbf{V}_1 \cap \mathbf{V}_2 \neq \{\mathbf{o}\}$. Hence there is at least one common non-zero vector $\mathbf{v}$ in each subspace (Example 1). Now, we know that there exists a basis of $\mathbf{V}_1$ which includes $\mathbf{v}$, and, similarly, a basis of $\mathbf{V}_2$ which includes $\mathbf{v}$ (Section 4.7, Example 2). Consequently, there exists a set of $p + q - 1$ generators of $\mathbf{V}$. But then $\dim \mathbf{V} < p + q$ (Section 4.6, Theorem 2), which is a contradiction. Therefore $\mathbf{V}_1 \cap \mathbf{V}_2 = \{\mathbf{o}\}$, which means that $\mathbf{V}$ is the direct sum $\mathbf{V}_1 \dotplus \mathbf{V}_2$. q.e.d.

EXAMPLE 2. The vectors in common to two subspaces $\mathbf{V}_1$ and $\mathbf{V}_2$ (that is, the vectors in their intersection $\mathbf{V}_1 \cap \mathbf{V}_2$) constitute a subspace. Let $\mathbf{V}_1$ and $\mathbf{V}_2$ be any two subspaces of $\mathbf{V}$. Denote their intersection by $\mathbf{W}_0$ and denote the subspace they generate by $\mathbf{V}_0$:

$$\mathbf{W}_0 = \mathbf{V}_1 \cap \mathbf{V}_2 \quad \text{and} \quad \mathbf{V}_0 = [\mathbf{V}_1, \mathbf{V}_2].$$

Since $\mathbf{W}_0$ is a subspace of $\mathbf{V}_1$, we can extend a basis of $\mathbf{W}_0$ to a basis of $\mathbf{V}_1$, and the vectors in this basis which are not in $\mathbf{V}_1$ will generate another subspace $\mathbf{V}_1'$ such that $\mathbf{V}_1 = \mathbf{W}_0 \dotplus \mathbf{V}_1'$ (see Example 1). Similarly, we have $\mathbf{V}_2 = \mathbf{W}_0 \dotplus \mathbf{V}_2'$. Now, $\mathbf{V}_0 = [\mathbf{W}_0, \mathbf{V}_1', \mathbf{V}_2']$ because $\mathbf{W}_0 \cup \mathbf{V}_1' \cup \mathbf{V}_2'$ contains a basis of $\mathbf{V}_1$ and one of $\mathbf{V}_2$. If $\mathbf{o} = \mathbf{w}_0 + \mathbf{v}_1' + \mathbf{v}_2'$, where the summands are in $\mathbf{W}_0$, $\mathbf{V}_1'$, $\mathbf{V}_2'$, respectively, then $\mathbf{v}_2' = -\mathbf{w}_0 - \mathbf{v}_1'$ is in $\mathbf{V}_1 \cap \mathbf{V}_2$, hence in $\mathbf{W}_0$. But this forces $\mathbf{v}_2' = \mathbf{o}$ and therefore $-\mathbf{w}_0 = -\mathbf{v}_1' = \mathbf{o}$. So $\mathbf{V}_0 = \mathbf{W}_0 \dotplus \mathbf{V}_1' \dotplus \mathbf{V}_2'$. By Theorem 4, extended to three summands, we get

$$\dim \mathbf{V}_0 = \dim \mathbf{W}_0 + \dim \mathbf{V}_1' + \dim \mathbf{V}_2' = \dim \mathbf{V}_1 + \dim \mathbf{V}_2 - \dim \mathbf{W}_0.$$

Hence,

$$\dim \mathbf{V}_1 + \dim \mathbf{V}_2 = \dim [\mathbf{V}_1, \mathbf{V}_2] + \dim [\mathbf{V}_1 \cap \mathbf{V}_2].$$

(b) *Factor spaces.* If $\mathbf{V}_0$ is a subspace of $\mathbf{V}$, then we have illustrated, in particular cases (Sections 3.7, 4.3), the idea of a *factor space* $\mathbf{V}/\mathbf{V}_0$, called "$\mathbf{V}$ *modulo* $\mathbf{V}_0$." The idea generalizes readily, using the same notation and proofs. A "vector" in the factor space $\mathbf{V}/\mathbf{V}_0$ is a *coset* $\mathbf{v} + \mathbf{V}_0$ of $\mathbf{V}_0$,

$$\mathbf{v} + \mathbf{V}_0 = \{\mathbf{v} + \mathbf{v}_0 \mid \mathbf{v}_0 \text{ in } \mathbf{V}_0\} = \bar{\mathbf{v}},$$

where $\mathbf{v}$ is a *representative* of the coset; and $\bar{\mathbf{v}} = \bar{\mathbf{v}}'$ if and only if $\mathbf{v}' = \mathbf{v} + \mathbf{v}_0$ for some $\mathbf{v}_0$ in $\mathbf{V}_0$. The notation $\bar{\mathbf{v}}$, where $\bar{\mathbf{v}} = \mathbf{v} + \mathbf{V}_0$, indicates which representative is used, but does not indicate the subspace with respect to which the coset is formed. As before, the rules

$$\bar{\mathbf{v}}_1 + \bar{\mathbf{v}}_2 = \overline{\mathbf{v}_1 + \mathbf{v}_2} \quad \text{and} \quad c\bar{\mathbf{v}} = \overline{c\mathbf{v}}$$

define the vector addition and scalar multiple in $\mathbf{V}/\mathbf{V}_0$.

Theorem 5. Let $\mathbf{V}_0$ be a subspace of $\mathbf{V}$. Then

$$\dim \mathbf{V}/\mathbf{V}_0 = \dim \mathbf{V} - \dim \mathbf{V}_0.$$

Proof: Let $\mathbf{M}_0 = \{\mathbf{u}_1, \ldots, \mathbf{u}_p\}$ be a basis of $\mathbf{V}_0$. Extend $\mathbf{M}_0$ to a basis $\{\mathbf{M}_0, \mathbf{v}_1, \ldots, \mathbf{v}_q\}$ of $\mathbf{V}$. Now, if $\sum c_i\bar{\mathbf{v}}_i = \bar{\mathbf{o}}$, then $\sum c_i\mathbf{v}_i$ is in $\mathbf{V}_0$ and therefore equal to $\mathbf{o}$, so each c_i equals 0. Hence $\{\bar{\mathbf{v}}_1, \ldots, \bar{\mathbf{v}}_q\}$ is a linearly independent set of vectors in $\mathbf{V}/\mathbf{V}_0$. Furthermore, if $\bar{\mathbf{v}}$ is any vector in $\mathbf{V}/\mathbf{V}_0$, then

$$\bar{\mathbf{v}} = \overline{\sum a_i\mathbf{u}_i + \sum b_i\mathbf{v}_i} = \overline{\sum b_i\mathbf{v}_i} = \sum b_i\bar{\mathbf{v}}_i.$$

Now we have that $\{\bar{\mathbf{v}}_1, \ldots, \bar{\mathbf{v}}_q\}$ *is a basis of* $\mathbf{V}/\mathbf{V}_0$; therefore $q = \dim \mathbf{V}/\mathbf{V}_0 = (p + q) - p = \dim \mathbf{V} - \dim \mathbf{V}_0$. q.e.d.

EXAMPLE 3. Suppose a factor space $\mathbf{V}/\mathbf{V}_0$ is given. Let $\{\bar{\mathbf{w}}_1, \ldots, \bar{\mathbf{w}}_q\}$ be a basis of $\mathbf{V}/\mathbf{V}_0$. *The set* $\{\mathbf{w}_1, \ldots, \mathbf{w}_q\}$ *must then be a linearly independent subset of* $\mathbf{V}$, as is easily verified, so $\dim[\mathbf{w}_1, \ldots, \mathbf{w}_q] = q$. If $\{\mathbf{u}_1, \ldots, \mathbf{u}_p\}$ is a basis of $\mathbf{V}_0$, then $\{\mathbf{u}_1, \ldots, \mathbf{u}_p, \mathbf{w}_1, \ldots, \mathbf{w}_q\}$ generates $\mathbf{V}$ and hence is a basis of $\mathbf{V}$, by Theorem 5. Thus, *for any given subspace* $\mathbf{V}_0$, *we can use the representatives of a basis of* $\mathbf{V}/\mathbf{V}_0$ *to generate a subspace* $\mathbf{W}$ *such that* $\mathbf{V} = \mathbf{V}_0 \dotplus \mathbf{W}$. In view of the *proof* of Theorem 5, the set of all possible such direct summands $\mathbf{W}$ coincides with the set of all subspaces each of which is generated by the vectors which extend a basis of $\mathbf{V}_0$ to basis of $\mathbf{V}$. However, if $\mathbf{V}_0$ is an invariant subspace with respect to some linear transformation $\boldsymbol{a}$, then the space $\mathbf{W}$ is not necessarily invariant and generally can not be picked to be invariant (see, for instance, Section 3.7). But *a factor linear transformation of* $\mathbf{V}/\mathbf{V}_0$ *will exist whenever* $\mathbf{V}_0$ *is invariant.*

PROBLEMS

1. From Example 2 and Theorem 5 show that $\dim[\mathbf{V}_1, \mathbf{V}_2]/\mathbf{V}_2 = \dim \mathbf{V}_1/(\mathbf{V}_1 \cap \mathbf{V}_2)$.
2. Let $\mathbf{V}_1$ and $\mathbf{V}_2$ be subspaces of a 5-dimensional vector space, and suppose $\dim \mathbf{V}_1 = 3$ and $\dim \mathbf{V}_2 = 4$. What are the possible dimensions of $\mathbf{V}_1 \cap \mathbf{V}_2$?
3. If $\mathbf{V} = \mathbf{V}_1 \dotplus \mathbf{V}_2 = \mathbf{V}_1 \dotplus \mathbf{V}_2'$ and $\dim \mathbf{V}_1 < (\frac{1}{2}) \dim \mathbf{V}$, show that $\mathbf{V}_2 \cap \mathbf{V}_2' \neq \{\mathbf{o}\}$. Illustrate this in real 3-dimensional space.
4. If $\mathbf{V} = \mathbf{V}_1 \dotplus \mathbf{V}_2$, show that $\mathbf{V}_2$ and $\mathbf{V}/\mathbf{V}_1$ are isomorphic vector spaces under the correspondence $\mathbf{v}_2 \leftrightarrow \bar{\mathbf{v}}_2 = \mathbf{v}_2 + \mathbf{V}_1$.
5. Suppose $\mathbf{V} = [\mathbf{V}_1, \mathbf{V}_2, \mathbf{V}_3]$ and that

$$\mathbf{V}_1 \cap [\mathbf{V}_2, \mathbf{V}_3] = \mathbf{V}_2 \cap [\mathbf{V}_1, \mathbf{V}_3] = \mathbf{V}_3 \cap [\mathbf{V}_1, \mathbf{V}_2] = \{\mathbf{o}\}.$$

Show that $\mathbf{o} = \mathbf{v}_1 + \mathbf{v}_2 + \mathbf{v}_3$ if and only if $\mathbf{v}_1 = \mathbf{v}_2 = \mathbf{v}_3 = \mathbf{o}$, hence

$$\mathbf{V} = \mathbf{V}_1 \dotplus \mathbf{V}_2 \dotplus \mathbf{V}_3.$$

6. If $\mathbf{V} = \mathbf{V}_1 \dotplus \mathbf{V}_2$ and $\mathbf{V}_2 = \mathbf{V}_{21} \dotplus \mathbf{V}_{22}$, show that

$$\mathbf{V} = \mathbf{V}_1 \dotplus \mathbf{V}_{21} \dotplus \mathbf{V}_{22},$$

and generalize.

4.9 COORDINATE TESTS FOR LINEAR DEPENDENCE

Let $\{\mathbf{v}_1, \ldots, \mathbf{v}_t\}$ be some finite set of vectors from an n-dimensional vector space $\mathbf{V}$. If $\{\mathbf{u}_1, \ldots, \mathbf{u}_n\}$ is a coordinate basis of $\mathbf{V}$, then we can express the coordinates of $\mathbf{v}_j$ by the equation

$$\mathbf{v}_j = \sum_{i=1}^{n} \mathbf{u}_i a_{ij}.$$

This choice of notation yields a coordinate column

$$V_j = (a_{1j}, \ldots, a_{nj})^t$$

to represent $\mathbf{v}_j$. Hence we can associate with the ordered set of vectors $\{\mathbf{v}_1, \ldots, \mathbf{v}_t\}$ a matrix $A = (a_{ij})$ which partitions naturally into the above coordinate columns:

$$A = (V_1, V_2, \ldots, V_t).$$

Conversely, any $n \times t$ matrix with scalar entries can be partitioned into an array of t column matrices each of which may be regarded as a coordinate column of a vector in $\mathbf{V}$ with respect to the given coordinate basis.

Theorem 6. A set $\{\mathbf{v}_1, \ldots, \mathbf{v}_t\}$ of vectors from $\mathbf{V}$ is linearly dependent if and only if the set of coordinate columns $\{V_1, \ldots, V_t\}$ formed with respect to a given coordinate basis are linearly dependent (as column vectors), hence, if and only if $AC = O$ for some non-zero column matrix C with scalar entries, where $A = (V_1, \ldots, V_t)$. The vectors need not be distinct.

Proof: Using the notation above, suppose $\sum c_j \mathbf{v}_j$ is a linear dependence. This is equivalent to the existence of c_i's, not all zero, such that

$$\textstyle\sum c_j \sum \mathbf{u}_i a_{ij} = \sum \mathbf{u}_i \sum a_{ij} c_j = \mathbf{o}, \quad \text{or} \quad \sum a_{ij} c_j = 0 \quad \text{for each } i.$$

This means that $\sum c_j V_j = O$, which is the same as $AC = O$, with

$$C = (c_1, \ldots, c_t)^t \neq O. \qquad \text{q.e.d.}$$

EXAMPLE 1. From a slightly different point of view, let A be a given $n \times t$ matrix with scalar entries and first regard its columns as column vectors. Then, from the definition of linear dependence, $AX = O$ has a *non-zero* solution for $X = (x_1, \ldots, x_t)^t$, with the x_i's scalars, if and only if the columns of A are linearly dependent (as column vectors). Now, let C be a non-zero solution. Then $AC = O$ can be interpreted, with respect to a coordinate basis of a suitable n-dimensional vector space, as a statement of the linear dependence of a set of vectors whose coordinate columns are the columns of A.

Suppose A is a $p \times q$ matrix with entries from some field. We can interpret its columns as coordinate columns of p-dimensional vectors and its rows as coordinate rows of q-dimensional vectors. These columns and rows can also be regarded as vectors in respective column and row vector spaces. Then, it is convenient in matrix algebra to speak of (a) the ***column space of*** A, meaning the *subspace of p-dimensional column vector space generated by the "columns" of* A, (b) the ***row space of*** A, meaning the *subspace of q-dimensional row vector space generated by the "rows" of* A.

EXAMPLE 2. The matrix $A = \begin{pmatrix} 2 & 0 & 1 \\ 0 & 1 & 2 \end{pmatrix}$ has a row space of dimension 2 and a column space of dimension 2. The equality of these two dimensions is not an accident, as we shall see later. Now, let $X = (x_1, x_2, x_3)^t$ and $Y = (y_1, y_2)$. Then $AX = O$ has a non-zero solution because any three or more vectors in a 2-dimensional vector space must be linearly dependent; but $YA = O$ has only the zero solution because the two rows of A are linearly independent.

EXAMPLE 3. The row and column spaces of certain matrices have obvious dimensions. Thus a diagonal matrix has as many linearly independent rows as non-zero entries (same for columns). More generally, *a matrix in which each row has its first non-zero entry (if any) further to the right than the first non-zero entries of the preceding rows* (if any) *has a row space of dimension equal to the number of these first non-zero entries*, that is, equal to the number of non-zero rows. A matrix in this simplified form is called a ***row-echelon matrix*** (see also Section 6.7, Problem 14). Thus

$$\begin{pmatrix} 0 & 2 & 4 & 1 & 0 \\ 0 & 0 & 0 & 1 & 2 \\ 0 & 0 & 0 & 0 & 0 \end{pmatrix}$$

has a row space of dimension 2, and it is in row-echelon form.

Suppose $\dim \mathbf{V} = n > 0$. As we have remarked, the justification for the technique of switching from $\mathbf{V}$ to a vector space of row or column vectors (see also Section 3.6) is based on the natural mapping of $\mathbf{V}$ onto the vector space of n-tuples, namely, the isomorphism of Section 1.5, Equation (3), generalized to higher dimensions. Suppose $\{\mathbf{u}_1, \ldots, \mathbf{u}_n\}$ is a given coordinate basis and $\mathbf{v} = \sum x_i \mathbf{u}_i$. Let (x_i), temporarily, denote the n-tuple vector $(x_1, \ldots, x_n)$ that is uniquely determined by $\mathbf{v}$ and the given basis. Then the mapping $\mathbf{v} \to (x_i)$ is one-to-one onto. If $\mathbf{w} \leftrightarrow (y_i)$ and c, d are any scalars, then

$$c\mathbf{v} + d\mathbf{w} \leftrightarrow c(x_i) + d(y_i).$$

This preservation of linear combinations (image of a sum equals the sum of the images, and the image of a scalar multiple is the same multiple of the image) is used in the proof of Theorem 6, *with* (x_i) *regarded as a column vector*. The correspondence thus displayed allows us to pass freely between coordinatized and abstract versions of any relations among vectors expressed by linear combinations, and it preserves linear independence (see Problem 3, below). These two vector spaces are isomorphic and the mapping $\mathbf{v} \to (x_i)$ is an isomorphism.

If X is an n-dimensional column vector or row vector, then the correspondence $X \leftrightarrow X^t$ is another simple but useful isomorphism. In some computational situations it is handier to use coordinate rows to represent vectors, rather than coordinate columns. For instance, suppose we wish to find a basis of some subspace $[\mathbf{w}_1, \ldots, \mathbf{w}_t]$ of an n-dimensional vector space $\mathbf{V}$. Suppose also that we do not insist on this basis being a subset of the given generating set $\{\mathbf{w}_1, \ldots, \mathbf{w}_t\}$. Then we can proceed by listing the coordinate rows of these vectors, with respect to any convenient basis, in the form of a partitioned matrix, say

$$B = \begin{pmatrix} W_1 \\ \vdots \\ W_t \end{pmatrix},$$

where W_i is the *coordinate row* of $\mathbf{w}_i$. *Any basis of the row space of B coincides with the set of coordinate rows of a basis of* $[\mathbf{w}_1, \ldots, \mathbf{w}_t]$, *and vice versa.* So, our problem is equivalent to finding a basis of this row space. For this purpose, the successive application to the *rows* of B of the same operations applied to the *equations* of a linear system in Section 4.2, will reduce B to a row-echelon matrix, the form described in Example 3. From this form, *a basis can be read off at sight* because each of these operations, usually called ***elementary row operations***, yields, in turn, a set of row vectors which generates *the same row space with which we started.* (See Problem 2 below.) These ideas will be elaborated in Section 6.7.

EXAMPLE 4. Suppose a set of vectors is represented with respect to some basis by the rows of a 4×5 matrix

$$\begin{pmatrix} 2 & -2 & 0 & 4 & 4 \\ 1 & 1 & 1 & 1 & 1 \\ 1 & 0 & 1 & 0 & 1 \\ 3 & -2 & 1 & 4 & 5 \end{pmatrix}.$$

Among the infinite number of ways to proceed, suppose we decide to *multiply the first row by $\frac{1}{2}$ and then use multiples of the new first row* to obtain

$$\begin{pmatrix} 1 & -1 & 0 & 2 & 2 \\ 0 & 2 & 1 & -1 & -1 \\ 0 & 1 & 1 & -2 & -1 \\ 0 & 1 & 1 & -2 & -1 \end{pmatrix}.$$

Next, *interchange the second and third rows and then subtract suitable multiples of the new second row from the third and fourth* to get the row-echelon matrix

$$\begin{pmatrix} 1 & -1 & 0 & 2 & 2 \\ 0 & 1 & 1 & -2 & 0 \\ 0 & 0 & -1 & 3 & 1 \\ 0 & 0 & 0 & 0 & 0 \end{pmatrix}.$$

The three non-zero rows are *a basis of the row space.* If we were to perform, simultaneously, the *same row operations in succession on a* 4×4 *identity matrix*, then the final fourth row of the modified identity matrix would display the coefficients of *a linear dependence* of the four given vectors. This, in fact, applies to any zero row of a row-echelon matrix constructed by elementary row operations (see also Section 6.7, Example 5 below). In our present case, skipping some intermediate steps, we find that our row operations change I as follows:

$$I \to \begin{pmatrix} \frac{1}{2} & 0 & 0 & 0 \\ -\frac{1}{2} & 1 & 0 & 0 \\ -\frac{1}{2} & 0 & 1 & 0 \\ -\frac{3}{2} & 0 & 0 & 1 \end{pmatrix} \to \begin{pmatrix} \frac{1}{2} & 0 & 0 & 0 \\ -\frac{1}{2} & 0 & 1 & 0 \\ -\frac{1}{2} & 1 & 0 & 0 \\ -1 & 0 & -1 & 1 \end{pmatrix} \to \begin{pmatrix} \frac{1}{2} & 0 & 0 & 0 \\ -\frac{1}{2} & 0 & 1 & 0 \\ \frac{1}{2} & 1 & -2 & 0 \\ -1 & 0 & -1 & 1 \end{pmatrix}.$$

The last row gives a linear dependence on the rows of the original 4×5 matrix, namely,

$$-(2, -2, 0, 4, 4) - (1, 0, 1, 0, 1) + (3, -2, 1, 4, 5) = (0, 0, 0, 0, 0).$$

PROBLEMS

1. Transpose the matrix in Example 4 and find a basis of the column space and a linear dependence in the columns by the method of Example 4.
2. Show that the following row operations do not alter the row space of a matrix: (a) *interchange two rows*, (b) *multiply a row by a non-zero scalar*, (c) *add to a row a multiple of some other row.*
3. (a) Show that a set of column vectors $X_1, \ldots, X_p$ are linearly dependent if and only if the vectors $X_1^t, \ldots, X_p^t$ are linearly dependent. (b) For *any* two isomorphic vector spaces, show that linear dependence is invariant under a given isomorphism.
4. Represent a polynomial $p(x) = a_0 + a_1x + \cdots + a_nx^n$ by the infinite row matrix $(a_0, \ldots, a_n, 0, \ldots)$. Find a basis of the subspace generated by the row matrices which represent
$$p(x), \quad p^{(1)}(x), \ldots, p^{(n)}(x),$$
where $p^{(i)}(x)$ is the i-th derivative:
$$p^{(i)}(x) = i!a_i + \cdots + [n(n-1)\cdots(n-i+1)]a_nx^{n-i}.$$
5. Suppose $\{\mathbf{v}_1, \ldots, \mathbf{v}_p\}$ is a linearly independent subset of an n-dimensional vector space $\mathbf{V}$, and that $\mathbf{V} = [\mathbf{v}_1, \ldots, \mathbf{v}_p, \mathbf{u}_1, \ldots, \mathbf{u}_q]$. Devise a row-echelon procedure for eliminating $p + q - n$ of the $\mathbf{u}_k$'s, thus enlarging $\{\mathbf{v}_1, \ldots, \mathbf{v}_p\}$ to a basis which is a *subset of the given generating set* (see Section 4.7, Example 2). (The set $\{\mathbf{u}_1, \ldots, \mathbf{u}_q\}$ need not be a basis.)

5

Invertibility

5.1 INVERTIBILITY AND BASES

An automorphism of a vector space **V** (see Section 1.5) is a one-to-one mapping of **V** onto **V** which has the property that the image of any linear combination of vectors in **V** equals the same linear combination of their images. Therefore *an automorphism of* **V** *is an invertible linear transformation of* **V**, first defined in Section 2.13.

We recall that a linear transformation $\boldsymbol{a}$ of **V** is called *invertible* if and only if there exists a linear transformation $\boldsymbol{b}$ such that

$$\boldsymbol{ab} = \boldsymbol{ba} = \boldsymbol{i}.$$

The linear transformation $\boldsymbol{b}$ is denoted by $\boldsymbol{a}^{-1}$ and is called the *inverse* of $\boldsymbol{a}$. Let the matrix A represent $\boldsymbol{a}$ with respect to some basis of the vector space **V** (finite-dimensional, as always hereafter). Then, assuming $A(\text{adj-}A) = |A|I$ for all square matrices, the results of Sections 2.12 and 2.13 are readily verified for the general finite-dimensional case. In particular, we still have that *a linear transformation* $\boldsymbol{a}$ *of* **V** *is invertible if and only if any one of the following equivalent statements is true:*

(1) $\text{im}\ \boldsymbol{a} = \mathbf{V}$, or what is the same, $\boldsymbol{a}$ is onto **V**.
(2) $\ker \boldsymbol{a} = \{\mathbf{o}\}$.
(3) $\boldsymbol{a}$ is one-to-one.
(4) $\boldsymbol{ab} = \boldsymbol{i}$ for some linear transformation $\boldsymbol{b}$ of **V**.
(5) $\boldsymbol{ba} = \boldsymbol{i}$ for some linear transformation $\boldsymbol{b}$ of **V**.
(6) A is an invertible matrix, where $A \leftrightarrow \boldsymbol{a}$.
(7) $|A| \neq 0$.

For matrices, we again say that a *square matrix* A is *invertible* if and only if there exists a square matrix B such that

$$AB = BA = I.$$

The matrix B is denoted by A^{-1} and is called the *inverse* of A. Since A may be regarded as the representation of a linear transformation, we deduce that A *is invertible if and only if any one of the following equivalent statements is true:*

(1) Given Y, then $AX = Y$ always has a solution for X.

(2) $AX = O$ has only $X = O$ as a solution (that is, A has linearly independent columns).

(3) Given Y, then $AX = Y$ has at most one solution for X (that is, if $AX_1 = AX_2$ then $X_1 = X_2$).

(4) $AB = I$ for some square matrix B (that is, the unit column vectors are linear combinations of the columns of A).

(5) $BA = I$ for some square B (that is, the unit row vectors are linear combinations of the rows of A).

(6) $\boldsymbol{a}$ is invertible, where $\boldsymbol{a} \leftrightarrow A$.

(7) $|A| \neq 0$.

The entries in the matrices B and X can be considered in any field containing the entries of A (in (2), (4), (5)), or of A and Y (in (1), (3)), because if a solution of a linear system of equations exists at all it exists also within the confines of such a field. We shall consider this later in a more general situation (Chapter 6).

EXAMPLE 1. From $AA^{-1} = I$ we see that the i-th column of A^{-1} is the unique solution of $AX = E_i$, where E_i is the i-th column of I. Or, by a partition of A^{-1} into "unknown" columns, we can solve simultaneously for the columns of A^{-1} from $A^{-1}A = I$ by maintaining the partition into columns until the end (see Problem 6). We also know (Section 2.13, Equation (43)) that $A(\text{cof-}A)^t = |A|I$. Recalling that $(\text{cof-}A)^t$ is denoted by adj-A ("adjugate of A"), and that

$$(\text{adj-}A)A = A(\text{adj-}A) = |A|I,$$

we have the expression of A^{-1} in the form

$$A^{-1} = (1/|A|)\text{adj-}A.$$

But other methods and formulas will turn up later.

If $\boldsymbol{a}$ *is not invertible, it is called* **singular**. *The same terminology is applied to a square matrix.* For a while we shall concentrate on invertible linear transformations and matrices. In terms of invertible linear transformations, the connection between automorphisms and coordinate bases can be stated by the following theorem.

Theorem 1. There is a *one-to-one correspondence* between the set of all possible changes (including no change) from a fixed coordinate basis of $\mathbf{V}$ to another coordinate basis of $\mathbf{V}$, and the set of invertible linear transformations of $\mathbf{V}$.

Proof: Let $\{\mathbf{u}_1, \ldots, \mathbf{u}_n\}$ be one coordinate basis of $\mathbf{V}$ and let $\{\mathbf{v}_1, \ldots, \mathbf{v}_n\}$ be another. Just as in Section 2.6 (see Theorem 2 below), we can determine a unique linear transformation $\boldsymbol{p}$ of $\mathbf{V}$ such that $\mathbf{v}_i = \boldsymbol{p}\mathbf{u}_i$ $(i = 1, \ldots, n)$. There exist unique scalars p_{ij} such that for each i, $\mathbf{v}_i = \sum \mathbf{u}_j p_{ji}$, and the matrix $P = (p_{ij})$, therefore, represents $\boldsymbol{p}$. As in Section 2.13, Example 4, we can show that P, hence $\boldsymbol{p}$, is invertible. Or, we can observe directly that the equations $\mathbf{u}_i = \boldsymbol{q}\mathbf{v}_i$ $(i = 1, \ldots, n)$ determine a unique linear transformation $\boldsymbol{q}$, so $\mathbf{u}_i = \boldsymbol{qp}\mathbf{u}_i$ $(i = 1, \ldots, n)$. This implies that $\boldsymbol{qp} = \boldsymbol{i}$, hence $\boldsymbol{p}$ is invertible. *Conversely*, if $\boldsymbol{p}$ is a given invertible linear transformation, then one readily verifies that $\{\boldsymbol{p}\mathbf{u}_1, \ldots, \boldsymbol{p}\mathbf{u}_n\}$ is linearly independent, hence a basis. No linear transformation different from $\boldsymbol{p}$ can give the same basis, since a linear transformation is determined by its effect on a basis. q.e.d.

As in Section 3.2, Example 3, it can be shown that $\boldsymbol{p}$ is represented by P with respect to *either one* of the bases it connects. Also, as in Section 3.2, Equation (3), *the connection between first and second coordinate columns of a vector is given by*

$$X = PY,$$

where X is the coordinate column with respect to the *first* basis, Y is the coordinate column with respect to the *second* basis, and P is the coefficient matrix which *expresses the second basis in terms of the first basis.*

EXAMPLE 2. Suppose a real matrix P expresses a change of basis and has the following property: If Y is the second coordinate column of a vector whose first coordinate column is X, then $X^tX = Y^tY$, for every X. Since $X = PY$, we have $Y^tP^tPY = Y^tY$ for every Y. By Section 3.4, Problem 4(b), it follows that $P^tP = I$. So P is a *real orthogonal matrix*, as defined in Section 3.4.

EXAMPLE 3. If $\boldsymbol{a}$ is singular then im $\boldsymbol{a} \neq \mathbf{V}$. *Since* im $\boldsymbol{a}$ *is then a proper subspace*, we can find a coordinate basis with respect to which

$$\boldsymbol{a} \leftrightarrow \begin{pmatrix} A_1 \\ O \end{pmatrix},$$

where the number of rows of A_1 equals dim im $\boldsymbol{a}$. (Recall that the columns of a matrix representation display the coordinates of the images of the basis vectors.)

PROBLEMS

1. Show that the product a finite number of invertible linear transformations (or matrices) is again invertible.
2. If matrices A and AB are both invertible, is B invertible? If A and $A + B$ are invertible, is B invertible?

3. If $\boldsymbol{p}$ is an invertible linear transformation of $\mathbf{V}$ and $\{\mathbf{u}_1, \ldots, \mathbf{u}_t\}$ is a subset of $\mathbf{V}$, show that $\{\boldsymbol{p}\mathbf{u}_1, \ldots, \boldsymbol{p}\mathbf{u}_t\}$ is linearly independent if and only if $\{\mathbf{u}_1, \ldots, \mathbf{u}_t\}$ is linearly independent.

4. For what values of s and t are the following matrices invertible?

(a) $\mathrm{diag}(s, t, s - t)$, (b) $\begin{pmatrix} 0 & 1 & 0 \\ 0 & 0 & 1 \\ s & 0 & 0 \end{pmatrix}$, (c) $\begin{pmatrix} 1 & s & t \\ 1 & s^2 & t^2 \\ 1 & s^3 & t^3 \end{pmatrix}$.

5. Find the inverse of each matrix in Problem 4, when the inverse exists.

6. Let $A = (a_{ij})$ be an invertible 2×2 matrix, let $X = (X_1, X_2)$ be a partitioned 2×2 matrix, and let $I = (E_1, E_2)$ be the partitioned 2×2 identity matrix. Show that the system

$$\sum X_i a_{ij} = E_j \quad (j = 1, 2)$$

has the solution

$$X_1 = (a_{22}E_1 - a_{21}E_2)/|A|, \quad X_2 = (-a_{12}E_1 + a_{11}E_2)/|A|.$$

Thus, express A^{-1} and compare with $(\text{adj-}A)/|A|$. Do the same with a row partition of X. Find corresponding formulas for the 3×3 case.

7. Suppose A and B are invertible. Solve for X, Y, Z if

$$\begin{pmatrix} A & C \\ O & B \end{pmatrix} \begin{pmatrix} X & Z \\ O & Y \end{pmatrix} = I.$$

8. Let $\{U_1, \ldots, U_n\}$ be a basis of an n-dimensional column vector space, and B any n-rowed matrix whose columns are in this space. Show that the equation $(U_1, \ldots, U_n)X = B$ is always solvable, that $(U_1, \ldots, U_n)$ is invertible, and that there exists a set $\{V_1, \ldots, V_n\}$ of $n \times 1$ column vectors such that

$$\begin{aligned} V_i^t U_j &= 0 \quad \text{if} \quad i \neq j, \\ &= 1 \quad \text{if} \quad i = j. \end{aligned}$$

9. Suppose a given coordinate basis of an n-dimensional vector space $\mathbf{V}$ is changed by permuting the vectors in the basis. Describe the matrix representation of the associated invertible linear transformation.

5.2 MAPPING THEOREM

The effect of a linear transformation $\boldsymbol{a}$ on a generating set of $\mathbf{V}$ determines its effect on every vector in $\mathbf{V}$. If the generating set is linearly independent (hence a basis), then every linear transformation of $\mathbf{V}$ is determined, as described in the following theorem, by a choice of images of the basis vectors.

Theorem 2. Let $\{\mathbf{u}_1, \ldots, \mathbf{u}_n\}$ be a basis of $\mathbf{V}$ and let $\{\mathbf{v}_1, \ldots, \mathbf{v}_n\}$ be any finite set of n vectors from $\mathbf{V}$. Then there exists a unique linear transformation $\boldsymbol{a}$ of $\mathbf{V}$ such that $\mathbf{v}_i = \boldsymbol{a}\mathbf{u}_i$ $(i = 1, \ldots, n)$.

Proof: The proof is just an extension of the discussion in Section 2.6. If $\mathbf{w}$ is any vector in $\mathbf{V}$, then

$$\mathbf{w} = \sum x_i \mathbf{u}_i,$$

uniquely. Now we define $\mathbf{w}'$ by

$$\mathbf{w}' = \sum x_i \mathbf{v}_i.$$

We can assign $\mathbf{w}'$ as the image of $\mathbf{w}$ and thus create a mapping, which we denote by $\boldsymbol{a}$, that is,

$$\mathbf{w}' = \boldsymbol{a}\mathbf{w}.$$

The mapping $\boldsymbol{a}$ is a linear transformation because $\mathbf{v}_i = \boldsymbol{a}\mathbf{u}_i$ $(i = 1, \ldots, n)$ implies $\mathbf{w}' = \sum x_i \boldsymbol{a}\mathbf{u}_i$. Finally, $\boldsymbol{a}$ is unique because it is determined by its effect on a basis. (With respect to the coordinate basis $\{\mathbf{u}_1, \ldots, \mathbf{u}_n\}$, we get a matrix representation of $\boldsymbol{a}$, from $\mathbf{v}_i = \sum \mathbf{u}_j a_{ji}$.) q.e.d.

Corollary. If $\{U_1, \ldots, U_n\}$ is a basis of an n-dimensional column vector space, and if $\{V_1, \ldots, V_n\}$ is any set of n vectors from the same space, then a unique linear transformation $\boldsymbol{a}$ of this space is determined by the rules:

$$\boldsymbol{a}U_i = V_i \quad (i = 1, \ldots, n),$$
$$\boldsymbol{a}\sum s_i U_i = \sum s_i V_i \quad (\text{all scalars } s_i).$$

The matrix representation of $\boldsymbol{a}$ is given by:

(a) $A = (U_1, \ldots, U_n)^{-1}(V_1, \ldots, V_n)$, with respect to the coordinate basis $\{U_1, \ldots, U_n\}$.
(b) $B = (U_1', \ldots, U_n')^{-1}(U_1, \ldots, U_n)A(U_1, \ldots, U_n)^{-1}(U_1', \ldots, U_n') = (U_1', \ldots, U_n')^{-1}(V_1, \ldots, V_n)(U_1, \ldots, U_n)^{-1}(U_1', \ldots, U_n')$, with respect to any other coordinate basis $\{U_1', \ldots, U_n'\}$.
(c) $C = (V_1, \ldots, V_n)(U_1, \ldots, U_n)^{-1}$, with respect to the coordinate basis $\{E_1, \ldots, E_n\}$, where $(E_1, \ldots, E_n) = I$ is the identity matrix.
(d) A again, with respect to $\{V_1, \ldots, V_n\}$ as a coordinate basis, *if* the V_i's happen to be linearly independent.

Proof: The first statement follows from Theorem 2 applied to the column vector space. The matrix representations follow analogously to the ones in Section 3.6, Example. Thus, setting $U = (U_1, \ldots, U_n)$, and so forth, we find:

$$\boldsymbol{a}U = V = U(U^{-1}V), \quad \boldsymbol{a} \leftrightarrow U^{-1}V;$$
$$\boldsymbol{a}U = (\boldsymbol{a}U')(U'^{-1}U) = V = U'(U'^{-1}V), \quad \boldsymbol{a} \leftrightarrow U'^{-1}VU^{-1}U';$$
$$\boldsymbol{a}U = (\boldsymbol{a}I)U = IV, \quad \boldsymbol{a} \leftrightarrow VU^{-1};$$
$$\boldsymbol{a}U = (\boldsymbol{a}V)(V^{-1}U) = V, \quad \boldsymbol{a} \leftrightarrow U^{-1}V.$$

q.e.d.

It is handy to abbreviate the description of $\boldsymbol{a}$ given in the hypotheses of the Corollary to

$$U_i \rightarrow V_i \quad (i = 1, \ldots, n).$$

Note that *when we are given a coordinate equation* as the description of the linear transformation $\boldsymbol{a}$ above, say $X' = AX$, then X is a *coordinate column* and so in general it does not coincide with the column vector it represents. But from the coordinate equation we know that $E_i \rightarrow$ (i-th column of A), so the Corollary gives a representation of $\boldsymbol{a}$ by A with respect to $\{E_1, \ldots, E_n)$ and a representation of $\boldsymbol{a}$ by $(U'_1, \ldots, U'_n)^{-1}A(U'_1, \ldots, U'_n)$ with respect to an arbitrary coordinate basis $\{U'_1, \ldots, U'_n\}$.

We may, of course, regard an n-dimensional column vector space as the isomorphic image of an n-dimensional vector space $\mathbf{V}$, *with the unit column vectors* $\{E_1, \ldots, E_n\}$ *corresponding to the vectors of an unspecified coordinate basis of* $\mathbf{V}$. From this convenient point of view, the column vectors coincide with coordinate columns of vectors in $\mathbf{V}$; hence the above Corollary describes a linear transformation $\boldsymbol{a}$ of $\mathbf{V}$ in terms of how $\boldsymbol{a}$ affects the *coordinate columns* $\{U_1, \ldots, U_n\}$ of n linearly independent vectors in $\mathbf{V}$. The given matrix representations and the coordinate equations are identical for $\boldsymbol{a}$ regarded as a linear transformation of $\mathbf{V}$, and for $\boldsymbol{a}$ regarded as a linear transformation of the isomorphic column vector space.

Now suppose, in terms of coordinate columns with respect to an unspecified coordinate basis of an n-dimensional vector space $\mathbf{V}$, we know that a linear transformation $\boldsymbol{a}$ of $\mathbf{V}$ maps n linearly independent vectors of $\mathbf{V}$ whose coordinate columns are $\{U_1, \ldots, U_n\}$ onto n vectors whose coordinate columns are $\{V_1, \ldots, V_n\}$: $U_i \rightarrow V_i$ $(i = 1, \ldots, n)$. Then the matrix representations of $\boldsymbol{a}$, with respect to various bases whose *coordinate column* descriptions are given, are exactly as described in the Corollary. In particular,

$$C = (V_1, \ldots, V_n)(U_1, \ldots, U_n)^{-1}$$

represents $\boldsymbol{a}$ with respect to the unspecified basis of $\mathbf{V}$, and $CX = X'$ is the corresponding coordinate equation (see Problem 4 below). Moreover, if $U_i = E_i$ $(i = 1, \ldots, n)$, then $C = A$, and the formula

$$B = (U'_1, \ldots, U'_n)^{-1}A(U'_1, \ldots, U'_n)$$

reflects a change of coordinate basis in $\mathbf{V}$, from a basis (the unspecified one) with coordinate columns $\{E_1, \ldots, E_n\}$ to a basis with coordinate columns $\{U'_1, \ldots, U'_n\}$, in agreement with the remark following the Corollary.

EXAMPLE 1. Suppose it is desired to create a linear transformation $\boldsymbol{a}$ such that $\ker \boldsymbol{a} = [\mathbf{u}_1, \ldots, \mathbf{u}_t]$ for some *prescribed* linear independent set $\{\mathbf{u}_1, \ldots, \mathbf{u}_t\}$. Extend this set to a basis $\{\mathbf{u}_1, \ldots, \mathbf{u}_n\}$ and determine $\boldsymbol{a}$ by: $\boldsymbol{a}\mathbf{u}_i = \mathbf{o}$ $(i = 1, \ldots, t)$; $\boldsymbol{a}\mathbf{u}_i = \mathbf{u}_i$ $(i = t + 1, \ldots, n)$. This is a linear transformation which has an especially simple representation with respect to $\{\mathbf{u}_1, \ldots, \mathbf{u}_n\}$ as coordinate basis, namely, $A = \operatorname{diag}(0, \ldots, 0, 1, \ldots, 1)$. If we wish the representation with respect to some other (second) coordinate basis, say $\{\mathbf{w}_1, \ldots, \mathbf{w}_n\}$ where $\mathbf{w}_i = \boldsymbol{p}\mathbf{u}_i$ and $\boldsymbol{p} \leftrightarrow P$, then we compute the matrix $P^{-1}AP$.

The set $\{\mathbf{v}_1, \ldots, \mathbf{v}_n\}$ in Theorem 2 may be linearly dependent. If so, there exists some linear dependence, say $\sum c_i\mathbf{v}_i = \mathbf{o}$, which is the same assumption as either

$$\text{(a) } \sum a_{ji}c_i = 0 \quad (j = 1, \ldots, n), \quad \text{where} \quad \boldsymbol{a} \leftrightarrow A = (a_{ij}),$$

or

$$\text{(b) } \sum c_i\boldsymbol{a}\mathbf{u}_i = \boldsymbol{a}\sum c_i\mathbf{u}_i = \mathbf{o},$$

for a non-trivial set of c_i's. In matrix notation, (a) says that $AC = O$ where $C = (c_1, \ldots, c_n)^t$ is non-zero. Hence $AX = O$ has a non-trivial solution, which means that A is a singular matrix. But (b) says this better, for $\sum c_i\mathbf{u}_i \neq \mathbf{o}$ implies $\ker \boldsymbol{a} \neq \{\mathbf{o}\}$; hence $\boldsymbol{a}$ is a *singular* linear transformation. Thus once again we find that when A is a square matrix with entries in the field of scalars of $\mathbf{V}$, then *A is invertible if and only if any linear transformation $\boldsymbol{a}$ of $\mathbf{V}$ that it represents is invertible.*

EXAMPLE 2. By Theorem 2, we can define a unique linear transformation, say $\boldsymbol{a}$, of a 3-dimensional column vector space, such that

$$\begin{aligned} \boldsymbol{a}(3, 1, 1)^t &= (0, 1, 1)^t, \\ \boldsymbol{a}(0, 1, 1)^t &= (2, 1, 0)^t, \\ \boldsymbol{a}(1, 0, 3)^t &= (0, 0, 0)^t, \end{aligned}$$

because the indicated counterimages are linearly independent. Let us see how to get the representations A and C in the above Corollary, Parts (a) and (c), using the same notation for the vectors. We can proceed in a manner similar to that described in Section 3.3, Example 1. Without any computation, we have

$$(U_1, U_2, U_3) = P^{-1} = \begin{pmatrix} 3 & 0 & 1 \\ 1 & 1 & 0 \\ 1 & 1 & 3 \end{pmatrix}$$

and

$$(V_1, V_2, V_3) = P^{-1}A = \begin{pmatrix} 0 & 2 & 0 \\ 1 & 1 & 0 \\ 1 & 0 & 0 \end{pmatrix},$$

where P expresses the unit column vectors $\{E_1, E_2, E_3\}$ in terms of the given column vectors $\{U_1, U_2, U_3\}$, and A represents $\boldsymbol{a}$ with respect to the columns of P^{-1} (the given counterimages) as a coordinate basis. Now, if we compute P, then we can compute A (see Problem 2 below) from

$$A = P(P^{-1}A) = (U_1, U_2, U_3)^{-1}(V_1, V_2, V_3).$$

Finally, we can compute C, which represents $\boldsymbol{a}$ with respect to the unit column vectors as coordinate basis, from $C = (V_1, V_2, V_3)(U_1, U_2, U_3)^{-1}$. This gives us

$$C = P^{-1}AP = \frac{1}{9}\begin{pmatrix} -6 & 16 & 2 \\ 0 & 9 & 0 \\ 3 & 1 & -1 \end{pmatrix}.$$

Note that if $Y = (1, -2, 2)$ and if $X = (1, 0, 3)^t$, then $YA = O$ and $AX = O$. Also $|A| = 0$. These all corroborate the singularity of $\boldsymbol{a}$, which we knew from the given fact that $(1, 0, 3)^t$ is in ker $\boldsymbol{a}$.

Of course, all the above suggestions are an evasion of the direct elementary procedure which merely expresses each of the three images and three counterimages as a linear combination of the prescribed basis, and then substitutes in the vector equation which determines $\boldsymbol{a}$.

PROBLEMS

1. If A is a square matrix, show that $AY = O$ has a non-zero solution for a column matrix Y if and only if $XA = O$ has a non-zero solution for some row matrix X.
2. Compute the matrix A in Example 2, which represents $\boldsymbol{a}$ with respect to $\{(3, 1, 1)^t, (0, 1, 1)^t, (1, 0, 3)^t\}$.
3. Verify Part (c) of the Corollary in another way by expressing $\boldsymbol{a}U_i$ and V_i in terms of $\{\boldsymbol{a}E_1, \ldots, \boldsymbol{a}E_n\}$ and $\{E_1, \ldots, E_n\}$, where E_i is the i-th unit column vector.
4. The coordinate equations of a certain linear transformation $\boldsymbol{a}$, with respect to some unspecified coordinate basis, are given by

$$X' = AX, \quad \text{with} \quad A = \begin{pmatrix} 1 & 1 & -1 \\ 1 & -1 & 1 \\ -1 & 1 & 1 \end{pmatrix}.$$

Let the set $\mathrm{M} = \{(1, 1, 0)^t, (1, 2, 3)^t, (0, 0, 1)^t\}$ consist of the coordinate columns of three vectors $\{\mathbf{u}_1, \mathbf{u}_2, \mathbf{u}_3\}$, in the indicated order.

(a) Show that the set $\{\mathbf{u}_1, \mathbf{u}_2, \mathbf{u}_3\}$ is linearly independent.

(b) Find the coordinate columns of the images under $\boldsymbol{a}$ of the vectors $\{\mathbf{u}_1, \mathbf{u}_2, \mathbf{u}_3\}$.

(c) Use $\{\mathbf{u}_1, \mathbf{u}_2, \mathbf{u}_3\}$, in the given order, as a coordinate basis and find the matrix representation of $\boldsymbol{a}$ with respect to it.

(d) Show that the image set $\{\boldsymbol{a}\mathbf{u}_1, \boldsymbol{a}\mathbf{u}_2, \boldsymbol{a}\mathbf{u}_3\}$ constitutes a coordinate basis, and find the matrix representation of $\boldsymbol{a}$ with respect to it.

(e) Find the matrix representation of $\boldsymbol{a}$ with respect to the coordinate basis $\{\mathbf{u}_2, \mathbf{u}_3, \mathbf{u}_1\}$.

5.3 CAYLEY-HAMILTON THEOREM

If $p(x)$ is a polynomial, say

$$p(x) = \sum_{i=0}^{n} b_i x^i = b_0 + b_1 x + \cdots + b_n x^n,$$

where x is an indeterminate (Section 4.4) and the b_i's are scalars, then the definitions and properties of $p(\boldsymbol{a})$ and $p(A)$ discussed in Section 2.9, apply to any linear transformation $\boldsymbol{a}$ and square matrix A. For instance, suppose A represents a linear transformation $\boldsymbol{a}$ of $\mathbf{V}$ with respect to some basis, and let the polynomial $p(x)$ have coefficients that are in the scalar field of $\mathbf{V}$. Then $p(\boldsymbol{a}) = \boldsymbol{o}$ if and only if $p(A) = O$, just as in Section 2.8, Example 8.

EXAMPLE 1. Suppose the constant b_0 in the polynomial $p(x)$ is not zero, $b_0 \neq 0$. If $\boldsymbol{a}$ is a linear transformation such that $p(\boldsymbol{a}) = \boldsymbol{o}$, we have

$$\boldsymbol{a}[(-1/b_0)(b_1\boldsymbol{i} + b_2\boldsymbol{a} + \cdots + b_n\boldsymbol{a}^{n-1})] = \boldsymbol{i},$$

and, equivalently, if $\boldsymbol{a} \leftrightarrow A$,

$$A[(-1/b_0)(b_1I + b_2A + \cdots + b_nA^{n-1})] = I.$$

So the polynomials in the brackets are $\boldsymbol{a}^{-1}$ and A^{-1}, respectively.

EXAMPLE 2. Suppose the constant in the polynomial $p(x)$ is zero, $b_0 = 0$. If also, $\boldsymbol{a} \leftrightarrow A$ and $p(\boldsymbol{a}) = \boldsymbol{o}$, then $p(x) = xq(x)$ and $\boldsymbol{a}q(\boldsymbol{a}) = \boldsymbol{o}$, as well as $Aq(A) = O$. If $q(\boldsymbol{a}) \neq \boldsymbol{o}$, then $q(\boldsymbol{a})\mathbf{u} \neq \mathbf{o}$ and $\boldsymbol{a}q(\boldsymbol{a})\mathbf{u} = \mathbf{o}$ for some non-zero vector $\mathbf{u}$, so $\ker \boldsymbol{a} \neq \{\mathbf{o}\}$. This means that $\boldsymbol{a}$ is singular. Equivalently, if $q(A) \neq O$, then some column of $q(A)$ is not zero, so $AX = O$ has a non-trivial solution. This means that A is singular. Certainly, therefore, if $p(x)$ is a polynomial of *minimal degree* with the property $p(\boldsymbol{a}) = \boldsymbol{o}$, then $b_0 = 0$ if and only if $\boldsymbol{a}$ is singular.

For any linear transformation $\boldsymbol{a}$ of an n-dimensional $\mathbf{V}$ and its representing matrix A there is a polynomial, of degree equal to n and with constant term b_0 equal to $(-1)^n|A|$, such that $\boldsymbol{a}$ and A are zeros of the polynomial (Theorem 3 below). This polynomial is the *characteristic polynomial* $\psi(x)$ defined by

$$\psi(x) = |xI - A|,$$

already introduced in Section 2.17. Its coefficients are alternating (in sign) sums of *principal minors* of A (Section 2.17, Example 3). If A is invertible and $\psi(A) = O$, then the latter equation can be used to express A^{-1} as a polynomial in A. To prove that $\psi(A) = O$, we shall use a determinant type procedure, which will be corroborated later in a more abstract setting. The result is known as the ***Cayley-Hamilton Theorem.*** (Note that $|xI - A|$ should be expanded *before* A replaces x.)

Theorem 3. If A is an $n \times n$ matrix and if $\psi(x) = |xI - A|$, then $\psi(A) = O$. If A represents a linear transformation $\boldsymbol{a}$, then $\psi(\boldsymbol{a}) = \boldsymbol{o}$.

Proof: Set $B = \text{adj-}(xI - A)$. Then we have

$$B(xI - A) = |xI - A|\, I = \psi(x)I.$$

Since A is $n \times n$, and each entry of B is a polynomial, we can express B as $B = \sum_0^{n-1} B_i x^i$, where no positive power of x appears in the entries of the B_i's. Express $\psi(x)$ as

$$\psi(x) = \sum_{k=0}^{n} b_k x^k, \quad \text{where} \quad b_n = 1,$$

and multiply out the product $B(xI - A)$. Then equating coefficients of like powers of x (matrices are equal if and only if their corresponding entries are equal), we find that

$$\begin{aligned} -B_0A &= b_0I, \\ -B_1A + B_0 &= b_1I, \\ &\vdots \\ -B_{n-1}A + B_{n-2} &= b_{n-1}I, \\ B_{n-1} &= I. \end{aligned}$$

Multiply each side of these equations on the right by $I, A, \ldots, A^n$, respectively, and add up to get $O = \psi(A)$. q.e.d.

EXAMPLE 3. If

$$A = \begin{pmatrix} 0 & 1 \\ 1 & 0 \end{pmatrix} \quad \text{then} \quad xI - A = \begin{pmatrix} x & -1 \\ -1 & x \end{pmatrix}.$$

In the above notation,

$$B = \begin{pmatrix} x & 1 \\ 1 & x \end{pmatrix} = B_0 + B_1x \quad \text{where} \quad B_0 = A \quad \text{and} \quad B_1 = I.$$

Then

$$\psi(x) = x^2 - 1 \quad \text{and} \quad B(xI - A) = \operatorname{diag}(\psi(x), \psi(x)).$$

Also, we verify that $\psi(A) = A^2 - I = O$, as claimed in Theorem 3.

EXAMPLE 4. If b_0 is the constant term in the characteristic polynomial $\psi(x)$ of A, then $b_0 = (-1)^n|A|$ and we see that $b_0 \neq 0$ if and only if A is invertible. So the equations $\psi(\boldsymbol{a}) = \boldsymbol{o}$ and $\psi(A) = O$ can always be used to express $\boldsymbol{a}^{-1}$ and A^{-1}, respectively, when the latter exist. As we have seen, there may exist polynomials of smaller degree of which $\boldsymbol{a}$ and A are zeros, and we shall consider this later. In any case, A^{-1} can be expressed as a polynomial in A.

PROBLEMS

1. Find the characteristic polynomial for each of the following matrices and verify Theorem 3 by direct substitution:

(a) $\operatorname{diag}(s_1, \ldots, s_n)$,

(b) $\begin{pmatrix} 0 & l & n \\ -l & 0 & m \\ -n & -m & 0 \end{pmatrix}$,

(c) $\operatorname{diag}(A_1, \ldots, A_t)$, where each A_i is square and has a corresponding known characteristic polynomial $\psi_i(x)$,

(d) $\begin{pmatrix} A & C \\ O & B \end{pmatrix}$, where $A = \begin{pmatrix} 2 & 0 \\ 1 & 5 \end{pmatrix}$, $B = \begin{pmatrix} 0 & 0 & 0 \\ 1 & 0 & 0 \\ 0 & 1 & 0 \end{pmatrix}$, $C = \begin{pmatrix} 0 & 0 & 1 \\ 0 & 0 & 0 \end{pmatrix}$.

2. If A is an invertible $n \times n$ matrix, show that: (a) $(-A)^{-1} = -A^{-1}$, (b) $B_0 = (-1)^{n+1}|A|A^{-1}$, (c) adj-$A$ is a polynomial in A (even if A is singular).

3. Use the method of Example 1 to find the inverses of:

$$\text{(a)} \begin{pmatrix} 0 & 1 \\ 2 & 0 \end{pmatrix}, \quad \text{(b)} \begin{pmatrix} 0 & 1 & 0 \\ 0 & 0 & 1 \\ 1 & 0 & 0 \end{pmatrix}, \quad \text{(c)} \begin{pmatrix} 1 & 1 & 0 \\ 0 & 1 & 1 \\ 0 & 0 & 1 \end{pmatrix}.$$

4. If an invertible $n \times n$ matrix A has characteristic polynomial $\psi(x)$, show that A^{-1} has characteristic polynomial

$$(x^n/b_0)\psi(1/x), \quad \text{where} \quad b_0 = (-1)^n|A|.$$

5.4 UNITARY MATRICES

In Section 3.4, a special basis of the vector space of real 2×1 column vectors was encountered. It has the property that the basis vectors are orthogonal and normal (briefly, *orthonormal*). For the case of an n-dimensional column vector space (and a similar theory applies to row vector space) with real or complex scalars, there is a natural extension of the definition of orthogonality. We shall not discuss the underlying abstraction for general vector spaces and its implications for linear transformations. Rather, we settle for some facts in matrix algebra that will be applicable later. In this section, let **V** denote an n-dimensional column vector space consisting of all $n \times 1$ real (or complex) column vectors.

Suppose $X = (x_1, \ldots, x_n)^t$ is a column vector, real or complex. *If each entry x_i is replaced by its conjugate $\bar{x}_i$, then the resulting column vector is called the conjugate of X and is denoted by X^c,*

$$X^c = (\bar{x}_1, \ldots, \bar{x}_n)^t.$$

(Recall that the conjugate of a complex number $x + iy(= re^{i\theta})$ is $x - iy(= re^{-i\theta})$.) This operation of *conjugation*, commutes with the operation of *transposition*,

$$(X^c)^t = (X^t)^c,$$

so we can write X^{ct} for either of the equal *row* vectors $(X^c)^t$, $(X^t)^c$. *We call X^{ct} the* ***conjugate transpose*** *of X, and usually denote it by X^*, rather than X^{ct},*

$$X^* = X^{ct}.$$

Similar terminology is applied to row vectors, row matrices, and column matrices; and in Example 2 below we extend it to $p \times q$ matrices. With respect to any scalar field contained in the field of real numbers, the operation conjugate transpose is merely that of ordinary transpose. Thus, if X is real, then $X^* = X^t$.

EXAMPLE 1.

$$X^*X = \sum \bar{x}_i x_i = \sum |x_i|^2 > 0, \quad \text{unless} \quad X = O.$$

Therefore, when $X \neq O$, we can ***normalize*** X by dividing it by $\sqrt{X^*X}$. This gives the ***normalized vector***

$$X/\sqrt{X^*X}\,.$$

For instance, if $X = (1, i, 1 + i)^t$, then $X^* = (1, -i, 1 - i)$, $X^*X = 4$, and $X/\sqrt{X^*X} = (\frac{1}{2})X$.

EXAMPLE 2. *If $A = (a_{ij})$ is any $p \times q$ matrix with real or complex entries, then the* ***conjugate transpose*** *of A is a $q \times p$ matrix denoted by A^* and defined by:*

$$A^* = (b_{ij}), \quad \text{where} \quad b_{ij} = \bar{a}_{ji}, \quad \text{for all} \quad i \quad \text{and} \quad j.$$

For instance,

$$\text{when } A = \begin{pmatrix} 1+i & 1 \\ 0 & 1-i \\ -1 & 0 \end{pmatrix}, \quad \text{then } A^* = \begin{pmatrix} 1-i & 0 & -1 \\ 1 & 1+i & 0 \end{pmatrix}.$$

If we use the notation

$$A^c = (\bar{a}_{ij}),$$

then $(A^c)^t = (A^t)^c$, so we write, in general,

$$A^* = A^{ct}.$$

If A is real, then $A^* = A^t$, which is the usual transpose of A.

Now, two column vectors X and Y, real or complex, are called ***orthogonal*** if and only if $\sum \bar{x}_i y_i = 0$, or equivalently, if and only if

$$X^*Y = 0. \tag{1}$$

Equation (1) is also equivalent to the condition $Y^*X = 0$. When X and Y are real, this definition coincides with our previous definition of orthogonality (Section 3.4). By Example 1, X is not orthogonal to itself unless $X = 0$.

If a set $\{U_1, \ldots, U_t\}$, $t \geq 1$, consists of *normalized and pairwise orthogonal column vectors*, which means that for all i, j,

$$U_i^* U_j = 0 \quad \text{when} \quad i \neq j, \quad U_i^* U_i = 1, \tag{2}$$

then this set is called ***orthonormal.*** The condition of normalization implies $U_i \neq O$ $(i = 1, \ldots, t)$. Although a real orthonormal set is what we called orthonormal when the scalar field was real, here we use the term orthonormal to cover the real and complex case.

EXAMPLE 3. An orthonormal set $\{U_1, \ldots, U_t\}$ of column vectors is linearly independent. For, if $\sum s_j U_j = O$ and we pre-multiply by any U_i^*, we get

$$U_i^* \sum s_j U_j = \sum s_j U_i^* U_j = s_i = 0.$$

In particular, the rows (and the columns) of a real orthogonal matrix are linearly independent.

An orthonormal set $\{U_1, \ldots, U_t\}$ of $n \times 1$ column vectors is called an ***orthonormal basis*** of the subspace $[U_1, \ldots, U_t]$. If $t = n$, then it is an orthonormal basis of **V** (n-dimensional column vector space). Every subspace of **V** has an orthonormal basis, and every orthonormal subset of **V** can be extended to an orthonormal basis of **V**. We shall show this in detail for the real case. But first, we give an example in real 3-dimensional column vector space.

EXAMPLE 4. The $n \times 1$ unit column vectors $E_1, \ldots, E_n$, that is, the columns of the n-rowed identity matrix I, furnish a simple orthonormal basis of either real or complex column vector space. But suppose we want an orthonormal basis of real 3-dimensional column vector space to include a given normalized vector, say the vector $U_1 = (1/\sqrt{3})(1, 1, 1)^t$. In this case, we can see by inspection that $U_2 = (1/\sqrt{2})(1, -1, 0)^t$ and $U_3 = (1/\sqrt{6})(1, 1, -2)^t$ will do as the second and third basis vectors. Note that the matrix $P = (U_1, U_2, U_3)$ is real orthogonal. It has the property $P^tP = I$, hence $P^t = P^{-1}$ and $PP^t = I$ also. The latter equation shows that the *rows* of P define three row vectors which constitute an orthonormal basis of real 3-dimensional *row* vector space.

If $\{U_1, \ldots, U_n\}$ is an orthonormal basis of **V**, then the matrix $P = (U_1, \ldots, U_n)$ has the equivalent properties

$$P^{-1} = P^*, \quad P^*P = PP^* = I. \tag{3}$$

Any square complex matrix with the property $P^*P = I$ is called a ***unitary matrix.*** A real unitary matrix is therefore what we have called a real orthogonal matrix. Since rotation matrices are real orthogonal, they are unitary.

One can convert any given basis of **V** to an orthonormal basis in a very useful way, changing one vector at a time. We shall show a particular construction, for a real column vector space. The complex case is similar. Let $\{X_1, \ldots, X_n\}$ be a given basis of a real n-dimensional column vector space **V**. Starting with this given basis, we can construct an orthonormal basis such that *for each* $t \leq n$,

$$[X_1, \ldots, X_t] = [U_1, \ldots, U_t], \quad U_i^tU_j = 0 \text{ if } i \neq j, \text{ and } U_i^tU_i = 1, \tag{4}$$

by first constructing an orthogonal basis $\{Y_1, \ldots, Y_n\}$. Consider the equations:

$$\begin{aligned} Y_1 &= X_1, \\ Y_2 &= X_2 - a_{21}Y_1, \\ Y_3 &= X_3 - a_{31}Y_1 - a_{32}Y_2, \\ &\vdots \\ Y_n &= X_n - a_{n1}Y_1 - a_{n2}Y_2 - \cdots - a_{n,n-1}Y_{n-1}. \end{aligned} \tag{5}$$

We seek real scalars a_{ij} and real vectors Y_i such that the Y_i's will be non-zero and orthogonal, that is,

$$Y_i^t Y_j = 0 \quad \text{if} \quad i \neq j, \quad \text{and} \quad Y_i^t Y_i \neq 0. \tag{6}$$

This can be accomplished recursively. First, multiply the second equation by Y_1^t and use (6) to get

$$0 = Y_1^t X_2 - a_{21} Y_1^t Y_1.$$

Since $Y_1 \neq O$, we can solve for a_{21}. Then, multiply the third equation by Y_1^t and Y_2^t, in turn, to get two equations:

$$0 = Y_1^t X_3 - a_{31} Y_1^t Y_1 \quad \text{and} \quad 0 = Y_2^t X_3 - a_{32} Y_2^t Y_2.$$

From these we solve for a_{31} and a_{32}. Continuing this way, we obtain an orthogonal set. Now define U_i by

$$U_i = Y_i/\sqrt{Y_i^t Y_i} \quad (i = 1, \ldots, n), \tag{7}$$

hence U_i is a normalization of Y_i. Then, the set $\{U_1, \ldots, U_t\}$ is orthonormal and satisfies Equations (4) for each $t \leq n$.

EXAMPLE 5. Suppose we express the X_i's in terms of the Y_i's, and set $R = (X_1, \ldots, X_n)$, $S = (Y_1, \ldots, Y_n)$. Then, by Equations (5),

$$R = ST,$$

where $T = (t_{ij})$ is an upper triangular matrix, that is, $t_{ij} = 0$ when $i > j$.

EXAMPLE 6. Suppose a subspace $\mathbf{V}_0$ of our real column vector space $\mathbf{V}$ is generated by an orthonormal set $\{U_1, \ldots, U_t\}$, that is, $\mathbf{V}_0 = [U_1, \ldots, U_t]$ and Equation (2) holds. Hence $\dim \mathbf{V}_0 = t \leq n$ and we can extend $\{U_1, \ldots, U_t\}$ to a basis $\{U_1, \ldots, U_t, Z_1, \ldots, Z_{n-t}\}$ of $\mathbf{V}$. Now we can proceed with the $(t + 1)$-st step of the above process, and finally obtain *an orthonormal basis of* $\mathbf{V}$ *which contains the given orthonormal basis of* $\mathbf{V}_0$.

EXAMPLE 7. Let P and Q be $n \times n$ unitary matrices. Set $A = PQ$. Then A is also unitary. Furthermore, if B is any $n \times n$ complex matrix such that PB is unitary, then B must be unitary. These facts mean: *Any two orthonormal bases of a complex column vector space are connected by a unitary matrix;* in particular, *this matrix is real orthogonal when the space is real.* For, such bases can always be arranged in the form of a unitary matrix.

PROBLEMS

1. Show that for complex column matrices, one has:
   (a) $(sX)^* = \bar{s}X^*$, (b) $(X + Y)^* = X^* + Y^*$, (c) $X^*Y = (Y^*X)^c$.
2. Show that for square complex $n \times n$ matrices A, B and $n \times 1$ column matrices X, Y, one has:
   (a) $(A + B)^* = A^* + B^*$, (b) $(AB)^* = B^*A^*$, (c) $(AX)^* = X^*A^*$,
   (d) $(X^*AY)^* = Y^*A^*X$, (e) $|A^*| = \overline{|A|}$, (f) $(A^*)^{-1} = (A^{-1})^*$.

3. If $A = \begin{pmatrix} E & F \\ G & H \end{pmatrix}$ is a partitioned complex matrix, express A^* in terms of E^*, F^*, G^*, H^*.

4. Let A be an invertible complex $p \times p$ matrix, and suppose $A^*A = \operatorname{diag}(d_1, \ldots, d_p)$. Show that: (a) $d_i > 0$ $(i = 1, \ldots, p)$, and (b) there exists a diagonal matrix F such that AF is unitary.

5. Let $\{X_1, X_2, X_3\}$ be the columns of

$$\begin{pmatrix} -1 & 1 & 1 \\ 1 & -1 & 1 \\ 1 & 1 & -1 \end{pmatrix}.$$

Use Equations (5), (6), and (7) to construct an orthonormal set containing $X_1/\sqrt{X_1^t X_1}$.

6. Let **V** be an n-dimensional vector space with complex scalars. Use the isomorphism of **V** with a column vector space to define *orthogonality* for vectors in **V**. How would you define a *unitary* linear transformation of **V**?

7. Let $\{X_1, \ldots, X_n\}$ be a basis of complex column vector space. Let c_{ij} be the cofactor of the j-th entry in the last row of

$$\begin{vmatrix} X_1^t X_1 & X_1^t X_2 & \cdots & X_1^t X_i \\ \vdots & \vdots & & \vdots \\ X_{i-1}^t X_1 & X_{i-1}^t X_2 & \cdots & X_{i-1}^t X_i \\ 1 & 1 & \cdots & 1 \end{vmatrix},$$

and $c_{11} = 1$. Define Y_i by $Y_i = \sum_{j=1}^{i} c_{ij} X_j$. Show that the set $\{Y_1, \ldots, Y_n\}$ is orthogonal. Apply this to Problem 5. (Note: $\sum_j c_{ij} X_k^t X_j = 0$ if $k < i$.)

6

Linear Transformations from V into W

6.1 LINEAR SYSTEMS

The solution of a linear system of equations in the manner of Section 4.2 uses elimination processes and a vector interpretation that are valid in any field containing the coefficients of the system. The simplicity of each step makes it easy to keep track of a number of properties (to see if they are preserved or lost) on the way to the final expression. We abstract from this special situation a more general context and derive consequences for matrix algebra.

A $p \times q$ system of linear equations can be given the alternative descriptions:

$$\sum_{j=1}^{q} a_{ij}x_j = x'_i \quad (i = 1, \ldots, p);$$

or

$$AX = X', \tag{1}$$

where $A = (a_{ij})$ is $p \times q$, $X = (x_1, \ldots, x_q)^t$, and $X' = (x'_1, \ldots, x'_p)^t$. In harmony with our previous approach, we shall emphasize an interpretation of the matrix equation $AX = X'$ as the *coordinate equation* of a mapping from a q-dimensional vector space **V** into a p-dimensional vector space **W**, both spaces having the same field of scalars.

W *may be a subspace of* **V** but coordinate bases in **V** and **W** are to be picked independently. Let X be regarded as the coordinate column of a vector **v** in **V** with respect to a fixed coordinate basis in **V**; and let X' be regarded as the coordinate column of a vector **w** in **W** with respect to a fixed coordinate basis in **W**. If Y and Y', with $AY = Y'$, are also coordinate columns of vectors in **V** and **W**, respectively, then for any two scalars c, d, the rules of matrix multiplication imply

$$A(cX + dY) = cX' + dY'. \tag{2}$$

Of course, we can regard X and X' as column vectors. If we do, then the assignment of X' as the image of X by Equation (1), defines an obvious mapping from a q-dimensional space of *column vectors* into a p-dimensional space of *column vectors*, having the property described by Equation (2). But consider the general vector spaces $\mathbf{V}$ and $\mathbf{W}$. Then with respect to the pair of fixed coordinate bases in $\mathbf{V}$ and $\mathbf{W}$, Equation (1) also defines a mapping from $\mathbf{V}$ into $\mathbf{W}$ wherein we regard X and X' as coordinate columns of the vectors $\mathbf{v}$ and $\mathbf{w}$. If we denote the latter mapping by $\boldsymbol{a}$, then Equation (1) is a coordinate representation of the vector equation

$$\boldsymbol{a}\mathbf{v} = \mathbf{w}; \tag{3}$$

that is, Equation (1) is a coordinate equation of the mapping $\boldsymbol{a}$ from $\mathbf{V}$ into $\mathbf{W}$. This mapping $\boldsymbol{a}$ is a generalization of a linear transformation of $\mathbf{V}$. Its essential properties can be described by:

$$\begin{aligned} &\boldsymbol{a}\mathbf{v} \text{ is a single vector in } \mathbf{W} \text{ defined for every } \mathbf{v} \text{ in } \mathbf{V}; \\ &\boldsymbol{a}(c\mathbf{u} + d\mathbf{v}) = c\boldsymbol{a}\mathbf{u} + d\boldsymbol{a}\mathbf{v} \text{ for all vectors } \mathbf{u}, \mathbf{v} \text{ in } \mathbf{V} \\ &\qquad \text{and all scalars } c, d. \end{aligned} \tag{4}$$

Now, *we define a* ***linear transformation from a vector space*** $\mathbf{V}$ ***into a vector space*** $\mathbf{W}$ *to be any mapping* $\boldsymbol{a}$ *from* $\mathbf{V}$ *into* $\mathbf{W}$ *which has the properties described in* (4). In particular, an isomorphism between $\mathbf{V}$ and $\mathbf{W}$ is the same thing as a one-to-one linear transformation from $\mathbf{V}$ onto $\mathbf{W}$. In the special case where $\mathbf{V}$ and $\mathbf{W}$ are *column vector spaces* with X in $\mathbf{V}$ and X' in $\mathbf{W}$, then Equation (1) defines a linear transformation from $\mathbf{V}$ into $\mathbf{W}$ which we may indicate by $X \rightarrow AX$ or $\boldsymbol{a}X = AX$. The latter equation is not a coordinate equation, but a definition of a mapping; however A does represent $\boldsymbol{a}$ with respect to a suitable pair of bases (see Section 6.3 below).

As we shall soon verify, every linear transformation from a vector space $\mathbf{V}$ into a vector space $\mathbf{W}$ corresponds to a suitable coordinate equation, uniquely determined once a pair of coordinate bases is chosen. This allows us to use a linear transformation from the vector space of $q \times 1$ column vectors into the vector space of $p \times 1$ column vectors as a faithful substitute for the linear transformation $\boldsymbol{a}$ from $\mathbf{V}$ into $\mathbf{W}$. This substitution depends on a choice of coordinate bases in $\mathbf{V}$ and $\mathbf{W}$, just as it does in the case of a linear transformation of $\mathbf{V}$. Even when $\mathbf{V} = \mathbf{W}$, a linear transformation from $\mathbf{V}$ into $\mathbf{W}$ is, in general, treated with respect to a pair of coordinate bases.

EXAMPLE 1. When $p = \dim \mathbf{W} = 1$, then $AX = X'$ has the special form

$$\textstyle\sum a_j x_j = x', \quad A = (a_1, \ldots, a_q).$$

When $q = \dim \mathbf{V} = 1$, then $AX = X'$ has the form

$$a_i x = x'_i \quad (i = 1, \ldots, p), \quad A = (a_1, \ldots, a_p)^t.$$

The omission of the row index or of the column index on the entries of a matrix is compensated for by the indicated physical presentation of the matrix. (A $p \times q$ matrix is perhaps best thought of as a function, its values denoted by $a(i, j)$, its domain consisting of ordered pairs of integers restricted by $1 \leq i \leq p$, $1 \leq j \leq q$, and its range a subset of a given field.)

EXAMPLE 2. Let X be a $p \times q$ matrix regarded as a vector in the vector space of all $p \times q$ matrices with entries in a given field. Let A be a fixed $1 \times p$ row and B a fixed $q \times 1$ column with entries in the given field. Then the assignment of AXB as the image of X, $X \to AXB$, is a mapping which is a linear transformation from the vector space of $p \times q$ matrices into the vector space of 1-tuples.

EXAMPLE 3. Suppose $f(A)$ is a polynomial in a fixed square matrix A, and suppose there exists an invertible matrix P such that $P^{-1}AP = D$, where D is a diagonal matrix. Then $P^{-1}f(A)P$ is also diagonal. Let $\mathbf{V}$ be the vector space of polynomials in A (see Problem 1 below), and $\mathbf{W}$ the vector space of diagonal matrices, where all entries and coefficients are in a common field. Then $f(A) \to P^{-1}f(A)P$ defines a linear transformation from $\mathbf{V}$ into $\mathbf{W}$. Of course, such a P does not exist for every A.

EXAMPLE 4. For any linear transformation $\boldsymbol{a}$ from $\mathbf{V}$ into $\mathbf{W}$, define the ***kernel*** of $\boldsymbol{a}$ by

$$\ker \boldsymbol{a} = \{\mathbf{u} \mid \mathbf{u} \text{ in } \mathbf{V} \text{ and } \boldsymbol{a}\mathbf{u} = \mathbf{o}\}, \tag{5}$$

and the ***image*** of $\boldsymbol{a}$ by

$$\operatorname{im} \boldsymbol{a} = \{\mathbf{v} \mid \mathbf{v} \text{ in } \mathbf{W} \text{ and } \mathbf{v} = \boldsymbol{a}\mathbf{u} \text{ for some } \mathbf{u} \text{ in } \mathbf{V}\}, \tag{6}$$

where we use our previously introduced abbreviations: $\ker \boldsymbol{a}$ and $\operatorname{im} \boldsymbol{a}$. As in the case of a linear transformation of $\mathbf{V}$, we find that $\ker \boldsymbol{a}$ *is a subspace of* $\mathbf{V}$ *while* $\operatorname{im} \boldsymbol{a}$ *is a subspace of* $\mathbf{W}$.

EXAMPLE 5. Let $\boldsymbol{a}$ be a linear transformation of $\mathbf{V}$ and let $\mathbf{V}'$ be an m-dimensional subspace of $\mathbf{V}$. If $\{\mathbf{v}'_1, \ldots, \mathbf{v}'_m\}$ is a basis of $\mathbf{V}'$, we can define a subspace $\mathbf{W}$ of $\mathbf{V}$ by

$$\mathbf{W} = [\boldsymbol{a}\mathbf{v}'_1, \ldots, \boldsymbol{a}\mathbf{v}'_m].$$

Suppose we restrict our attention to the effect of $\boldsymbol{a}$ on the vectors in $\mathbf{V}'$. *This **restriction** of $\boldsymbol{a}$ to $\mathbf{V}'$ defines a mapping denoted by*

$$\boldsymbol{a} \mid \mathbf{V}'.$$

If $\mathbf{v}'$ is any vector in $\mathbf{V}'$, then $(\boldsymbol{a} \mid \mathbf{V}')\mathbf{v}' = \boldsymbol{a}\mathbf{v}'$. *This mapping is a linear transformation from* $\mathbf{V}'$ *into* $\mathbf{W}$. It is actually *onto* because $\operatorname{im}(\boldsymbol{a} \mid \mathbf{V}')$ is a subspace of $\mathbf{V}$. Hence,

$$\mathbf{W} = \operatorname{im}(\boldsymbol{a} \mid \mathbf{V}'),$$

and it is readily verified that $\dim \mathbf{W} \leq m = \dim \mathbf{V}'$. It is sometimes convenient to denote $\operatorname{im}(\boldsymbol{a} \mid \mathbf{V}')$ by $\boldsymbol{a}\mathbf{V}'$.

More generally, if $\boldsymbol{a}$ is a linear transformation from a vector space $\mathbf{V}$ into a vector space $\mathbf{W}$, and $\mathbf{V}'$ is a subspace of $\mathbf{V}$, then the restriction of $\boldsymbol{a}$ to $\mathbf{V}'$ is also denoted by $\boldsymbol{a} \mid \mathbf{V}'$. Its domain is $\mathbf{V}'$ and its range is a subspace of $\mathbf{W}$ denoted by $\operatorname{im}(\boldsymbol{a} \mid \mathbf{V}')$, or just $\boldsymbol{a}\mathbf{V}'$ (see Problem 5 below). Here, also, we have

$$\dim \operatorname{im}(\boldsymbol{a} \mid \mathbf{V}') \leq \dim \mathbf{V}'.$$

PROBLEMS

1. Consider the set of all polynomials in a given square $n \times n$ matrix A, the coefficients of the polynomials being in a fixed field containing the entries of A. Show that this set is a finite-dimensional vector space. (Embed it in an n^2-dimensional space.)
2. Show that a particular linear transformation from the vector space of all $n \times n$ matrices (entries in a fixed field) into a 1-dimensional vector space is defined by $\boldsymbol{a}A = \sum_{i=1}^{n} a_{ii}$. Compare $\boldsymbol{a}(AB)$ with $\boldsymbol{a}(BA)$.
3. In Example 3, show that
$$\boldsymbol{a}(f(A)g(A)) = \boldsymbol{a}f(A)\boldsymbol{a}g(A), \text{ and } \ker \boldsymbol{a} = \{O\}.$$
Show how to interpret $\boldsymbol{a}$ as a restriction of a linear transformation $X \to P^{-1}XP$, where X is variable with entries from a given field.
4. Let $\boldsymbol{a}$ be a linear transformation from $\mathbf{V}$ into $\mathbf{W}$. Show that $\ker \boldsymbol{a}$ and $\operatorname{im} \boldsymbol{a}$ are subspaces,
$$\ker \boldsymbol{a} = \ker \boldsymbol{qa} = \boldsymbol{p} \ker \boldsymbol{ap}$$
and
$$\operatorname{im} \boldsymbol{qa} = \boldsymbol{q} \operatorname{im} \boldsymbol{a}$$
for all invertible linear transformations $\boldsymbol{p}$ of $\mathbf{V}$ and $\boldsymbol{q}$ of $\mathbf{W}$. Show that the latter equality is true even if $\boldsymbol{q}$ is not invertible, and that $\dim(\operatorname{im} \boldsymbol{qa}) \leq \dim \operatorname{im} \boldsymbol{a}$.
5. In Example 5, show that $\boldsymbol{a}|\mathbf{V}'$ is one-to-one if and only if $\dim \mathbf{W} = m$. (Consider $\ker \boldsymbol{a}|\mathbf{V}'$.)
6. Let a $p \times q$ matrix A be given. Show that there always exists a pair of vector spaces $\mathbf{V}$ and $\mathbf{W}$ such that A can be regarded as the matrix of a linear transformation from $\mathbf{V}$ into $\mathbf{W}$.
7. If $\mathbf{V}_1$ and $\mathbf{V}_2$ are subspaces of $\mathbf{V}$, find a linear transformation from $[\mathbf{V}_1, \mathbf{V}_2]/\mathbf{V}_2$ onto $\mathbf{V}_1/(\mathbf{V}_1 \cap \mathbf{V}_2)$. Then apply Section 4.8, Theorem 5 to get the result of Section 4.8, Example 2. (Try $\mathbf{v}_1 + \mathbf{v}_2 + \mathbf{V}_2 \to \mathbf{v}_1 + \mathbf{V}_1 \cap \mathbf{V}_2$.)

6.2 MATRIX REPRESENTATION AND PRODUCTS

Consider a pair of vector spaces $\mathbf{V}$ and $\mathbf{W}$, with a common scalar field. Let $\{\mathbf{v}_1, \ldots, \mathbf{v}_q\}$ and $\{\mathbf{w}_1, \ldots, \mathbf{w}_p\}$ be coordinate bases of $\mathbf{V}$ and $\mathbf{W}$, respectively. Let $\boldsymbol{a}$ be a linear transformation from $\mathbf{V}$ into $\mathbf{W}$. As in the case of a linear transformation of $\mathbf{V}$, $\boldsymbol{a}$ *is determined by its effect on a basis of* $\mathbf{V}$. For, suppose we express the images $\boldsymbol{a}\mathbf{v}_j$ $(j = 1, \ldots, q)$ in terms of the given basis of $\mathbf{W}$. Then

$$\boldsymbol{a}\mathbf{v}_j = \sum_{i=1}^{p} \mathbf{w}_i a_{ij} \quad (j = 1, \ldots, q);$$

and if $\mathbf{v} = \sum x_j \mathbf{v}_j$ is any vector in $\mathbf{V}$, then by Section 6.1, Equation (4),

$$\boldsymbol{a}\mathbf{v} = \sum x_j \boldsymbol{a}\mathbf{v}_j = \sum x_j \mathbf{w}_i a_{ij} = \sum(\sum a_{ij}x_j)\mathbf{w}_i = \sum x'_i \mathbf{w}_i.$$

This implies the *coordinate equation* $AX = X'$, where $A = (a_{ij})$. *The* $p \times q$ *matrix* A *is the* ***matrix representation*** *of* $\boldsymbol{a}$ *with respect to the given pair of coordinate bases.*

The way in which the subscripts are assigned is motivated by the existence of a natural multiplication of linear transformations under restricted conditions. Let $\mathbf{U}$ be another vector space with the same scalars as $\mathbf{V}$ and $\mathbf{W}$, and let $\{\mathbf{u}_1, \ldots, \mathbf{u}_r\}$ be a coordinate basis of $\mathbf{U}$. If $\boldsymbol{b}$ is a linear transformation from $\mathbf{U}$ into $\mathbf{V}$, then *we define the* ***product ab*** *as the linear transformation* $\mathbf{c}$ *from* $\mathbf{U}$ *into* $\mathbf{W}$ *given by*

$$\mathbf{c}\mathbf{u} = \boldsymbol{a}(\boldsymbol{b}\mathbf{u}),$$

for every $\mathbf{u}$ in $\mathbf{U}$. For, $\boldsymbol{b}\mathbf{u}$ is in the domain of $\boldsymbol{a}$, and the linearity of the mapping is easily verified. Now, we make use of the given coordinate bases by writing

$$\boldsymbol{b}\mathbf{u}_j = \sum \mathbf{v}_i b_{ij},$$

so $\boldsymbol{b}$ is represented by the $q \times r$ matrix $B = (b_{ij})$. Then

$$\mathbf{c}\mathbf{u}_j = \sum(\boldsymbol{a}\mathbf{v}_i)b_{ij} = \sum(\sum \mathbf{w}_k a_{ki})b_{ij} = \sum \mathbf{w}_k(\sum a_{ki}b_{ij}) \quad (j = 1, \ldots, r).$$

Hence $\boldsymbol{c}$ *is represented by a* $p \times r$ *matrix*

$$C = (c_{ij}), \quad c_{ij} = \sum_k a_{ik}b_{kj},$$

for which we write:

$$C = AB. \tag{7}$$

This defines a ***multiplication of rectangular matrices*** *whenever the number of columns of the left factor equals the number of rows of the right factor.*

EXAMPLE 1. Suppose we partition A and B into row and column matrices, respectively,

$$A = \begin{pmatrix} A_1 \\ \vdots \\ A_p \end{pmatrix} \quad \text{and} \quad B = (B_1, \ldots, B_q).$$

Then

$$C = \begin{pmatrix} A_1 B \\ \vdots \\ A_p B \end{pmatrix} = (AB_1, \ldots, AB_q) = \begin{pmatrix} & \vdots & \\ \cdots & A_i B_j & \cdots \\ & \vdots & \end{pmatrix} = (c_{ij}).$$

In particular, we can verify that

$$(x, y, z)\begin{pmatrix} a & d \\ b & e \\ c & f \end{pmatrix} = (xa + yb + zc, \quad xd + ye + zf),$$

and

$$\begin{pmatrix} x \\ y \\ z \end{pmatrix}(a, b, c) = \begin{pmatrix} xa & xb & xc \\ ya & yb & yc \\ za & zb & zc \end{pmatrix}.$$

EXAMPLE 2. When some rows and columns of a given matrix are deleted, the resulting table is called a ***submatrix***. If $t \le p$ and $t \le r$, we can form a $t \times t$ square submatrix from the $p \times r$ matrix C in Equation (7) by retaining the entries at the intersections of those *rows whose indices are* $i_1, \ldots, i_t$ $(i_1 < i_2 < \cdots < i_t)$, with those *columns whose indices are* $j_1, \ldots, j_t$ $(j_1 < j_2 < \cdots < j_t)$. This amounts to a deletion of the rows and columns not having these indices. Denote this submatrix by

$$C\begin{pmatrix} i_1 & \cdots & i_t \\ j_1 & \cdots & j_t \end{pmatrix}.$$

It is clearly equal to the product of the following rectangular submatrices of A and B:

$$A\begin{pmatrix} i_1 & \cdots & i_t \\ 1 & \cdots & q \end{pmatrix} \quad \text{and} \quad B\begin{pmatrix} 1 & \cdots & q \\ j_1 & \cdots & j_t \end{pmatrix}.$$

The determinant of this product can be evaluated as follows, where we denote $a_{i_1k_1}$ by $a(i_1, k_1)$, and so forth:

$$\begin{vmatrix} \sum a(i_1, k_1)b(k_1, j_1) & \sum a(i_1, k_2)b(k_2, j_2) \cdots \\ \vdots & \\ \sum a(i_t, k_1)b(k_1, j_1) & \sum a(i_t, k_2)b(k_2, j_2) \cdots \end{vmatrix}$$

$$= \sum_{\substack{k_1, \ldots, k_t = 1 \\ \text{(independently)}}}^{q} \begin{vmatrix} \text{same entries except} \\ \text{that the } \sum\text{'s are} \\ \text{removed} \end{vmatrix}$$

$$= \sum_{\text{(same)}} \left| A\begin{pmatrix} i_1 & \cdots & i_t \\ k_1 & \cdots & k_t \end{pmatrix} \right| b(k_1, j_1)b(k_2, j_2) \cdots b(k_t, j_t).$$

Here we have used the submatrix symbol with *repeated* column indices allowed and have applied the following properties of determinants (see summary in Section 6.7, Example 10 below):

(a) the *addition theorem*, which in the 2×2 case is illustrated by

$$\begin{vmatrix} a + a' & b \\ c + c' & d \end{vmatrix} = \begin{vmatrix} a & b \\ c & d \end{vmatrix} + \begin{vmatrix} a' & b \\ c' & d \end{vmatrix};$$

(b) the property of *scalar multiples*, which is illustrated by

$$k\begin{vmatrix} a & b \\ c & d \end{vmatrix} = \begin{vmatrix} ka & b \\ kc & d \end{vmatrix} = \begin{vmatrix} a & kb \\ c & kd \end{vmatrix}.$$

If $t > q$ then *each*

$$A\begin{pmatrix} i_1 \cdots i_t \\ k_1 \cdots k_t \end{pmatrix}$$

has some equal columns, hence a zero determinant, and our last *sum equals zero too*. So, suppose $t \leq q$. Then only those selections of values for $k_1, \ldots, k_t$ which are distinct permutations of t integers from the set $1, \ldots, q$ can yield non-zero minors in the sum. Each such selection of $k_1, \ldots, k_t$ can be rearranged into a natural order which, after relabeling becomes, say, $l_1 < l_2 < \cdots < l_t$. Now, in our last sum, those terms with the *same set* $\{l_1, \ldots, l_t\}$ add up to

$$\left|A\begin{pmatrix} i_1 \cdots i_t \\ l_1 \cdots l_t \end{pmatrix}\right| \sum \pm b(k_1, j_1) \cdots b(k_t, j_t) = \left|A\begin{pmatrix} i_1 \cdots i_t \\ l_1 \cdots l_t \end{pmatrix}\right| \left|B\begin{pmatrix} l_1 \cdots l_t \\ j_1 \cdots j_t \end{pmatrix}\right|,$$

where the present sum is taken over all permutations $k_1, \ldots, k_t$ of $l_1, \ldots, l_t$. The sign of each summand is determined by the number of transpositions required to put the k_i's into the natural order. When this number is even, the sign is $+$, otherwise $-$. (See Problems 4, 5 below.) Hence we have the following relation between *t-rowed minors* of C, A, B when $C = AB$ and $t \leq q$:

$$\left|C\begin{pmatrix} i_1 \cdots i_t \\ j_1 \cdots j_t \end{pmatrix}\right| = \sum_{l_1 < \cdots < l_t} \left|A\begin{pmatrix} i_1 \cdots i_t \\ l_1 \cdots l_t \end{pmatrix}\right| \cdot \left|B\begin{pmatrix} l_1 \cdots l_t \\ j_1 \cdots j_t \end{pmatrix}\right|,$$

where $t \leq q$ *and* $l_1, \ldots, l_t$ *vary over all possible ordered choices of* t *distinct columns of* A *(hence, of the corresponding* t *rows of* B). In particular, there are the following cases:

(1) If A, B, C are $n \times n$, take $t = n$ to get $|C| = |A|\,|B|$, which is the *multiplication theorem for determinants*.

(2) If A, B, C are $n \times n$, take $t = n - 1$ and multiply through by $(-1)^{i+j}$ to get

$$\text{cof-}C = (\text{cof-}A)(\text{cof-}B),$$

or

$$\text{adj-}C = (\text{adj-}B)(\text{adj-}A).$$

(i and j are indices of the deleted row and column, respectively.)

(3) If A, B are $p \times q$, $q \times r$, respectively, then we get the usual rule for multiplication by taking $t = 1$.

EXAMPLE 3. Suppose four matrices are related by $A = BCD$, and assume associativity (see Problem 2 below). Then, *any given t-rowed minor of* A

is a linear combination of the t-rowed minors of C with coefficients which are products of t-rowed minors of B and D. If all the t-rowed minors of C equal zero, then every t-rowed minor of A equals zero. Here we have assumed that t does not exceed the number of rows or columns of any of the matrices; otherwise, as Example 2 shows, the t-rowed minors of A equal zero, if they exist.

EXAMPLE 4. If X is a $q \times r$ matrix and is regarded as a vector in the vector space of all $q \times r$ matrices with entries in a given field, then the mapping $X \to AX$ defines a linear transformation of this vector space into the vector space of $p \times r$ matrices. A more general linear transformation of this type is defined by $X \to AXB$ with B an $r \times s$ matrix, or in functional notation, $\boldsymbol{a}X = AXB$. The latter includes Section 6.1, Example 2 as a special case.

PROBLEMS

1. (a) Multiply out: $\begin{pmatrix} 1 & -1 & -1 \\ 2 & 0 & 1 \end{pmatrix}\begin{pmatrix} \frac{1}{2} & 1 \\ \frac{1}{2} & 2 \\ -1 & -1 \end{pmatrix}$.

(b) Show that $\begin{pmatrix} a & b & 0 \\ c & d & 0 \\ e & f & 0 \end{pmatrix}\begin{pmatrix} x & y & z \\ u & v & w \\ k & l & m \end{pmatrix} = \begin{pmatrix} a & b \\ c & d \\ e & f \end{pmatrix}\begin{pmatrix} x & y & z \\ u & v & w \end{pmatrix}$.

(c) Suppose A is a $p \times q$ matrix. For what size B and zero matrices is

$$(A, O)\begin{pmatrix} B \\ O \end{pmatrix} = AB?$$

2. Let $\boldsymbol{a}$, $\boldsymbol{b}$, $\boldsymbol{c}$ be linear transformations. Prove associativity of a product $\boldsymbol{abc}$, hence of any representation ABC, when the product can be defined. Multiply out:

(a) $(x, y, z)\begin{pmatrix} a & d \\ b & e \\ c & f \end{pmatrix}\begin{pmatrix} s \\ t \end{pmatrix}$, (b) $\begin{pmatrix} x \\ y \\ z \end{pmatrix}(a, b, c)\begin{pmatrix} e \\ f \\ g \end{pmatrix}$.

3. Work out the identity of Example 2 when A and B are row and column matrices in both orders. Verify case (2) also, and then prove it directly for invertible A and B.

4. If two of the distinct numbers $x_1, \ldots, x_n$ are interchanged in the product $\Pi_{i<j}(x_i - x_j)$ $(i, j = 1, \ldots, n)$, then show that the product changes sign. Hence distinguish between an even and an odd number of interchanges.

5. Show that any permutation of the integers $1, \ldots, n$ can be accomplished by a succession of interchanges (transpositions) two at a time. Apply this to the product in Problem 4 and show that the "parity" of a permutation is one of its invariants (number of interchanges is always *even* or always *odd*).

6. An $n \times n$ matrix A_n has its i-th row equal to $(x_1^{i-1}, x_2^{i-1}, \ldots, x_n^{i-1})$. Show that

$$|A_n| = |A_{n-1}|(x_n - x_1)(x_n - x_2)\cdots(x_n - x_{n-1}).$$

Compare $|A_n|$ to the product in Problem 4.

7. If X and Y are real $n \times 1$ column vectors, show that $|X^tY|^2 \leq (X^tX)(Y^tY)$. Extend the result to complex vectors.

6.3 MAPPING THEOREM

Suppose a $p \times q$ matrix $A = (a_{ij})$ has entries from the common scalar field of a q-dimensional vector space $\mathbf{V}$ and a p-dimensional vector space $\mathbf{W}$. With respect to a fixed pair of coordinate bases $\{\mathbf{v}_1, \ldots, \mathbf{v}_q\}$ and $\{\mathbf{w}_1, \ldots, \mathbf{w}_p\}$ of $\mathbf{V}$ and $\mathbf{W}$, respectively, we can define a unique linear transformation $\boldsymbol{a}$ from $\mathbf{V}$ into $\mathbf{W}$ by setting

(1) $\boldsymbol{a}\mathbf{v}_i = \sum \mathbf{w}_j a_{ji}$ $(i = 1, \ldots, q)$, and

(2) $\boldsymbol{a}\sum x_i\mathbf{v}_i = \sum x_i\boldsymbol{a}\mathbf{v}_i$, for every vector $\sum x_i\mathbf{v}_i$ in $\mathbf{V}$.

Because the x_i's are unique, this is certainly a mapping. To show that it is a linear transformation, we apply (2) to verify that

$$\boldsymbol{a}(c\sum x_i\mathbf{v}_i + d\sum y_i\mathbf{v}_i) = c\boldsymbol{a}\sum x_i\mathbf{v}_i + d\boldsymbol{a}\sum y_i\mathbf{v}_i.$$

It is represented by A because its effect on each $\mathbf{v}_i$ is determined by (1). If $\boldsymbol{a}\mathbf{v}_i = \boldsymbol{b}\mathbf{v}_i$ (for each i) for some linear transformation $\boldsymbol{b}$, then from (2) we get $\boldsymbol{a} = \boldsymbol{b}$. *Hence, the matrix A determines, by* (1) *and* (2) *with respect to the given pair of coordinate bases, a unique linear transformation* $\boldsymbol{a}$ *from* $\mathbf{V}$ *into* $\mathbf{W}$, *and this* $\boldsymbol{a}$ *is represented by A.*

The above construction of $\boldsymbol{a}$ from A is actually the following more general version of the *mapping theorem* (Section 5.2, Theorem 2).

Theorem 1. Given any set $\{\mathbf{w}'_1, \ldots, \mathbf{w}'_q\}$ of q vectors from $\mathbf{W}$ and a basis $\{\mathbf{v}_1, \ldots, \mathbf{v}_q\}$ of $\mathbf{V}$, then there exists a unique linear transformation $\boldsymbol{a}$ from $\mathbf{V}$ into $\mathbf{W}$ such that $\mathbf{w}'_i = \boldsymbol{a}\mathbf{v}_i$ $(i = 1, \ldots, q)$.

Proof: Define a mapping $\boldsymbol{a}$ by the rule

$$\boldsymbol{a}(\sum x_i\mathbf{v}_i) = \sum x_i\mathbf{w}'_i;$$

in particular, $\boldsymbol{a}\mathbf{v}_i = \mathbf{w}'_i$. Therefore

$$\boldsymbol{a}\sum x_i\mathbf{v}_i = \sum x_i\boldsymbol{a}\mathbf{v}_i,$$

from which we can verify that $\boldsymbol{a}$ is a linear transformation. The uniqueness follows from the fact that $\boldsymbol{a}$ is defined on a basis of $\mathbf{V}$. q.e.d.

If a matrix A is given, then in Theorem 1 we can set $\mathbf{w}'_i = \sum \mathbf{w}_j a_{ji}$ to find a linear transformation $\boldsymbol{a}$ determined and represented by A, a procedure equivalent to what we did at the start of this section. In view of Section 6.2 we now have, with respect to a fixed pair of coordinate bases, a *one-to-one correspondence between the set of linear transformations of a q-dimensional* $\mathbf{V}$ *into a p-dimensional*

W *and the set of all* $p \times q$ *matrices whose entries are in the common scalar field of* **V** *and* **W**. *Thus, by the introduction of coordinate bases, we can study a linear transformation* $\boldsymbol{a}$ *from* **V** *into* **W** *by means of a uniquely determined coordinate equation* $AX = X'$. The equation $AX = X'$ can, of course, be regarded as the defining equation of a linear transformation $X \to AX$ from a q-dimensional column vector space into a p-dimensional column vector space. *The coordinate equation of the latter linear transformation coincides with the coordinate equation* $AX = X'$ *of* $\boldsymbol{a}$ *if unit column vectors, in natural order, constitute the coordinate bases of the two column vector spaces.*

EXAMPLE 1. In the vector space of 2×2 matrices, we may choose as coordinate basis the ordered set $\{E_{11}, E_{12}, E_{21}, E_{22}\}$, where E_{ij} has a 1 in the i, j position and zeros elsewhere. If we call this vector space **V**, *and regard* **V** *as* **W** *also*, then the representation of a linear transformation $\boldsymbol{a}$ from **V** into **W** will generally involve two different coordinate bases of **V**. Suppose however, that we select these coordinate bases both equal to the ordered set $\{E_{11}, E_{12}, E_{21}, E_{22}\}$. Then for a variable X in **V** and a fixed $A = (a_{ij})$ in **V**, the particular linear transformation from **V** into **W** determined by $\boldsymbol{a}X = AX$ is represented with respect to the given coordinate bases by a 4×4 matrix (shown in partitioned form):

$$\boldsymbol{a} \leftrightarrow \begin{pmatrix} a_{11}I & a_{12}I \\ a_{21}I & a_{22}I \end{pmatrix},$$

where I is the 2×2 identity matrix.

But suppose we regard im $\boldsymbol{a}$ as **W**, where $\boldsymbol{a}$ is as above, namely, $X \to \boldsymbol{a}X = AX$. Then the selection of a coordinate basis of **W** is restricted by the nature of im $\boldsymbol{a}$. For example, let $A = \operatorname{diag}(1, 0)$. Then im $\boldsymbol{a} = [E_{11}, E_{12}]$ and

$$\boldsymbol{a} \leftrightarrow \begin{pmatrix} 1 & 0 & 0 & 0 \\ 0 & 1 & 0 & 0 \end{pmatrix}$$

with respect to the pair of coordinate bases $\{E_{11}, E_{12}, E_{21}, E_{22}\}$ of **V** and $\{E_{11}, E_{12}\}$ of $\mathbf{W} = \operatorname{im} \boldsymbol{a}$. But if $A = \begin{pmatrix} 1 & 1 \\ -1 & -1 \end{pmatrix}$, then

$$\mathbf{W} = \operatorname{im} \boldsymbol{a} = [E_{11} - E_{21}, E_{12} - E_{22}],$$

and if we take the latter two vectors in the given order as a coordinate basis of **W**, with the same ordered set $\{E_{11}, E_{12}, E_{21}, E_{22}\}$ again as the coordinate basis of **V**, then

$$\boldsymbol{a} \leftrightarrow \begin{pmatrix} 1 & 0 & 1 & 0 \\ 0 & 1 & 0 & 1 \end{pmatrix}.$$

EXAMPLE 2. Let a pair of fixed but unspecified bases be understood in q-dimensional vector space **V** and p-dimensional vector space **W**. Suppose a linear transformation $\boldsymbol{a}$ has the effect of mapping given coordinate columns $X_1, \ldots, X_q$ of q *linearly independent* vectors in $\mathbf{V}$ onto given coordinate columns $Y_1, \ldots, Y_q$ of q vectors from $\mathbf{W}$: $X_i \to Y_i$. Let A represent $\boldsymbol{a}$ with respect to the fixed pair of coordinate bases. Set $X = (X_1, \ldots, X_q)$ and $Y = (Y_1, \ldots, Y_q)$. Then $AX = Y$, hence

$$A = YX^{-1}.$$

(The solution for A can be arranged as a row-echelon process, suggested in Section 6.8, Problem 6.)

Now, consider a q-dimensional column vector space and a p-dimensional column vector space, with the same scalar field as that of $\mathbf{V}$ and $\mathbf{W}$. Establish isomorphisms of these column vector spaces with $\mathbf{V}$ and $\mathbf{W}$, respectively, by assigning the unit $q \times 1$ column vectors $\{E_1, \ldots, E_q\}$ as images of the vectors in the fixed basis of $\mathbf{V}$ and the unit $p \times 1$ column vectors $\{F_1, \ldots, F_p\}$ as images of the vectors in the fixed basis of $\mathbf{W}$. Then the X_i's and Y_i's above are column vectors which (besides serving as coordinate columns of vectors in $\mathbf{V}$ and $\mathbf{W}$, respectively) coincide with their own representations (coordinate columns) with respect to the bases $\{E_1, \ldots, E_q\}$ and $\{F_1, \ldots, F_p\}$. Hence, with respect to these unit column vector bases, the matrix A above also represents the column vector mapping $X_i \to Y_i$.

PROBLEMS

1. (a) If A and B are $p \times q$ matrices such that $AU = BU$ for every $q \times 1$ column vector U (using a common field of entries), show that $A = B$. What is the "smallest" set of column vectors which will always force $A = B$? (b) If $AB = B$ for some fixed $n \times p$ matrix A and every $p \times q$ matrix B, what is A?

2. Find a matrix representation of the linear transformation $\boldsymbol{a}$ in Section 6.1, Problem 2, for the case $n = 2$.

3. Apply Example 2 to find A when the mapping of the coordinate columns, $X_i \to Y_i$, is given by:

(a) $(1, 0)^t \to (0, 1, 1, 0)^t$,
$(0, 1)^t \to (0, 0, 0, 1)^t$;

(b) $(1, 1, 0)^t \to (1, 0)^t$,
$(1, 0, -1)^t \to (1, 0)^t$,
$(1, 1, 1)^t \to (1, 0)^t$.

4. Modify Example 1 by considering the vector space of 2×3 matrices X, and by defining six basis matrices $\{E_{11}, \ldots, E_{23}\}$ analogously to the square case. Show that $\boldsymbol{a}X = AX$ is still a linear transformation and modify the representations of $\boldsymbol{a}$ when

(a) $A = \operatorname{diag}(1, 0)$,

(b) $A = \begin{pmatrix} 1 & 1 \\ -1 & -1 \end{pmatrix}$.

5. If M is a fixed $p \times q$ matrix, N is a fixed $r \times s$ matrix, and X is a variable $q \times r$ matrix, show that MXN defines a linear transformation from the vector space of $q \times r$ matrices into the vector space of $p \times s$ matrices. Find a matrix representation when $p = q = r = s = 2$, $M = N = \operatorname{diag}(1, 0)$.

6. If $\mathbf{V}'$ is a subspace of a vector space $\mathbf{V}$, and $\boldsymbol{b}$ is a linear transformation from $\mathbf{V}'$ into $\mathbf{W}$, show that there exists a linear transformation $\boldsymbol{a}$ of $\mathbf{V}$ such that $\boldsymbol{b} = \boldsymbol{a} \mid \mathbf{V}'$.

7. Let f be a linear transformation from a q-dimensional $\mathbf{V}$ into a 1-dimensional $\mathbf{W}$. Let $\{\mathbf{u}_1, \ldots, \mathbf{u}_q\}$ and $\{\mathbf{w}_1\}$ be a pair of coordinate bases for these spaces. Show that the set of all such linear transformations is a q-dimensional vector space, call it $\mathbf{V}^t$. If $\boldsymbol{a}$ is a linear transformation of $\mathbf{V}$, define a linear transformation $\boldsymbol{a}^t$ of $\mathbf{V}^t$ by $f \to f\boldsymbol{a}$, that is,

$$\boldsymbol{a}^t f = f\boldsymbol{a},$$

and a coordinate basis $\{f_1, \ldots, f_q\}$ of $\mathbf{V}^t$ by

$$\begin{aligned} f_i\mathbf{u}_j &= \mathbf{w}_1 \quad \text{if} \quad i = j, \\ &= \mathbf{o} \quad \text{if} \quad i \neq j. \end{aligned}$$

Show that if $\boldsymbol{a} \leftrightarrow A$, then $\boldsymbol{a}^t$ exists and, with respect to the above basis of $\mathbf{V}^t$,

$$\boldsymbol{a}^t \leftrightarrow A^t.$$

6.4 EQUIVALENT LINEAR TRANSFORMATIONS AND MATRICES

Analogous to the idea of similar linear transformations $\boldsymbol{a}$ and $\boldsymbol{b}$ of $\mathbf{V}$ linked by an invertible linear transformation (automorphism) $\boldsymbol{p}$, there is the idea of two linear transformations $\boldsymbol{a}$ and $\boldsymbol{b}$ from $\mathbf{V}$ into $\mathbf{W}$ linked by a *pair* of invertible linear transformations $\boldsymbol{p}$ of $\mathbf{V}$ and $\boldsymbol{q}$ of $\mathbf{W}$.

Two linear transformations **a** *and* **b** *from* **V** *into* **W** *are called* ***equivalent*** *and are said to be* ***intertwined*** *by the invertible linear transformations* **p** *and* **q**, *if*

$$\boldsymbol{qa} = \boldsymbol{bp}.$$

The invertible linear transformations $\boldsymbol{p}$ and $\boldsymbol{q}$ match the action of $\boldsymbol{b}$ to the action of $\boldsymbol{a}$. This behavior is summarized schematically in Figure 44, if the condition $\boldsymbol{qa}\mathbf{v} = \boldsymbol{bp}\mathbf{v}$ for every $\mathbf{v}$ in $\mathbf{V}$ is added. With respect to a pair of coordinate bases of $\mathbf{V}$ and $\mathbf{W}$, suppose $\boldsymbol{a} \leftrightarrow A$, $\boldsymbol{b} \leftrightarrow B$, $\boldsymbol{p} \leftrightarrow P$, and $\boldsymbol{q} \leftrightarrow Q$. Then

$$\boldsymbol{qa} = \boldsymbol{bp} \leftrightarrow QA = BP.$$

However, an invertible linear transformation like $\boldsymbol{p}$ or $\boldsymbol{q}$ can also be uniquely associated with a change of coordinate basis, so we may regard $\boldsymbol{p}$ and $\boldsymbol{q}$ as the source of *another matrix representation of the linear transformation* $\boldsymbol{a}$, this time with respect to a second pair of coordinate bases associated with $\boldsymbol{p}$ and $\boldsymbol{q}$. Depending on which interpretation we make, it turns out that either one matrix represents a pair of equivalent linear transformations, or one linear transformation is represented by a pair of equivalent matrices (defined below). Let us discuss this distinction. (The use of subscripts p and q is not related to the notation $\boldsymbol{p}$ and $\boldsymbol{q}$.)

Suppose the coordinate basis of a q-dimensional vector space $\mathbf{V}$ is changed from $\{\mathbf{v}_1, \ldots, \mathbf{v}_q\}$ to $\{\mathbf{v}'_1, \ldots, \mathbf{v}'_q\}$ and that $\boldsymbol{p}$ is the associated invertible linear transformation. So $\mathbf{v}'_i = \sum \mathbf{v}_j p_{ji}$ and $P = (p_{ij})$ is the matrix representation of the invertible linear transformation $\boldsymbol{p}$. ($\boldsymbol{p}$ has the same representation with respect to either basis, as previously verified.) We have already encountered the following *two meanings for the matrix equation* $X = PX'$, *where* X *and* X' *are coordinate columns*:

1. X and X' are coordinate columns of the *same vector* $\mathbf{v}$ in $\mathbf{V}$ with respect to the above *two coordinate bases of* $\mathbf{V}$; hence they are related by $X = PX'$, as we have seen in Sections 3.2 and 5.1 (our X' here is the Y there).

2. X is the coordinate column of a vector $\mathbf{v}$ in $\mathbf{V}$ and X' is the coordinate column of its *image under* $\boldsymbol{p}^{-1}$, namely, the coordinate column of $\boldsymbol{p}^{-1}\mathbf{v}$; hence the equation $P^{-1}X = X'$ is the *coordinate equation of the linear transformation* $\boldsymbol{p}^{-1}$, expressed with respect to $\{\mathbf{v}_1, \ldots, \mathbf{v}_q\}$ and evaluated at $\mathbf{v}$. (This agrees with Figure 44 if $\boldsymbol{p}$ is replaced by $\boldsymbol{p}^{-1}$.)

Analogous remarks apply to $\mathbf{W}$ and $\boldsymbol{q}$ (with $\boldsymbol{q}$ replaced by $\boldsymbol{q}^{-1}$ in Figure 44).

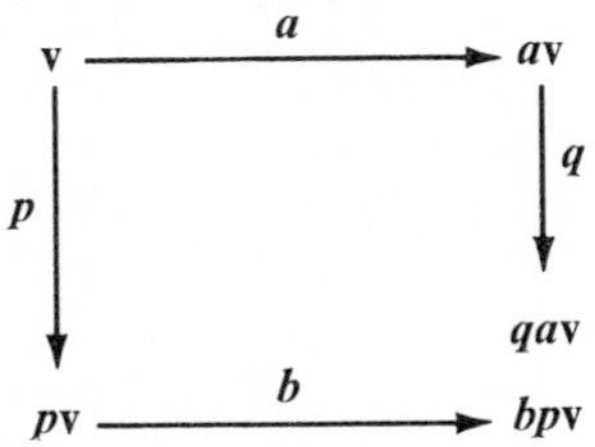

FIGURE 44

Now, let $\boldsymbol{a}$ and $\boldsymbol{b}$ be linear transformations from $\mathbf{V}$ into $\mathbf{W}$. Let A represent $\boldsymbol{a}$ with respect to $\{\mathbf{v}_1, \ldots, \mathbf{v}_q\}$ and B represent $\boldsymbol{b}$ with respect to the same coordinate basis $\{\mathbf{v}_1, \ldots, \mathbf{v}_q\}$. Also, let Q represent $\boldsymbol{q}$ with respect to a coordinate basis $\{\mathbf{w}_1, \ldots, \mathbf{w}_p\}$ of $\mathbf{W}$. Then we can associate *two meanings with the matrix equation*

$$QB = AP,$$

as shown in Figures 45 and 46, if the condition $Q^{-1}AX = BP^{-1}X$ for every X is added to the figures. Note that we are *supposing* $QB = AP$.

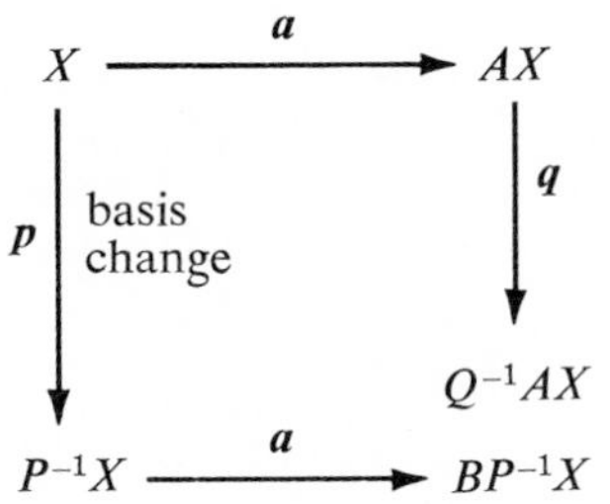

FIGURE 45

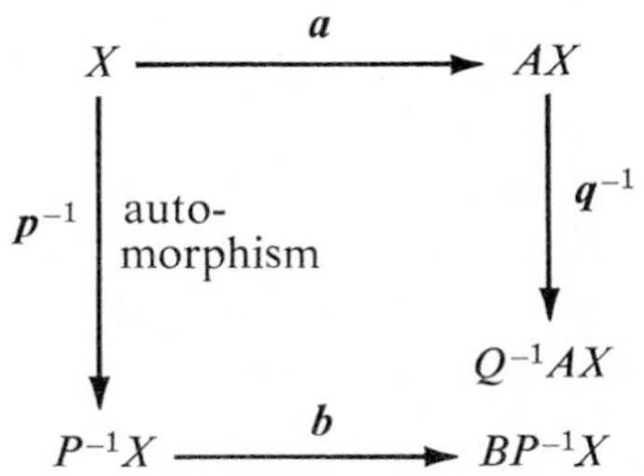

FIGURE 46

In Figure 45, $QB = AP$ is taken to mean that A and B represent, *with respect to generally different coordinate bases*, the same linear transformation $\boldsymbol{a}$. In Figure 46, $QB = AP$ is taken to mean that A represents $\boldsymbol{a}$ and B represents $\boldsymbol{b}$, *with respect to the same coordinate bases*, where $\boldsymbol{a}$ and $\boldsymbol{b}$ are *equivalent linear transformations* such that $\boldsymbol{qb} = \boldsymbol{ap}$. So, the matrix B can represent $\boldsymbol{a}$ and $\boldsymbol{b}$, with respect to different pairs of bases. (Note that Figure 46 would be a coordinate representation of Figure 44 if $\boldsymbol{p}$ and $\boldsymbol{q}$ in the latter were replaced by $\boldsymbol{p}^{-1}$ and $\boldsymbol{q}^{-1}$, respectively.)

Now, *when any two $p \times q$ matrices A and B happen to be related by an equation of the form*

$$QB = AP \tag{8}$$

where P and Q are some pair of invertible matrices, then A and B are called **equivalent matrices,** *intertwined by P and Q*. We see that *equivalent linear transformations are represented by equivalent matrices*, intertwined by matrices whose entries are in the field of scalars common to **V** and **W**. To express the equivalence of two matrices, we shall favor the $QB = AP$ form when $\boldsymbol{a} \leftrightarrow A$ with respect the first pair of bases and $\boldsymbol{b} \leftrightarrow B$ with respect to the second pair of bases. In case $\mathbf{V} = \mathbf{W}$ and $\boldsymbol{q} = \boldsymbol{p}$, this notation for equivalent *matrices* agrees with that for similar *matrices* in Section 3.3.

EXAMPLE 1. Referring to Figure 45, some facts we already know can be reestablished. Suppose $\mathbf{V} = \mathbf{W}$ and set $\dim \mathbf{V} = n = p = q$. Use the same bases in **V** and **W**, that is, let $\mathbf{v}_i = \mathbf{w}_i$ $(i = 1, \ldots, n)$. Then if $\boldsymbol{p} = \boldsymbol{i}$, we end up with $B = Q^{-1}A$; which means that if X is the coordinate column of $\mathbf{v}$ with respect to $\{\mathbf{v}_1, \ldots, \mathbf{v}_q\}$, then $Q^{-1}AX$ is the coordinate column of $\boldsymbol{a}\mathbf{v}$ with respect to $\{\boldsymbol{q}\mathbf{v}_1, \ldots, \boldsymbol{q}\mathbf{v}_q\}$. If in addition we have $\boldsymbol{a} = \boldsymbol{i}$, then $B = Q^{-1}$; which means that $Q^{-1}X$ is the coordinate column of $\mathbf{v}$ with respect to the new coordinate basis $\{\boldsymbol{q}\mathbf{v}_1, \ldots, \boldsymbol{q}\mathbf{v}_q\}$ of **V**.

EXAMPLE 2. Suppose A and B are equivalent, say $QB = AP$. If we transpose both sides of this equation, we get $B^tQ^t = P^tA^t$, which is the same as $(P^t)^{-1}B^t = A^t(Q^t)^{-1}$, hence A^t and B^t also are equivalent.

EXAMPLE 3. Let **V** be 3-dimensional, **W** 2-dimensional, and suppose a linear transformation $\boldsymbol{a}$ from **V** into **W** causes coordinate columns X_1, X_2, X_3 of a basis of **V** to map onto coordinate columns Y_1, Y_2, Y_3, respectively, of three vectors from **W**: $X_i \rightarrow Y_i$ $(i = 1, 2, 3)$. To find representations of $\boldsymbol{a}$, we can work in a pair of column vector spaces, *with unit column vectors corresponding to the unspecified basis vectors of* **V** *and* **W**.

(a) The representation of $\boldsymbol{a}$ with respect to the unspecified coordinate bases of **V** and **W** is (see Section 6.3, Example 2) given by,

$$\boldsymbol{a} \leftrightarrow (Y_1, Y_2, Y_3)(X_1, X_2, X_3)^{-1}.$$

Compare this with Section 5.2, Corollary, Part (c).

(b) The representation of $\boldsymbol{a}$ with respect to a coordinate basis of **V** with coordinate columns $\{X_1, X_2, X_3\}$, and a coordinate basis of **W** with coordinate columns $\{Y_1', Y_2'\}$, is given by

$$\boldsymbol{a} \leftrightarrow (Y_1', Y_2')^{-1}(Y_1, Y_2, Y_3).$$

Compare this with Section 5.2, Corollary, Part (a).
(c) The representation of $\boldsymbol{a}$ with respect to a coordinate basis of **V** with coordinate columns $\{X_1', X_2', X_3'\}$, and a coordinate basis of **W** with coordinate columns $\{Y_1', Y_2'\}$, is given by

$$\boldsymbol{a} \leftrightarrow (Y_1', Y_2')^{-1}(Y_1, Y_2, Y_3)(X_1, X_2, X_3)^{-1}(X_1', X_2', X_3').$$

Compare this with Section 5.2, Corollary, Part (b).

To derive these formulas one can use again an easy matrix device. Set $X = (X_1, X_2, X_3)$, $\boldsymbol{a}X = (\boldsymbol{a}X_1, \boldsymbol{a}X_2, \boldsymbol{a}X_3)$, and similarly with the other vectors. Then:

$$\boldsymbol{a}X = (\boldsymbol{a}I)X = IY \quad \text{implies} \quad \boldsymbol{a}I = I(YX^{-1}), \text{ giving case (a);}$$
$$\boldsymbol{a}X = (Y'Y'^{-1})Y \quad \text{implies} \quad \boldsymbol{a}X = Y'(Y'^{-1}Y), \text{ giving case (b);}$$
$$\boldsymbol{a}X = \boldsymbol{a}X'(X'^{-1}X) = Y = Y'(Y'^{-1}Y)$$

implies

$$\boldsymbol{a}X' = Y'Y'^{-1}YX^{-1}X', \text{ giving case (c).}$$

PROBLEMS

1. With respect to some unspecified pair of coordinate bases, a linear transformation $\boldsymbol{a}$ from a 3-dimensional **V** into a 2-dimensional **W** maps coordinate columns X_i onto the coordinate columns Y_i as follows:

$$X_1 = (1, 0, 1)^t \to Y_1 = (2, 1)^t,$$
$$X_2 = (1, 1, 0)^t \to Y_2 = (1, 2)^t,$$
$$X_3 = (0, 0, 1)^t \to Y_3 = (1, 0)^t.$$

(a) Find the matrix representation of $\boldsymbol{a}$ with respect to the unspecified pair of coordinate bases.

(b) Find the matrix representation of $\boldsymbol{a}$ with respect to a coordinate basis in **V** whose coordinate columns are $\{X_1, X_2, X_3\}$ and one in **W** whose coordinate columns are $\{Y_1, Y_2\}$.

2. Do the same as in Problem 1(a) with $\boldsymbol{a}$ a linear transformation from a 2-dimensional **V** into a 3-dimensional **W**, as follows:

$$X_1 = (1, 2)^t \to Y_1 = (0, 1, 1)^t,$$
$$X_2 = (1, 0)^t \to Y_2 = (1, 0, 1)^t.$$

3. Suppose in Problems 1(a), and 2 we change the unspecified pairs of bases of **V** and **W** to new pairs, by invertible $\boldsymbol{p}$ and $\boldsymbol{q}$ respectively, whose matrices are

(a) $P = \begin{pmatrix} 1 & 0 & 1 \\ 0 & 1 & 0 \\ 0 & 0 & 1 \end{pmatrix}$, $\quad Q = \begin{pmatrix} 0 & 1 \\ -1 & 0 \end{pmatrix}$ in Problem 1,

(b) $P = \begin{pmatrix} 1 & 1 \\ 0 & 1 \end{pmatrix}$, $\quad Q = \begin{pmatrix} 2 & 0 & 0 \\ 0 & 0 & 1 \\ 0 & 1 & 0 \end{pmatrix}$ in Problem 2.

Find the new matrix representations of $\boldsymbol{a}$.

6.5 KERNEL AND IMAGE

With respect to a suitably chosen pair of coordinate bases of a q-dimensional vector space $\mathbf{V}$ and a p-dimensional vector space $\mathbf{W}$, the matrix representation of a linear transformation $\boldsymbol{a}$ from $\mathbf{V}$ into $\mathbf{W}$ is extremely simple, see Equation (9) below. We first relate the dimensions of ker $\boldsymbol{a}$ and im $\boldsymbol{a}$.

Theorem 2. If $\boldsymbol{a}$ is a linear transformation from $\mathbf{V}$ into $\mathbf{W}$ and if $\{\bar{\mathbf{v}}_1, \ldots, \bar{\mathbf{v}}_r\}$ is a basis of $\mathbf{V}/\ker \boldsymbol{a}$, then $\{\boldsymbol{a}\mathbf{v}_1, \ldots, \boldsymbol{a}\mathbf{v}_r\}$ is a basis of im $\boldsymbol{a}$ and

$$\dim \mathbf{V} = \dim \ker \boldsymbol{a} \dotplus \dim \operatorname{im} \boldsymbol{a}.$$

Proof: We know that ker $\boldsymbol{a}$ is an invariant subspace of $\mathbf{V}$ and that for any basis $\{\bar{\mathbf{v}}_1, \ldots, \bar{\mathbf{v}}_r\}$ of the factor space $\mathbf{V}/\ker \boldsymbol{a}$, the whole space $\mathbf{V}$ is a direct sum

$$\mathbf{V} = [\mathbf{v}_1, \ldots, \mathbf{v}_r] \dotplus \ker \boldsymbol{a},$$

although the first summand is generally not invariant under $\boldsymbol{a}$. If there were a linear dependence, say $\sum c_i \boldsymbol{a}\mathbf{v}_i = \mathbf{o}$, then $\boldsymbol{a}\sum c_i\mathbf{v}_i = \mathbf{o}$. This would imply that $\sum c_i\mathbf{v}_i$ is in ker $\boldsymbol{a}$, so $\sum c_i\bar{\mathbf{v}}_i = \bar{\mathbf{o}}$, a contradiction. Hence $\{\boldsymbol{a}\mathbf{v}_1, \ldots, \boldsymbol{a}\mathbf{v}_r\}$ is a linearly independent subset of $\mathbf{W}$. Furthermore, if $\mathbf{w}$ is a vector in im $\boldsymbol{a}$, then $\mathbf{w} = \boldsymbol{a}\mathbf{v}$ for some vector $\mathbf{v} = \sum c_i\mathbf{v}_i + \mathbf{v}_0$ in $\mathbf{V}$, where $\mathbf{v}_0$ is in ker $\boldsymbol{a}$. Hence

$$\mathbf{w} = \boldsymbol{a}\mathbf{v} = \sum c_i \boldsymbol{a}\mathbf{v}_i,$$

so

$$\operatorname{im} \boldsymbol{a} = [\boldsymbol{a}\mathbf{v}_1, \ldots, \boldsymbol{a}\mathbf{v}_r] \quad \text{and} \quad \dim \operatorname{im} \boldsymbol{a} = \dim(\mathbf{V}/\ker \boldsymbol{a}) = r.$$

Also,

$$\dim \ker \boldsymbol{a} = \dim \mathbf{V} - r$$

because ker $\boldsymbol{a}$ is a direct summand, which implies the desired result. q.e.d.

EXAMPLE 1. Let $\mathbf{V} = \mathbf{W}$, where $\mathbf{V}$ is the vector space of all the real polynomials of degree at most n, including the constants. If $\boldsymbol{a}$ is the linear transformation d^2/dx^2, that is, the "second derivative with respect to x," then

$$\ker \boldsymbol{a} = [1, x] \quad \text{and} \quad \operatorname{im} \boldsymbol{a} = [1, \ldots, x^{n-2}].$$

Since $\dim \mathbf{V} = n + 1$, we verify that

$$\dim \mathbf{V} = \dim \ker \boldsymbol{a} + \dim \operatorname{im} \boldsymbol{a}.$$

Note that im $\boldsymbol{a}$ contains ker $\boldsymbol{a}$ in this case, provided $n > 2$.

Now, let $\{\mathbf{u}_1, \ldots, \mathbf{u}_s\}$ be a basis of ker $\boldsymbol{a}$, where $\boldsymbol{a}$ is a linear transformation from a q-dimensional $\mathbf{V}$ into a p-dimensional $\mathbf{W}$ and $r = \dim \mathbf{V}/\ker \boldsymbol{a}$, so $s = q - r$ by Theorem 2. If $\{\bar{\mathbf{v}}_1, \ldots, \bar{\mathbf{v}}_r\}$ is a basis of $\mathbf{V}/\ker \boldsymbol{a}$, then $\{\mathbf{v}_1, \ldots, \mathbf{v}_r, \mathbf{u}_1, \ldots, \mathbf{u}_s\}$ can be chosen as coordinate basis of $\mathbf{V}$ (Section 4.8, Example 3). Also, we can augment $\{\boldsymbol{a}\mathbf{v}_1, \ldots, \boldsymbol{a}\mathbf{v}_r\}$, which by Theorem 2 is a basis of im $\boldsymbol{a}$, to a coordinate basis $\{\boldsymbol{a}\mathbf{v}_1, \ldots, \boldsymbol{a}\mathbf{v}_r, \mathbf{w}_1, \ldots, \mathbf{w}_{p-r}\}$ of $\mathbf{W}$. *With respect to this pair of coordinate bases,* $\boldsymbol{a}$ *is represented by a* $p \times q$ *matrix* A *whose entries are all zero except for* $a_{11} = \cdots = a_{rr} = 1$. For, if we recall that the columns of A give the coordinates of the images of the vectors which constitute the coordinate basis of $\mathbf{V}$, we see that

$$A = \operatorname{diag}(I_r, O) = \begin{pmatrix} I_r & O \\ O & O \end{pmatrix}, \tag{9}$$

where I_r is the r-rowed identity and the lower right-hand O is a $(p - r) \times (q - r)$ zero matrix.

EXAMPLE 2. Suppose $\dim \mathbf{W} = 1$ and $\boldsymbol{a} \neq \boldsymbol{o}$. Then dim im $\boldsymbol{a} = 1$, hence dim ker $\boldsymbol{a} = q - 1$ where $q = \dim \mathbf{V}$. So $\boldsymbol{a}$ is represented, with respect to the special pair of coordinate bases described above, by the $1 \times q$ matrix $(1, 0, \ldots, 0)$, a special case of Equation (9).

PROBLEMS

1. If a linear transformation $\boldsymbol{a}$ of $\mathbf{V}$ is represented by $A = \begin{pmatrix} 0 & 1 \\ 0 & 0 \end{pmatrix}$, show that im $\boldsymbol{a}$ = ker $\boldsymbol{a}$ and each is of dimension 1. If this same matrix A represents a linear transformation $\boldsymbol{a}$ *from* $\mathbf{V}$ *into* $\mathbf{V}$, does the same conclusion hold? Can im $\boldsymbol{a}$ = ker $\boldsymbol{a}$ if $\mathbf{V}$ is 3-dimensional?

2. Suppose $\boldsymbol{a}$ is a linear transformation from $\mathbf{V}$ into $\mathbf{W}$. Show that *if* $\boldsymbol{p}$ and $\boldsymbol{q}$ *are invertible linear transformations of* $\mathbf{V}$ *and* $\mathbf{W}$, *respectively, then*

$$\text{dim im } \boldsymbol{a} = \text{dim im } \boldsymbol{qa} = \text{dim im } \boldsymbol{ap}.$$

Show that $\boldsymbol{a}$ is one-to-one if and only if dim im $\boldsymbol{a} = \dim \mathbf{V}$.

3. If $\boldsymbol{p}$ is an invertible linear transformation of $\mathbf{V}$, and if $\boldsymbol{b}$ is a linear transformation from $\mathbf{V}$ into $\mathbf{W}$, show (Section 6.1, Problem 6) that

$$\ker \boldsymbol{b} = \boldsymbol{p} \ker(\boldsymbol{bp}) = \{\boldsymbol{p}\mathbf{u} \mid \boldsymbol{bp}\mathbf{u} = \mathbf{o}\}$$

and therefore dim ker $\boldsymbol{b}$ = dim ker $\boldsymbol{bp}$. Show that the latter follows also from the fact that im $\boldsymbol{b}$ = im $\boldsymbol{bp}$ and Theorem 2.

4. By use of Section 6.2, Example 3, show that if A is equivalent to $\operatorname{diag}(I_r, 0)$ and also to $\operatorname{diag}(I_t, 0)$, then $t = r$.

5. Show that the largest order of the non-zero minors of A is the same as that of A^t. (The *order* of a minor is the number of rows in the square submatrix whose determinant is evaluated.)

6. If $\mathbf{V}'$ is a subspace of $\mathbf{V}$ and $\boldsymbol{a}$ is a linear transformation from $\mathbf{V}$ into $\mathbf{W}$, show that

$$\dim \mathbf{V}' \geq \dim \operatorname{im}(\boldsymbol{a} \mid \mathbf{V}') \geq \dim \mathbf{V}' - \dim \ker \boldsymbol{a}.$$

6.6 RANK AND EQUIVALENCE

We know that when $\boldsymbol{a}$ and $\boldsymbol{b}$ are equivalent linear transformations from $\mathbf{V}$ into $\mathbf{W}$ then, with respect to a fixed pair of coordinate bases of $\mathbf{V}$ and $\mathbf{W}$, their representing matrices A and B are intertwined by matrices whose entries are in the field of scalars. On the other hand, our definition (Section 6.4, Equation (8)) of equivalent matrices allows intertwining matrices whose entries are in *any* field containing the entries of A and B. However, when A and B are equivalent, then there do exist intertwining matrices with entries in a given field (containing the entries of A and B) as we shall see below, in Theorem 5. Hence it is true that when A represents $\boldsymbol{a}$ and B represents $\boldsymbol{b}$, then A is equivalent to B if and only if $\boldsymbol{a}$ is equivalent to $\boldsymbol{b}$. First, we consider the basic invariant quantity of equivalent linear transformations, namely, $\dim \operatorname{im} \boldsymbol{a}$.

Theorem 3. $\boldsymbol{a}$ is equivalent to $\boldsymbol{b}$ if and only if $\dim \operatorname{im} \boldsymbol{a} = \dim \operatorname{im} \boldsymbol{b}$.

Proof: If $\boldsymbol{a}$ is equivalent to $\boldsymbol{b}$, there exist invertible linear transformations, say $\boldsymbol{p}$ of $\mathbf{V}$ and $\boldsymbol{q}$ of $\mathbf{W}$, such that $\boldsymbol{qa} = \boldsymbol{bp}$. Because $\boldsymbol{q}$ is invertible, $\ker \boldsymbol{qa} = \ker \boldsymbol{a}$, hence we have $\dim \ker \boldsymbol{bp} = \dim \ker \boldsymbol{a}$. By Section 6.5, Theorem 2, this means also that $\dim \operatorname{im} \boldsymbol{bp} = \dim \operatorname{im} \boldsymbol{a}$. But $\dim \operatorname{im} \boldsymbol{bp} = \dim \operatorname{im} \boldsymbol{b}$, because $\operatorname{im} \boldsymbol{bp} = \operatorname{im} \boldsymbol{b}$. This proves the "only if" part. Now, conversely, suppose

$$\dim \operatorname{im} \boldsymbol{a} = \dim \operatorname{im} \boldsymbol{b} = r.$$

Let

$$\mathbf{V}/\ker \boldsymbol{a} = [\bar{\mathbf{v}}_1, \ldots, \bar{\mathbf{v}}_r], \quad \ker \boldsymbol{a} = [\mathbf{v}_{r+1}, \ldots, \mathbf{v}_q], \quad \mathbf{V}/\ker \boldsymbol{b} = [\bar{\mathbf{v}}'_1, \ldots, \bar{\mathbf{v}}'_r],$$
$$\ker \boldsymbol{b} = [\mathbf{v}'_{r+1}, \ldots, \mathbf{v}'_q],$$

as in proof of Section 6.5, Theorem 2. There exists an invertible $\boldsymbol{p}$ such that

$$\mathbf{v}'_i = \boldsymbol{p}\mathbf{v}_i \quad (i = 1, \ldots, q).$$

We extend bases of $\operatorname{im} \boldsymbol{a}$ and $\operatorname{im} \boldsymbol{b}$ to bases of $\mathbf{W}$ as follows:

$$\{\boldsymbol{a}\mathbf{v}_1, \ldots, \boldsymbol{a}\mathbf{v}_r, \mathbf{w}_{r+1}, \ldots, \mathbf{w}_p\} \quad \text{and} \quad \{\boldsymbol{b}\mathbf{v}'_1, \ldots, \boldsymbol{b}\mathbf{v}'_r, \mathbf{w}'_{r+1}, \ldots, \mathbf{w}'_p\}.$$

Then there exists an invertible $\boldsymbol{q}$ such that

$$\boldsymbol{b}\mathbf{v}'_i = \boldsymbol{qa}\mathbf{v}_i \quad (i = 1, \ldots, r), \quad \text{and} \quad \mathbf{w}'_j = \boldsymbol{q}\mathbf{w}_j \quad (j = r+1, \ldots, p).$$

Therefore

$$\boldsymbol{qa}\mathbf{v}_i = \boldsymbol{b}\mathbf{v}'_i = \boldsymbol{bp}\mathbf{v}_i \quad (i = 1, \ldots, r);$$

and

$$\boldsymbol{qa}\mathbf{v}_i = \mathbf{o} = \boldsymbol{b}\mathbf{v}'_i = \boldsymbol{bp}\mathbf{v}_i \quad (i = r + 1, \ldots, q).$$

Since $\boldsymbol{qa}$ and $\boldsymbol{bp}$ agree on a basis of $\mathbf{V}$, they are equal, hence $\boldsymbol{a}$ and $\boldsymbol{b}$ are equivalent. q.e.d.

The integer dim im $\boldsymbol{a}$ *is called the* ***rank*** *of* $\boldsymbol{a}$, *and the integer* dim ker $\boldsymbol{a}$ *is called the* ***nullity*** *of* $\boldsymbol{a}$. Thus, by Section 6.5, Problem 2, we have

$$\text{rank } \boldsymbol{a} = \text{rank } \boldsymbol{qa} = \text{rank } \boldsymbol{ap}$$

for invertible $\boldsymbol{p}$ and $\boldsymbol{q}$; and by Section 6.5, Theorem 2, we have

$$\dim \mathbf{V} = \text{nullity } \boldsymbol{a} + \text{rank } \boldsymbol{a}.$$

Theorem 4. If A is any matrix which represents a linear transformation $\boldsymbol{a}$ from $\mathbf{V}$ into $\mathbf{W}$, then the dimension of the column space of A equals the rank of $\boldsymbol{a}$. If P and Q represent any pair of invertible linear transformations, $\boldsymbol{p}$ of $\mathbf{V}$ and $\boldsymbol{q}$ of $\mathbf{W}$, then the column spaces of A, QA, and AP all have the same dimension, and the row spaces of A, QA, and AP all have the same dimension.

Proof: The columns of A are coordinate columns of images of a basis of $\mathbf{V}$, hence of a generating set of im $\boldsymbol{a}$. Therefore, rank $\boldsymbol{a}$ (= dim im $\boldsymbol{a}$) equals the dimension of the column space of A. Also, from the fact that

$$\text{rank } \boldsymbol{a} = \text{rank } \boldsymbol{qa} = \text{rank } \boldsymbol{ap},$$

we have the equality of the dimensions of the column spaces of their representing matrices, by the first part of this theorem. Finally, A is actually arbitrary, since we can always find a linear transformation it represents. Hence, using the invertible matrices P^t and Q^t, we can apply the same arguments to A^t, A^tQ^t, and P^tA^t, whose columns are the rows of A, QA, and AP transposed, and whose column spaces are isomorphic, respectively, to the row spaces of A, QA, and AP. q.e.d.

Theorem 5. With respect to some pair of coordinate bases of $\mathbf{V}$ and $\mathbf{W}$, suppose A and B represent two linear transformations $\boldsymbol{a}$ and $\boldsymbol{b}$, respectively. Then A is equivalent to B if and only if $\boldsymbol{a}$ is equivalent to $\boldsymbol{b}$.

Proof: We know (Section 6.4) that when $\boldsymbol{a}$ is equivalent to $\boldsymbol{b}$, then A is equivalent to B, intertwined by matrices with scalar entries. On the other hand, suppose $B = MAN$ (that is, $M^{-1}B = AN$) for invertible matrices M and N, whose entries are in some field which contains the scalar field of $\mathbf{V}$ and $\mathbf{W}$. If rank $\boldsymbol{a} = r$, then by Section 6.5, Equation (9), there are invertible matrices S and T with scalar entries, such that $SAT = \text{diag}(I_r, O)$. Since $A = M^{-1}BN^{-1}$, we have $SM^{-1}BN^{-1}T = \text{diag}(I_r, O)$. We may regard B as the representation of a linear transformation $\boldsymbol{b}'$ from a vector space $\mathbf{V}'$ into a vector space $\mathbf{W}'$, where the scalar field of $\mathbf{V}'$ and $\mathbf{W}'$ includes the scalar field of $\mathbf{V}$ and $\mathbf{W}$ as well as the entries of M and N (Section 6.1, Problem 6). Hence $\operatorname{diag}(I_r, O)$ also represents $\boldsymbol{b}'$, so by Theorem 4, rank $\boldsymbol{b}' = r$, and r therefore equals the dimension of the column space of B. Since B also represents $\boldsymbol{b}$, rank $\boldsymbol{b} = r$. Thus $\boldsymbol{a}$ is equivalent to $\boldsymbol{b}$, by Theorem 3. (See also Example 1, below.) q.e.d.

Corollary. If two matrices A and B have entries in a given field and if $B = MAN$ for some pair of invertible matrices M and N, then there exist invertible matrices M_0 and N_0 with entries in the given field such that $B = M_0AN_0$.

Proof: By the above theorem, the equivalence of A and B implies the equivalence of linear transformations of which A and B can be considered representations, hence A and B are intertwined in the given field, say $QB = AP$. Now choose $M_0 = Q^{-1}$ and $N_0 = P$. q.e.d.

EXAMPLE 1. Another way to prove that the equivalence of A and B implies the equivalence of $\boldsymbol{a}$ and $\boldsymbol{b}$ is as follows: Let rank $\boldsymbol{a} = r$ and rank $\boldsymbol{b} = t$. Then $SAT = \operatorname{diag}(I_r, O)$ and $JBK = \operatorname{diag}(I_t, O)$ for invertible matrices S, T, J, K. Hence, from $B = MAN$, we get

$$\operatorname{diag}(I_t, O) = JMS^{-1} \operatorname{diag}(I_r, O)T^{-1}NK.$$

This contradicts Section 6.2, Example 3 unless $t = r$. So $\boldsymbol{a}$ and $\boldsymbol{b}$ have the same rank. Therefore, they are equivalent.

EXAMPLE 2. Since rank $\boldsymbol{a}$ is the integer r in the matrix representation $\operatorname{diag}(I_r, O)$, we get that rank $\boldsymbol{a}$ equals the *largest order of the non-zero minors of any representing matrix*, and hence this order equals the dimension of the column space of any representing matrix. (See Section 6.5, Problem 4.)

EXAMPLE 3. Let s and t be the respective dimensions of the row and column spaces of a $p \times q$ matrix A. The columns of A may be permuted, without changing these dimensions. Therefore we shall assume that the first t columns of A are linearly independent and notice that A can be expressed in the partitioned form

$$A = (A_0, A_0P) = A_0(I, P),$$

where A_0 is $p \times t$. Hence, the t linearly independent rows of (I, P) generate the row space of A, that is, $s \leq t$. Similarly, we can show that $t \leq s$, hence $s = t$.

Theorem 6. The row space and column space of a $p \times q$ matrix A have equal dimensions.

Proof: We could quote Example 3, or we could apply Theorem 4 to the representation $\operatorname{diag}(I_r, O) = SAT$ and its transpose. Instead, let us practice with the fact that the largest order of the non-zero minors of A equals the dimension of the column space of A (Example 2). Suppose this dimension is r. Then $SAT = \operatorname{diag}(I_r, O)$, from which

$$T^t A^t S^t = \operatorname{diag}(I_r, O).$$

Thus A^t is equivalent to $\operatorname{diag}(I_r, O)$, hence the largest order of its non-zero minors also equals r which equals the rank of the linear transformation represented by A^t, and hence equals the dimension of the column space of A^t. But this space is isomorphic to the row space of A. q.e.d.

The rank of $\boldsymbol{a}$ is also what we mean by the ***rank of any representing matrix*** A, denoted by rank A. We therefore have that rank A *equals the common dimension of its column space and row space, as well as the largest order of its non-zero minors*. Our work also shows that the set of all the matrices which represent a given linear transformation from $\mathbf{V}$ into $\mathbf{W}$ is characterized by the fact that these matrices have the same rank. Dually, the set of all linear transformations from $\mathbf{V}$ into $\mathbf{W}$ which are equivalent to a particular one is characterized by the fact that all its members have the same rank. (Since every matrix, with entries from a field, represents some linear transformation, the rank of A is always defined.)

The *rank of any matrix A is independent of the field in which the entries of A are embedded*, because the computation of the largest order non-zero minor does not depend on this field. Thus, *the linear dependence or independence of a given set of row or column vectors is not affected by an enlargement of the scalar field.* (This appeal to determinants can be avoided, for example, by considering the possible equivalence of A to $\operatorname{diag}(I_r, O)$ over one field and to $\operatorname{diag}(I_t, O)$ over a larger field, and then applying Theorem 4.)

Theorem 7. If $\boldsymbol{a}$ and $\boldsymbol{b}$ are linear transformations from $\mathbf{V}$ into $\mathbf{W}$, then

$$\operatorname{rank}(\boldsymbol{a} + \boldsymbol{b}) \leq \operatorname{rank} \boldsymbol{a} + \operatorname{rank} \boldsymbol{b}.$$

If $\boldsymbol{b}$ is a linear transformation from $\mathbf{U}$ into $\mathbf{V}$ and $\boldsymbol{a}$ is a linear transformation from $\mathbf{V}$ into $\mathbf{W}$, then

(1) $\operatorname{rank} \boldsymbol{ab} \leq \operatorname{minimum} \{\operatorname{rank} \boldsymbol{a}, \operatorname{rank} \boldsymbol{b}\}$, and
(2) $\operatorname{rank} \boldsymbol{ab} \geq \operatorname{rank} \boldsymbol{a} + \operatorname{rank} \boldsymbol{b} - \dim \mathbf{V}$.

Proof: Suppose $\boldsymbol{a}$ and $\boldsymbol{b}$ are linear transformations from $\mathbf{V}$ into $\mathbf{W}$. Since $(\boldsymbol{a} + \boldsymbol{b})\mathbf{u} = \boldsymbol{a}\mathbf{u} + \boldsymbol{b}\mathbf{u}$, we have that $\operatorname{im}(\boldsymbol{a} + \boldsymbol{b})$ is a subspace of $[\operatorname{im} \boldsymbol{a}, \operatorname{im} \boldsymbol{b}]$. Therefore

$$\dim \operatorname{im}(\boldsymbol{a} + \boldsymbol{b}) \leq \dim \operatorname{im} \boldsymbol{a} + \dim \operatorname{im} \boldsymbol{b}$$

(see Section 4.8, Example 2). This gives the desired result for the corresponding ranks. Now suppose $\boldsymbol{a}$ and $\boldsymbol{b}$ are linear transformations from $\mathbf{V}$ into $\mathbf{W}$ and from $\mathbf{U}$ into $\mathbf{V}$, respectively. Then $\dim(\operatorname{im} \boldsymbol{ab}) = \dim(\boldsymbol{a} \operatorname{im} \boldsymbol{b}) \leq \dim \operatorname{im} \boldsymbol{b}$, and $\operatorname{im} \boldsymbol{ab}$

is contained in the im $\boldsymbol{a}$. These imply, in turn, that rank $\boldsymbol{ab} \leq$ rank $\boldsymbol{b}$ and rank $\boldsymbol{ab} \leq$ rank $\boldsymbol{a}$. Finally,

$$\text{im } \boldsymbol{ab} = \boldsymbol{a} \text{ im } \boldsymbol{b} = \text{im}(\boldsymbol{a} \mid \text{im } \boldsymbol{b}),$$

so

$$\dim \text{im } \boldsymbol{ab} = \dim \text{im}(\boldsymbol{a} \mid \text{im } \boldsymbol{b}) = \dim(\text{im } \boldsymbol{b}) - \dim \ker(\boldsymbol{a} \mid \text{im } \boldsymbol{b}).$$

But $\ker(\boldsymbol{a} \mid \text{im } \boldsymbol{b})$ is contained in $\ker \boldsymbol{a}$, hence

$$\dim \ker(\boldsymbol{a} \mid \text{im } \boldsymbol{b}) \leq \dim \ker \boldsymbol{a} = q - \dim \text{im } \boldsymbol{a}, \quad q = \dim \mathbf{V}.$$

Therefore

$$\text{rank } \boldsymbol{ab} = \text{rank } \boldsymbol{b} - \dim \ker(\boldsymbol{a} \mid \text{im } \boldsymbol{b})$$

and

$$\dim \ker(\boldsymbol{a} \mid \text{im } \boldsymbol{b}) \leq q - \text{rank } \boldsymbol{a}.$$

Altogether, this yields

$$\text{rank } \boldsymbol{ab} \geq \text{rank } \boldsymbol{b} + \text{rank } \boldsymbol{a} - q.$$

q.e.d.

PROBLEMS

1. If $A = \begin{pmatrix} 1 & 1 \\ 0 & 1 \end{pmatrix}$ and $B = \begin{pmatrix} 0 & 1 \\ 1 & 0 \end{pmatrix}$ are considered over the rational numbers, show that A and B are intertwined (Section 6.4, Equation (8)) by $P = \begin{pmatrix} 1 & 0 \\ 0 & i \end{pmatrix}$ and $Q = \begin{pmatrix} i & 1 \\ i & 0 \end{pmatrix}$ $(i^2 = -1)$; hence that A and B represent equivalent linear transformations $\boldsymbol{a}$ and $\boldsymbol{b}$ between vector spaces with the rational numbers as field of scalars. Find a pair of rational intertwining matrices.

2. Let $\boldsymbol{a}$ and $\boldsymbol{b}$ be linear transformations from a real 3-dimensional space into a real 2-dimensional space, such that, in terms of coordinates x', y' in the latter space,

$$\text{im } \boldsymbol{a} = \{\text{locus of } x' + y' = 0\},$$

and

$$\text{im } \boldsymbol{b} = \{\text{locus of } x' - y' = 0\}.$$

Show that $\boldsymbol{a}$ and $\boldsymbol{b}$ are equivalent and give an example of such a pair, with explicit coordinate equations.

3. If $\boldsymbol{a}$ is a linear transformation from $\mathbf{V}$ into $\mathbf{W}$ such that $\mathbf{V}$ contains $\mathbf{W}$ and $\ker \boldsymbol{a} \cap \text{im } \boldsymbol{a} = \{\mathbf{o}\}$, show that

$$\mathbf{V} = [\ker \boldsymbol{a}, \text{im } \boldsymbol{a}] = \ker \boldsymbol{a} \dotplus \text{im } \boldsymbol{a}.$$

4. If $\boldsymbol{a}$ and $\boldsymbol{b}$ are similar linear transformations of a vector space, show that

$$\dim[\ker \boldsymbol{a} \cap \text{im } \boldsymbol{a}] = \dim[\ker \boldsymbol{b} \cap \text{im } \boldsymbol{b}].$$

5. Let $\boldsymbol{a}$ be a linear transformation of an n-dimensional $\mathbf{V}$ and let $\boldsymbol{a}$ have rank r. Show that when $\ker \boldsymbol{a} \cap \text{im } \boldsymbol{a} = \{\mathbf{o}\}$, then $\boldsymbol{a} \leftrightarrow \text{diag}(B, O)$ where B is $n - r$ rowed and O is $r \times r$ (zero matrix), for a suitable choice of coordinate basis. If $\ker \boldsymbol{a} = \text{im } \boldsymbol{a}$, find a simple representation of $\boldsymbol{a}$.

6. If AB is defined and $AB = O$, show that rank A + rank $B \leq$ number of columns of A.

7. If $\boldsymbol{a}$ is a linear transformation from $\mathbf{V}$ into $\mathbf{W}$, and $\mathbf{b}$ is a linear transformation from $\mathbf{U}$ into $\mathbf{V}$, show that:

(a) nullity $\boldsymbol{ab}$ = nullity $(\boldsymbol{a} \mid \text{im } \boldsymbol{b})$ + nullity $\boldsymbol{b} \leq$ nullity $\boldsymbol{a}$ + nullity $\boldsymbol{b}$,

(b) nullity $(\boldsymbol{a} \mid \text{im } \boldsymbol{b})$ = rank $\boldsymbol{b}$ − rank $\boldsymbol{ab}$.

8. If $\boldsymbol{a}$, $\boldsymbol{b}$, $\boldsymbol{c}$ are linear transformations such that $\boldsymbol{abc}$ is defined, show that

$$\text{rank } \boldsymbol{bc} - \text{rank } \boldsymbol{abc} \leq \text{rank } \boldsymbol{b} - \text{rank } \boldsymbol{ab}.$$

6.7 ELEMENTARY LINEAR TRANSFORMATIONS

Any invertible linear transformation can be associated with a change of coordinate basis in $\mathbf{V}$. Here, we show how it can be factored into a product of invertible linear transformations, each of which effects a very simple change in the coordinate basis.

Suppose $\{\mathbf{v}_1, \ldots, \mathbf{v}_q\}$ and $\{\mathbf{v}'_1, \ldots, \mathbf{v}'_q\}$ are two coordinate bases and $\mathbf{v}'_i = \boldsymbol{p}\mathbf{v}_i$. We start changing the first coordinate basis to the second, beginning with a change of the vector $\mathbf{v}_1$. We can write $\mathbf{v}'_1 = \sum c_i\mathbf{v}_i$. If $c_1 \neq 0$, then multiply $\mathbf{v}_1$ by c_1, add $c_2\mathbf{v}_2$ to it, then add $c_3\mathbf{v}_3$, and so on, until $\mathbf{v}_1$ is changed to $\mathbf{v}'_1$. The set $\{\mathbf{v}'_1, \mathbf{v}_2, \ldots, \mathbf{v}_q\}$ is a basis, because each of the successive modifications of $\mathbf{v}_1$ preserves linear independence. If, however, $c_1 = 0$, let c_k be the earliest coefficient for which $c_k \neq 0$ and *interchange* $\mathbf{v}_1$ with $\mathbf{v}_k$ to get a new coordinate basis which starts with $\mathbf{v}_k$. Then, multiply $\mathbf{v}_k$ by c_k, add $c_{k+1}\mathbf{v}_{k+1}$ to it, and so on, until $\mathbf{v}_k$ is changed to $\mathbf{v}'_1$. Now, we can write $\mathbf{v}'_2 = d_1\mathbf{v}'_1 + \sum d_i\mathbf{v}_i$, where the sum excludes the deleted vector $\mathbf{v}_1$ or $\mathbf{v}_k$, and some $d_i \neq 0$ for some $i > 1$ because $\mathbf{v}'_1$ and $\mathbf{v}'_2$ are linearly independent. If $d_2 \neq 0$, we multiply $\mathbf{v}_2$ by d_2, add $d_1\mathbf{v}'_1$ to it, and so on, until it is changed to $\mathbf{v}'_2$. We have now reached the coordinate basis $\{\mathbf{v}'_1, \mathbf{v}'_2, \mathbf{v}_3, \ldots\}$. If, however, $d_2 = 0$, proceed with an interchange as before. After a finite number of such steps, we finally achieve the second coordinate basis $\{\mathbf{v}'_1, \ldots, \mathbf{v}'_q\}$. This process presents the invertible linear transformation $\boldsymbol{p}$ associated with the given pair of coordinate bases as a product of simple invertible linear transformations. It is clearly not a unique factorization, but each step defines an associated invertible linear transformation of $\mathbf{V}$.

We used three types of linear transformations determined by their effects on the successively altered coordinate bases. In terms of $\{\mathbf{v}_1, \ldots, \mathbf{v}_q\}$ they are:

(1) $\boldsymbol{t}_{ij}$, determined by: $\boldsymbol{t}_{ij}\mathbf{v}_i = \mathbf{v}_j$, $\boldsymbol{t}_{ij}\mathbf{v}_j = \mathbf{v}_i$, $\boldsymbol{t}_{ij}\mathbf{v}_k = \mathbf{v}_k$ if $k \neq i, j$.

(2) $\boldsymbol{t}_i(c)$, determined by: $\boldsymbol{t}_i(c)\mathbf{v}_i = c\mathbf{v}_i$, $\boldsymbol{t}_i(c)\mathbf{v}_k = \mathbf{v}_k$ if $k \neq i$, and $c \neq 0$.

(3) $\boldsymbol{t}_{ij}(c)$, determined by: $\boldsymbol{t}_{ij}(c)\mathbf{v}_i = \mathbf{v}_i + c\mathbf{v}_j$ with $i \neq j$, $\boldsymbol{t}_{ij}(c)\mathbf{v}_k = \mathbf{v}_k$ if $k \neq i$.

We see that: $\boldsymbol{t}_{ij}$ interchanges $\mathbf{v}_i$ and $\mathbf{v}_j$, and leaves the others fixed; $\boldsymbol{t}_i(c)$ multiplies $\mathbf{v}_i$ by a non-zero c and leaves the others fixed; $\boldsymbol{t}_{ij}(c)$ adds $c\mathbf{v}_j$ to $\mathbf{v}_i$ for some $j \neq i$ and leaves the others fixed.

These are called ***elementary linear transformations.*** *Each has an inverse which is also elementary.* The descriptions given above yield matrix representations for each, and these matrices *do not depend on which basis we alter.* We denote these representing matrices by T_{ij}, $T_i(c)$, $T_{ij}(c)$, respectively, and call them ***elementary matrices.*** They can be created from the identity matrix, as follows:

(1′) T_{ij}: created from I by interchanging rows i and j.

(2′) $T_i(c)$: created from I by replacing 1 by $c(\neq 0)$ in the i-th row.

(3′) $T_{ij}(c)$: created from I by replacing 0 by c in the i, j position.

Neither here nor on the symbols for the elementary linear transformations have we bothered to indicate the dimension of the vector space, because this will be clear from the context.

To find the effect of these coordinate basis changes on the matrix A of a linear transformation, we use Section 6.4, Equation (8) in the form

$$B = Q^{-1}AP$$

where P and Q represent the coordinate basis changes in **V** and **W**, respectively. For this purpose, note that

$$T_{ij}^{-1} = T_{ij}, \quad T_i(c)^{-1} = T_i(1/c), \quad T_{ij}(c)^{-1} = T_{ij}(-c).$$

EXAMPLE 1. Let **V** be 2-dimensional and **W** 3-dimensional. Take $\{\mathbf{v}_1, \mathbf{v}_2\}$ and $\{\mathbf{w}_1, \mathbf{w}_2, \mathbf{w}_3\}$ as notation for a pair of coordinate bases.

(a) Suppose in **V** we take a new basis $\{\mathbf{v}'_1, \mathbf{v}'_2\}$ such that

$$\mathbf{v}'_1 = \boldsymbol{t}_{12}(c)\mathbf{v}_1 = \mathbf{v}_1 + c\mathbf{v}_2,$$
$$\mathbf{v}'_2 = \boldsymbol{t}_{12}(c)\mathbf{v}_2 = \mathbf{v}_2,$$

and the matrix for this change,

$$T_{12}(c) = \begin{pmatrix} 1 & 0 \\ c & 1 \end{pmatrix}.$$

If a linear transformation $\boldsymbol{a}$ is represented by a 2×3 matrix $A = (a_{ij})$, then the change from $\{\mathbf{v}_1, \mathbf{v}_2\}$ to $\{\mathbf{v}'_1, \mathbf{v}'_2\}$ changes the representation of $\boldsymbol{a}$ from A to $AT_{12}(c)$, that is, it corresponds to a column operation on A which adds c times the second column to the first column.

(b) Suppose in **W** we take a new basis $\{\mathbf{w}'_1, \mathbf{w}'_2, \mathbf{w}'_3\}$ such that

$$\mathbf{w}'_1 = \boldsymbol{t}_{12}(c)\mathbf{w}_1 = \mathbf{w}_1 + c\mathbf{w}_2,$$
$$\mathbf{w}'_2 = \boldsymbol{t}_{12}(c)\mathbf{w}_2 = \mathbf{w}_2,$$
$$\mathbf{w}'_3 = \boldsymbol{t}_{12}(c)\mathbf{w}_3 = \mathbf{w}_3,$$

and the matrix

$$T_{12}(c) = \begin{pmatrix} 1 & 0 & 0 \\ c & 1 & 0 \\ 0 & 0 & 1 \end{pmatrix},$$

whose inverse is $T_{12}(-c)$. The change from $\{\mathbf{w}_1, \mathbf{w}_2, \mathbf{w}_3\}$ to $\{\mathbf{w}'_1, \mathbf{w}'_2, \mathbf{w}'_3\}$ changes the representation of $\boldsymbol{a}$ from A to $T_{12}(-c)A$, that is, it corresponds to a *row operation* on A which adds $-c$ times the second row to the first row.

EXAMPLE 2. The determinants of the elementary matrices have the values: $|T_{ij}| = -1$, $|T_i(c)| = c \neq 0$, $|T_{ij}(c)| = 1$. The invertibility of the elementary matrices implies that TA and A have the same row space, while A and AT have the same column space, for any elementary matrix T.

Since any invertible linear transformation can be factored into a product of elementary linear transformations, any invertible matrix can be factored into a product of elementary matrices, and for the entries of the factors we need not use elements outside the prescribed field. Conversely, any product of elementary linear transformations is invertible, and the same goes for their matrices. Hence, the set of $n \times n$ invertible matrices with entries in a specified field is the same as the set of products of elementary matrices with entries from the same field; and a similar statement holds for the set of invertible linear transformations of a vector space.

If two matrices are equivalent, say $B = MAN$ where M and N are invertible, we now see that B can be derived from A by a sequence of elementary row and column operations corresponding to the factorizations (not unique) of M and N into elementary matrices, in fact, corresponding to the factorization of any intertwining pair. In particular, we can describe the products RA and AS of a $p \times q$ matrix A pre-multiplied by an invertible R and post-multiplied by an invertible S, respectively, as the results of a succession of elementary row operations in the case RA, and elementary column operations in the case AS. In terms of linear transformations, RA reflects a change of coordinate basis in $\mathbf{W}$, while AS reflects a change of coordinate basis in $\mathbf{V}$. RA and A have the same row space while AS and A have the same column space, because R and S are products of elementary matrices (Example 2).

EXAMPLE 3. If a $p \times q$ matrix A is interpreted as the representation of a linear transformation from $\mathbf{V}$ into $\mathbf{W}$, then a suitable choice of coordinate basis of $\mathbf{W}$ will yield a new representation $B = MA$ such that the first (left to right) non-zero entry, if any, in the i-th row of B is further to the right than the first non-zero entry in the $(i - 1)$-th row of B, for $i = 2, 3, \ldots, p$. The matrix B has been called a *row-echelon matrix* (Section 4.9, Example 3) and it can be attained as follows:

1. Shift to the top row of A, if not already there, a row of A which has its *first non-zero entry* at least as far to the left as any other row. (This corresponds to a suitable $\boldsymbol{t}_{ij}$ applied to the first basis of $\mathbf{W}$.)
2. Subtract multiples of this row from non-zero multiples of each of the $p - 1$ rows beneath it to clear the first non-zero column of all non-zero entries under the first row. (This corresponds to a sequence of $\boldsymbol{t}_{ij}(c)$'s, possibly mingled with some non-trivial $\boldsymbol{t}_i(c)$'s.)

3. Operate on the rows 2 to p in a similar way, then on the rows 3 to p, and so on.

When the corresponding process is performed on the columns of A, then a *column-echelon* matrix is attained. These equivalent forms of A are handy for computations involving linear dependence, rank, linear equations, and inverses.

EXAMPLE 4. If $A = \begin{pmatrix} 1 & 2 & 3 & 4 \\ 5 & 16 & 7 & 18 \\ 4 & 14 & 4 & 14 \end{pmatrix}$ then A is row equivalent, in turn, to

$$A_1 = \begin{pmatrix} 1 & 2 & 3 & 4 \\ 0 & 6 & -8 & -2 \\ 0 & 6 & -8 & -2 \end{pmatrix} \quad \text{and} \quad A_2 = \begin{pmatrix} 1 & 2 & 3 & 4 \\ 0 & 3 & -4 & -1 \\ 0 & 0 & 0 & 0 \end{pmatrix}.$$

From this it is evident that the row space of A has a basis given by the first two rows of A_2. So rank $A = 2$. By a column-echelon reduction, one can get the corresponding facts about the column space of A. Column-echelon can also be effected by transposing the matrix and reducing it to row-echelon, and transposing again.

EXAMPLE 5. While reducing a matrix to some desired equivalent form, one can keep track of the product of the elementary matrices of row (or column) operations by applying them, at the same time, to an identity matrix, or to two identity matrices if both intertwining matrices need to be collected. For instance, applying only *row* operations,

$$A = \begin{pmatrix} 0 & 1 \\ 2 & 1 \end{pmatrix} \xrightarrow{T_{12}} \begin{pmatrix} 2 & 1 \\ 0 & 1 \end{pmatrix} \xrightarrow{T_1(\frac{1}{2})} \begin{pmatrix} 1 & \frac{1}{2} \\ 0 & 1 \end{pmatrix} \xrightarrow{T_{12}(-\frac{1}{2})} \begin{pmatrix} 1 & 0 \\ 0 & 1 \end{pmatrix} = B,$$

$$I \quad \rightarrow \quad \begin{pmatrix} 0 & 1 \\ 1 & 0 \end{pmatrix} \rightarrow \begin{pmatrix} 0 & \frac{1}{2} \\ 1 & 0 \end{pmatrix} \rightarrow \begin{pmatrix} -\frac{1}{2} & \frac{1}{2} \\ 1 & 0 \end{pmatrix} = M,$$

so $B = MA$. (Here we happen to have computed A^{-1}, an event which always occurs when A is invertible.) To illustrate application of only *column* operations, consider the extreme case,

$$A = (1, 2, 0, -5) \xrightarrow{T_{21}(-2)} (1, 0, 0, -5) \xrightarrow{T_{41}(5)} (1, 0, 0, 0) = B,$$

$$I \quad \rightarrow \quad \begin{pmatrix} 1 & -2 & 0 & 0 \\ 0 & 1 & 0 & 0 \\ 0 & 0 & 1 & 0 \\ 0 & 0 & 0 & 1 \end{pmatrix} \rightarrow \begin{pmatrix} 1 & -2 & 0 & 5 \\ 0 & 1 & 0 & 0 \\ 0 & 0 & 1 & 0 \\ 0 & 0 & 0 & 1 \end{pmatrix} = N,$$

so $B = AN$. Note, in the first illustration, that the i-th row of M gives the coefficients for the expression of the i-th row of B as a linear combination of the rows of A. In general, corresponding to each zero row of B, we find a linear dependence on the rows of A. Similarly, in the second illustration, the i-th column of N gives the coefficients for the expression of the i-th column of B as a linear combination of the columns of A.

EXAMPLE 6. In Section 3.5, Example 5 we mentioned the use of completion of squares to express a quadratic form X^tAX, $A = A^t$, as a weighted sum of squares of new variables. This process is equivalent to the performance of a sequence of simultaneous row and column operations on the matrix A, each pair of the *same* type, until it is diagonalized. The matrix description of this process is P^tAP, where P is a product of elementary matrices reflecting the column operations on A. The corresponding change of variables is given by $Y = P^{-1}X$; so

$$X^tAX = Y^tP^tAPY = \left(\sum^n d_i y_i^2\right).$$

These d_i's are not unique. Furthermore, it is necessary to assume that our field of numbers is such that $s + s \neq 0$ when $s \neq 0$ (see Section 4.4, Example 7). (The necessity of the condition can be seen when an attempt is made to diagonalize $\begin{pmatrix} 0 & 1 \\ 1 & 0 \end{pmatrix}$ by this process over the field of integers modulo 2.) To illustrate, take

$$A = \begin{pmatrix} 1 & -2 & 3 & 0 \\ & 4 & -6 & \frac{1}{2} \\ & & 8 & 0 \\ & * & & 0 \end{pmatrix} = A^t.$$

Condensing the simultaneous row and column operations, we find

$$A \xrightarrow{T_{21}(2)\ldots} \begin{pmatrix} 1 & 0 & 0 & 0 \\ 0 & 0 & 0 & \frac{1}{2} \\ 0 & 0 & -1 & 0 \\ 0 & \frac{1}{2} & 0 & 0 \end{pmatrix} \xrightarrow{T_{23}} \begin{pmatrix} 1 & 0 & 0 & 0 \\ 0 & -1 & 0 & 0 \\ 0 & 0 & 0 & \frac{1}{2} \\ 0 & 0 & \frac{1}{2} & 0 \end{pmatrix}$$

$$\xrightarrow{T_{34}(1)} \begin{pmatrix} 1 & 0 & 0 & 0 \\ 0 & -1 & 0 & 0 \\ 0 & 0 & 1 & \frac{1}{2} \\ 0 & 0 & \frac{1}{2} & 0 \end{pmatrix} \xrightarrow{T_{43}(-\frac{1}{2})} \operatorname{diag}(1, -1, 1, -\tfrac{1}{4});$$

$$I \to \begin{pmatrix} 1 & 0 & 0 & 0 \\ 2 & 1 & 0 & 0 \\ -3 & 0 & 1 & 0 \\ 0 & 0 & 0 & 1 \end{pmatrix} \to \cdots \to \begin{pmatrix} 1 & 0 & 0 & 0 \\ -3 & 0 & 1 & 0 \\ 2 & 1 & 0 & 1 \\ -1 & -\frac{1}{2} & 0 & \frac{1}{2} \end{pmatrix} = P^t,$$

where we keep track of the product of row operations by applying them to I. So

$$X^tAX = y_1^2 - y_2^2 + y_3^2 - (\tfrac{1}{4})y_4^2.$$

EXAMPLE 7. Let $A = \begin{pmatrix} a & b \\ c & d \end{pmatrix}$ with $a \neq 0$. Then using two identity matrices to keep track of row and column operations, we get:

$$A \to \begin{pmatrix} a & b \\ 0 & d - bc/a \end{pmatrix} \to \begin{pmatrix} a & 0 \\ 0 & |A|/a \end{pmatrix} = MAN,$$

$$I \to \begin{pmatrix} 1 & 0 \\ -c/a & 1 \end{pmatrix} = M, \quad I \to \begin{pmatrix} 1 & -b/a \\ 0 & 1 \end{pmatrix} = N.$$

This factors A into a shear times a strain times a shear, as follows:

$$A = \begin{pmatrix} 1 & 0 \\ c/a & 1 \end{pmatrix} \begin{pmatrix} a & 0 \\ 0 & |A|/a \end{pmatrix} \begin{pmatrix} 1 & b/a \\ 0 & 1 \end{pmatrix}.$$

EXAMPLE 8. Let $A = \begin{pmatrix} a & b \\ b & c \end{pmatrix}$ be a real symmetric 2×2 matrix with $a \neq 0$ and $ac - b^2 = d^2 \neq 0$ (that is, $|A| > 0$, hence $|A|$ equals the square of a non-zero number, say d). Then as in Example 7,

$$A \to \operatorname{diag}(a, d^2/a) = P^tAP, \quad \text{with} \quad P^t = \begin{pmatrix} 1 & 0 \\ -b/a & 1 \end{pmatrix}.$$

Now, if also $a > 0$, then

$$A = (P^t)^{-1}(\operatorname{diag}(a^{1/2}, d/a^{1/2}))^2P^{-1} = R^tR, \quad R = (1/a^{1/2}) \begin{pmatrix} a & b \\ 0 & d \end{pmatrix}.$$

Suppose, for some real matrix S, that $A = S^tS$. Then $S^tS = R^tR$, which implies $T^tT = I$, where $T = RS^{-1}$. So $TS = R$ for a real orthogonal T, that is, the most general factorization of A into a real matrix times the transpose of the same matrix is given by $A = S^tS$ with $TS = R$ for a real orthogonal T. For T we may take

$$T = \begin{pmatrix} \epsilon \cos\theta & \sin\theta \\ -\epsilon \sin\theta & \cos\theta \end{pmatrix}, \quad \text{where} \quad \epsilon = \pm 1,$$

so

$$S = T^tR = (1/a^{1/2}) \begin{pmatrix} \epsilon a \cos\theta & \epsilon b \cos\theta - \epsilon d \sin\theta \\ a \sin\theta & b \sin\theta + d \cos\theta \end{pmatrix}.$$

EXAMPLE 9. Because P^tAP has the same rank as A (P is invertible), the real symmetric matrix A in Example 6 always has the same number of non-zero entries when it is diagonalized in this way. Now, suppose $r = \operatorname{rank} A$ and that

$$Z^tQ^tAQZ = \sum_1^r e_i z_i^2$$

is the result of another diagonalization, by an invertible matrix Q. Let $d_1, \ldots, d_p$ and $e_1, \ldots, e_q$ be the *positive* coefficients in the two reductions, the other non-zero coefficients being *negative*. Assume $p < q$. Since $X = PY$ and $X = QZ$, we have $Y = P^{-1}QZ$, hence each y_i is a linear combination of the z_i's. Therefore, we can consider the system of linear homogeneous equations *in the* z_i's:

$$y_i = 0 \quad (i = 1, \ldots, p),$$
$$z_i = 0 \quad (i = q + 1, \ldots, n).$$

There are $n - (q - p)$ of these equations in n unknowns. Since $p < q$, this system has *less* than n equations and therefore has a non-trivial solution for $z_1, \ldots, z_n$, that is, some $z_k \neq 0$, with $k \leq q$, is part of a solution. Substitute such a solution into the identity

$$\sum d_i y_i^2 = \sum e_i z_i^2.$$

This gives

$$0 \geq \sum_{p+1}^{r} d_i y_i^2 = \sum_{1}^{q} e_i z_i^2 > 0,$$

which is a contradiction. Hence $q \leq p$, and so by symmetry of the argument, $p = q$. This so-called ***Sylvester Law of Inertia*** for real quadratic forms implies, in particular:

A *real* quadratic form has the property $X^tAX > 0$ for every real $X \neq O$, if and only if there exists a real invertible P such that

$$P^tAP = \operatorname{diag}(d_1, \ldots, d_n) \quad \text{with} \quad d_i > 0 \quad \text{for} \quad i = 1, \ldots, n.$$

A form X^tAX which has the property $X^tAX > 0$ when $X \neq O$, is called *positive definite*. The same terminology is applied to the real symmetric matrix A. Thus, if $A = B^tB$ for a real invertible B, then A is positive definite.

EXAMPLE 10. Since many elementary properties of the determinant can be expressed in terms of elementary matrices, let us review some determinant theory while we illustrate this fact. The "determinant" is a scalar-valued function whose domain consists of all square matrices and whose value $|A|$ at any $n \times n$ matrix $A = (a_{ij})$ is a scalar given by either of the formulas below, where the sums are taken over all permutations of the column and row indices, respectively:

$$|A| = \sum(\pm 1)a_{1j_1} \cdots a_{nj_n} = \sum(\pm 1)a_{i_1 1} \cdots a_{i_n n}.$$

In the first sum, one chooses -1 for those terms whose column indices $j_1, \ldots, j_n$ constitute an odd permutation of $1, \ldots, n$ (which means that it takes an odd number of interchanges (transpositions) to restore $j_1, \ldots, j_n$ to the natural order $1, \ldots, n$). In the second sum, one chooses -1 when the row indices $i_1, \ldots, i_n$ constitute an odd permutation of $1, \ldots, n$.

Now using elementary matrices where applicable, we list the elementary properties of $|A|$:

1. $|A^t| = |A|$.
2. $|T_{ij}A| = |AT_{ij}| = -|A|$ if $i \neq j$.
3. If $T_{ij}A = A$ for some $i \neq j$, then $|A| = 0$.
4. $|T_i(c)A| = |AT_i(c)| = c|A|$; $|cA| = c^n|A|$.
5. $|T_{ij}(c)A| = |AT_{ij}(c)| = |A|$. ($i \neq j$ by definition)
6. $A(\text{adj-}A) = (\text{adj-}A)A = |A|I$, where $\text{adj-}A = (\text{cof-}A)^t$.
7. If the i-th row A_i of A is written as a sum $A_i = \sum B_{ij}$ of row matrices B_{ij}, then $|A| = \sum|A^j|$ where A^j is derived from A by replacing A_i with B_{ij}. (This is the addition theorem for rows.)
8. If $C = AB$, where A is a $p \times q$ matrix, and B is a $q \times r$ matrix, then for $t \times t$ submatrices of C, $t \leq q$,

$$\left|C\begin{pmatrix} i_1 & \cdots & i_t \\ j_1 & \cdots & j_t \end{pmatrix}\right| = \sum \left|A\begin{pmatrix} i_1 & \cdots & i_t \\ l_1 & \cdots & l_t \end{pmatrix}\right| \left|B\begin{pmatrix} l_1 & \cdots & l_t \\ j_1 & \cdots & j_t \end{pmatrix}\right|,$$

summed over all ordered selections $l_1 < \cdots < l_t$ of t indices selected from $1, \ldots, q$.

9. If A is $n \times n$, then for any fixed ordered selection of rows, say $i_1 < \ldots < i_p$, one has

$$|A| = \sum(-1)^{\Sigma(i_s+j_s)}\left|A\begin{pmatrix} i_1 & \cdots & i_p \\ j_1 & \cdots & j_p \end{pmatrix}\right| \left|\not{A}\begin{pmatrix} i_1 & \cdots & i_p \\ j_1 & \cdots & j_p \end{pmatrix}\right|$$

summed over all ordered selections $j_1 < \cdots < j_p$ from $1, \ldots, n$, where $\not{A}$ means "strike out" the *indicated rows and columns*. (This is Laplace's Expansion by p-rowed minors.)

PROBLEMS

1. If A is an invertible matrix, how does the application to A of the three types of elementary row and column operations affect the structure of A^{-1}?

2. If rank $A \leq 1$, show that $A = XY^t$ for suitable column matrices X, Y.

3. If X and Y are column matrices, show that $XY^t + YX^t$ has rank at most 2.

4. Suppose A is a $p \times q$ matrix of rank r. What is the rank of

$$\begin{pmatrix} A & AQ \\ PA & PAQ \end{pmatrix}?$$

5. Factor

$$A = \begin{pmatrix} 0 & 0 & 0 \\ 0 & 13 & -3 \\ 0 & -3 & 13 \end{pmatrix}$$

into R^tR.

6. Reduce a t-columned matrix B of rank r to $\operatorname{diag}(I_r, O)$ and thus determine in another way that for any t-rowed C,

$$\operatorname{rank}(BC) \geq \operatorname{rank} B + \operatorname{rank} C - t.$$

7. Express $\sum_{i<j}^{n} (x_i - x_j)^2$ as X^tAX with $A = A^t$, and reduce to $\sum b_i y_i^2$.

8. Use the "addition theorem" for determinants to prove that for $n \times 1$ columns X, Y, and an $n \times n$ matrix $A = (a_{ij})$, one has

$$\begin{vmatrix} A & X \\ Y^t & e \end{vmatrix} = e|A| - \sum x_i y_j \operatorname{cof-}a_{ij}.$$

9. If A is positive definite, show that $A = P^tP$ for some invertible P. Does this extend to any real symmetric A for which $X^tAX \geq 0$?

10. Show that:

(a)

$$A_n = \begin{vmatrix} 1 & \cdots & 1 \\ x_1 & \cdots & x_n \\ x_1^2 & \cdots & x_n^2 \\ \vdots & & \\ x_1^{n-1} & \cdots & x_n^{n-1} \end{vmatrix} = A_{n-1} \prod_{k=1}^{n-1} (x_n - x_k) \quad \text{(the Alternant).}$$

(b)

$$B_n = \begin{vmatrix} x_1 & x_2 \cdots x_n \\ x_2 & x_3 \cdots x_1 \\ \vdots & \\ x_n & x_1 \cdots x_{n-1} \end{vmatrix} = (-1)^{n(n-1)/2} \prod_{j=1}^{n} \sum_{k=1}^{n} \omega^{jk} x_k \quad \text{(the Circulant),}$$

where $\omega = e^{2\pi i/n}$.

(c)

$$C_n = \begin{vmatrix} x_1 & 1 & 0 & \cdot & \cdot & \cdot & \cdot & 0 \\ -1 & x_2 & 1 & 0 & & \cdot & \cdot & 0 \\ 0 & -1 & x_3 & 1 & & 0 & \cdot & 0 \\ \vdots & & & & & & & \\ 0 & \cdot & \cdot & \cdot & \cdot & 0 & -1 & x_n \end{vmatrix} = x_n C_{n-1} + C_{n-2}, \quad n \geq 2$$

(the Continuant).

11. Show that if A is in lower triangular-block form, then so is adj-A. (By a ***lower triangular-block*** matrix we mean a partitioned matrix $A = (A_{ij})$ such that $A_{ij} = O$ if $i < j$, and each A_{ii} is square. Upper triangular-block is then the transposed type.) If $A = \operatorname{diag}(A_1, \ldots, A_t)$, what is the form of adj-A?

12. Show that T_{ij} can be factored into a product of $T_i(c)$'s and $T_{ij}(c)$'s. Show that every invertible lower triangular matrix is a product of $T_{ij}(c)$'s.

13. If A is a $p \times q$ matrix and B is a $q \times p$ matrix, show that by elementary row operations one can transform $\begin{pmatrix} I & A \\ B & I \end{pmatrix}$ into $\begin{pmatrix} I & A \\ O & I - BA \end{pmatrix}$, and by elementary column operations one can transform the same matrix into $\begin{pmatrix} I - AB & A \\ O & I \end{pmatrix}$, where I is a suitable identity matrix in each case. Hence show that $|I - AB| = |I - BA|$.

14. If, in the row-echelon form of a matrix, we require that the first non-zero entry in each row be equal to 1 and that the other entries in the corresponding *column* of this entry all be equal to 0, then show that this form is *uniquely* determined by the given matrix. Show that two sets of the same number of column matrices, say $\{X_1, \ldots, X_t\}$ and $\{Y_1, \ldots, Y_t\}$, from an n-tuple column vector space, generate the same subspace if and only if the matrices $(X_1, \ldots, X_t)^t$ and $(Y_1, \ldots, Y_t)^t$ have the same unique row echelon form; hence, there exists a one-to-one correspondence between distinct subspaces and unique row-echelon matrices without zero rows.

6.8 SYSTEMS OF LINEAR EQUATIONS

Consider a system of linear equations which in matrix form is the equation

$$AX = C,$$

where A is a known $p \times q$ coefficient matrix, X is a $q \times 1$ unknown column matrix, and C is a known $p \times 1$ column matrix. The entries of X are sought in some prescribed field which contains the entries of A and C. We regard this as a coordinate representation of the following abstract problem in linear transformations: To *solve the equation*

$$\boldsymbol{a}\mathbf{x} = \mathbf{c}.$$

Here, $\boldsymbol{a}$ *is a known linear transformation from a q-dimensional* $\mathbf{V}$ *into a p-dimensional* $\mathbf{W}$, $\mathbf{x}$ *is an unknown vector in* $\mathbf{V}$ *and* $\mathbf{c}$ *is a known vector in* $\mathbf{W}$, and all are referred to the same pair of coordinate bases, with respect to which they are represented by A, X, C, respectively.

We see that a solution of $\boldsymbol{a}\mathbf{x} = \mathbf{c}$ exists if and only if the vector $\mathbf{c}$ is in im $\boldsymbol{a}$. In coordinate terms, this means a solution of $AX = C$ exists if and only if C is in the column space of A. Since the rank of a matrix equals the dimension of its column space, we can phrase the condition as follows: *A solution X exists if and only if the matrices A and (A, C) have the same rank.* (A, C) is called the ***augmented matrix*** of the system. This criterion for the existence of a solution is independent of the field of reference because the rank of A is independent (Section 6.6); in particular, *if a solution exists in a larger field, then it exists in the given field.*

EXAMPLE 1. An effective procedure for analyzing $AX = C$ is provided by the row-echelon reduction of (A, C). When the basis of **W** is changed by an invertible linear transformation, say one whose matrix representation is Q, set $M = Q^{-1}$. Then the matrix representation of $\boldsymbol{a}$ changes from A to MA and the coordinate column of $\mathbf{c}$ changes from C to MC, while X, of course, *remains the same.* Hence, *by suitable choice of M, as reflected in a sequence of row operations on* (A, C), *we can replace* $AX = C$ *by an equivalent system* (one having the same solutions; it still represents $\boldsymbol{a}\mathbf{x} = \mathbf{c}$ with the original basis of **V** unchanged) *whose augmented matrix is in row-echelon form*:

$$(A, C) \to (MA, MC) = \begin{pmatrix} A' & C' \\ O & C'' \end{pmatrix},$$

where (A', C') *is an r-rowed matrix in row-echelon form*, $r = \text{rank } A$. The equation $\boldsymbol{a}\mathbf{x} = \mathbf{c}$ is now represented by

$$A'X = C',$$
$$O = C''.$$

Therefore, a reduction of (A, C) to row-echelon discovers whether a solution exists (C'' *must equal* O), at the same time it affords a recursive method for expressing r of the unknowns as linear combinations of $q - r$ unknowns and the entries (constants) from C'. These r unknowns, say $x_{j_1}, \ldots, x_{j_r}$, correspond to the non-zero corner entries $a'_{1j_1}, \ldots, a'_{rj_r}$ that are the first non-zero entries in the r non-zero rows of A' in (A', C'). Thus if (A, C) reduces to

$$\begin{pmatrix} A' & C' \\ O & C'' \end{pmatrix} = \begin{pmatrix} 0 & 1 & 2 & 0 & 3 & 3 \\ 0 & 0 & 0 & 1 & 1 & -1 \\ 0 & 0 & 0 & 0 & 0 & 0 \end{pmatrix},$$

then $AX = C$ is "consistent" (a solution exists), and $j_1 = 2, j_2 = 4$. So, a simplified equivalent system is:

$$x_2 = -2x_3 - 3x_5 + 3, \quad x_4 = -x_5 - 1.$$

In parametric coset form, the general solution is

$$X = (0, 3, 0, -1, 0)^t + t_1(1, 0, 0, 0, 0)^t$$
$$+ t_2(0, -2, 1, 0, 0)^t + t_3(0, -3, 0, -1, 1)^t,$$

where t_1, t_2, t_3 are the variable scalars defined by $t_1 = x_1$, $t_2 = x_3$, $t_3 = x_5$.

If desired, M can always be chosen so that r of the columns of MA are unit column vectors, as in the above example, where $r = 2$ (see Section 6.7, Problem 14). In this case, if a solution exists, the column MC is an obvious linear combination of the r unit column vectors, and the coefficients in this linear combination give r of the x_i's of a particular solution. The non-zero columns of MA are obvious linear combinations of the r unit column vectors, and the zero columns can be multiplied by 1, thus determining $q - r$ linearly independent solutions of $AX = O$. The system $AX = C$ can be solved by this algorithm, even without any interchange of rows.

Theorem 8. Suppose $\boldsymbol{a}\mathbf{x} = \mathbf{c}$ has a solution $\mathbf{u}$; then the set of all solutions of $\boldsymbol{a}\mathbf{x} = \mathbf{c}$ is the coset $\mathbf{u} + \ker \boldsymbol{a}$. Conversely, given a subspace $\mathbf{V}_0$ of $\mathbf{V}$ and a vector $\mathbf{u}$ in $\mathbf{V}$, there exists a linear transformation $\boldsymbol{a}$ from $\mathbf{V}$ into $\mathbf{W}$ and a vector $\mathbf{c}$ in $\mathbf{W}$ such that $\mathbf{V}_0 = \ker \boldsymbol{a}$ and $\mathbf{u} + \mathbf{V}_0$ is the coset of solutions of $\boldsymbol{a}\mathbf{x} = \mathbf{c}$.

Proof: If $\mathbf{u}$ and $\mathbf{u}'$ are solutions, then $\boldsymbol{a}\mathbf{u} = \boldsymbol{a}\mathbf{u}' = \mathbf{c}$, so $\boldsymbol{a}(\mathbf{u} - \mathbf{u}') = \mathbf{o}$. Hence $\mathbf{u} - \mathbf{u}'$ is in ker $\boldsymbol{a}$, which means that $\mathbf{u}$ and $\mathbf{u}'$ are in the same coset $\bar{\mathbf{u}} = \mathbf{u} + \ker \boldsymbol{a}$. For the other statement, we can apply Section 6.3, Theorem 1 (except that the images are in **W**, it is similar to the case in Section 5.2, Example 1), and then take $\mathbf{c} = \boldsymbol{a}\mathbf{u}$. The construction of $\boldsymbol{a}$ shows that it is generally not unique.

q.e.d.

Theorem 9. Suppose A is a $p \times q$ matrix and that U is a solution of $AX = C$ (in the prescribed field). Then every solution of $AX = C$ has the form $U + U_0$, where U_0 can be any vector such that $AU_0 = O$. The solutions of the homogeneous system $AX = O$ constitute a subspace (the *solution space* of $AX = O$) of the vector space of $q \times 1$ column vectors and this subspace is generated by $q - r$ linearly independent solutions of $AX = O$, where $r = \text{rank } A$. If $\{U_1, \ldots, U_{q-r}\}$ is a basis of the solution space of $AX = O$, then it is a basis of the solution space with respect to any larger field of reference. When A is square, say $n \times n$, then $AX = O$ has a non-zero solution if and only if A is singular ($|A| = 0$), and then it has a solution space of dimension $n - r$.

Proof: Consider $AX = C$ as a coordinate representation of $\boldsymbol{a}\mathbf{x} = \mathbf{c}$. Then the solutions of $\boldsymbol{a}\mathbf{x} = \mathbf{c}$ are represented one-to-one by those of $AX = C$. The solution space of $AX = O$ represents ker $\boldsymbol{a}$. Since $\dim \ker \boldsymbol{a} = q - \text{rank } \boldsymbol{a}$, we get that the dimension of the solution space of $AX = O$ equals $q - \text{rank } A$. The matrix $(U_1, \ldots, U_{q-r})$ will have rank equal to $q - r$ in any larger field, and A will continue to have rank r in any larger field; hence $\{U_1, \ldots, U_{q-r}\}$ continues to be a basis of the solution space of $AX = O$ in the larger field. If A is square, we recall that $\boldsymbol{a}$ is invertible if and only if $\ker \boldsymbol{a} = \{\mathbf{o}\}$, and invertibility is equivalent to $|A| \neq 0$.

q.e.d.

The determination of the coset of solutions of $AX = C$ (when it is solvable) by the row-echelon method leads naturally to a basis of the solution space of $AX = O$ and a representative of the solution coset; but only the solution space and coset are unique, that is, different row operations usually result in different representatives and bases.

EXAMPLE 2. If the $p \times q$ matrix A has rank r then there is at least one invertible $r \times r$ submatrix

$$A\begin{pmatrix} i_1 & \cdots & i_r \\ j_1 & \cdots & j_r \end{pmatrix}.$$

Hence the columns of A with indices $j_1, \ldots, j_r$ are linearly independent and constitute a $p \times r$ submatrix A_r. A reordering of the summands in each equation (in the same way) causes A_r to appear as the first r columns of the coefficient matrix of the altered system. Then the row-echelon reduction of this altered system changes A_r to MA_r, which is still of rank r. Hence in the row-echelon form, we have (choosing 1's for the non-zero corners)

$$a'_{11} = a'_{22} = \cdots = a'_{rr} = 1.$$

We can therefore solve for $x_{j_1}, \ldots, x_{j_r}$ in terms of the remaining $q - r$ unknowns. So, *for every non-zero minor of order r in A we can solve explicitly for the unknowns whose subscripts match the column indices of the minor.* And *the converse is also true.* For, a solution of $AX = C$ is also a solution of the equivalent row-echelon form of the equation. In this form, the unknowns $x_{j_1}, \ldots, x_{j_r}$, that we solve for explicitly, correspond to obviously linearly independent columns with indices $j_1, \ldots, j_r$.

EXAMPLE 3. Suppose A is a $p \times q$ matrix of rank 2 and for simplicity assume $\left| A\begin{pmatrix} 1 & 2 \\ 1 & 2 \end{pmatrix} \right| \neq 0$. We can illustrate the remarks of Example 2 by an adaptation of Cramer's Rule. For every row index i and every column index j we have

$$\begin{vmatrix} A\begin{pmatrix} 1 & 2 \\ 1 & 2 \end{pmatrix} & \begin{matrix} a_{1j} \\ a_{2j} \end{matrix} \\ \begin{matrix} a_{i1} & a_{i2} \end{matrix} & a_{ij} \end{vmatrix} = a_{i1}\left| A\begin{pmatrix} 1 & 2 \\ 2 & j \end{pmatrix} \right| - a_{i2}\left| A\begin{pmatrix} 1 & 2 \\ 1 & j \end{pmatrix} \right| + a_{ij}\left| A\begin{pmatrix} 1 & 2 \\ 1 & 2 \end{pmatrix} \right| = 0.$$

Hence, for $j = 3, \ldots, q$ we get $q - 2$ linear independent solutions of $AX = O$ whose entries are as follows:

$$\{x_1 = \left| A\begin{pmatrix} 1 & 2 \\ 2 & j \end{pmatrix} \right| \Big/ \left| A\begin{pmatrix} 1 & 2 \\ 1 & 2 \end{pmatrix} \right|, \quad x_2 = -\left| A\begin{pmatrix} 1 & 2 \\ 1 & j \end{pmatrix} \right| \Big/ \left| A\begin{pmatrix} 1 & 2 \\ 1 & 2 \end{pmatrix} \right|,$$

$$x_3 = \cdots = x_{j-1} = 0, \quad x_j = 1, \quad x_{j+1} = \cdots = x_q = 0\}.$$

EXAMPLE 4. Let an s-dimensional subspace $\mathbf{V}_0$ of a q-dimensional space $\mathbf{V}$ be generated by s given vectors whose coordinate columns with respect to some basis of $\mathbf{V}$ are $X_1, \ldots, X_s$. *Suppose we seek a homogeneous system* $AX = O$ *of smallest size such that* $[X_1, \ldots, X_s]$ *is the solution space of* $AX = O$. Since $s = q - \text{rank } A$, we must have rank $A = q - s$. Denoting the rank A by r, we see that the smallest possible A will be $r \times q$. Define a $q \times s$ matrix B by

$$B = (X_1, \ldots, X_s).$$

Since rank $B = s$, the system $B^tY = O$ has $q - s(=r)$ linearly independent solutions, say $Y_1, \ldots, Y_r$. *Now, set* $A = (Y_1, \ldots, Y_r)^t$. This is $r \times q$, has rank r, and $AB = O$. But B has rank $q - r$, so *the solution space of* $AX = O$ *is the column space of* B, and the latter space is $[X_1, \ldots, X_s]$, as desired.

An effective procedure for obtaining the matrix A of Example 4 is to reduce B to row-echelon MB and set A equal to the submatrix of M consisting of the last r rows of M. (Since M is invertible, A has rank r. Since B has rank s,

$AB = O$.) In fact, whether or not $\mathbf{V}_0 = [X_1, \ldots, X_s]$ has dimension s, a homogeneous linear system whose solution space is $\mathbf{V}_0$ can be computed in the same way. So also can a linear system whose set of solutions constitute a prescribed coset of $\mathbf{V}_0$ (see Problems 6 and 7 below).

PROBLEMS

1. If $A = \begin{pmatrix} 1 & -2 & 1 & -1 & 1 \\ -2 & 4 & 0 & 4 & 0 \end{pmatrix}$ find the solution spaces of $AX = O$ and $Y^tA = O$, where X and Y are column vectors.

2. If A is $n \times n$, find necessary and sufficient conditions for $AX = C$ to have more than one solution.

3. Show that $AX = C$ has a solution if and only if $Y^tC = 0$ whenever $Y^tA = O$ for some column vector Y.

4. Suppose A is the matrix of a linear transformation $\boldsymbol{a}$ of rank r. Let M be an invertible matrix such that MA^t is in row-echelon form. Show that M and MA^t have the partitioned forms

$$M = \begin{pmatrix} M_r \\ M_0 \end{pmatrix}, \quad MA^t = \begin{pmatrix} B_r \\ O \end{pmatrix},$$

where: (a) the rows of M_0 are coordinate rows of a basis of ker $\mathbf{a}$; (b) the rows of B_r are coordinate rows of a basis of im $\mathbf{a}$. Relate these to the solution space of $AX = O$ and the column space of A.

5. In Example 4, take $s = 1$ and find a particular $r \times q$ matrix A if $X_1 = (1, 1, \ldots, 1)^t$.

6. (a) If $\begin{pmatrix} * \\ M_0 \end{pmatrix} A = \begin{pmatrix} * \\ O \end{pmatrix}$ is a row echelon reduction of a $p \times q$ matrix A of rank r, show that the $r \times q$ system $M_0X = O$ has as its solution space the column space of A. (b) Find a homogeneous system whose solution space is the column space of

$$A = \begin{matrix} 0 & 3 & 1 \\ 4 & 0 & -1 \\ 1 & 0 & 0 \\ 1 & 1 & 0 \\ 0 & 2 & 1 \end{matrix}.$$

7. Find a linear system of equations whose solutions constitute a coset

$$(0, 3, 0, 2)^t + [(1, 0, 1, 3)^t, \quad (1, -2, 1, 1)^t, \quad (3, -2, 3, 7)^t].$$

8. Let $X_1, \ldots, X_s$ and $Y_1, \ldots, Y_t$ be two lists of q-dimensional column vectors and set $A = (X_1, \ldots, X_s)$, $B = (Y_1, \ldots, Y_t)$. If

$$\begin{pmatrix} * \\ M_0 \end{pmatrix} A = \begin{pmatrix} * \\ O \end{pmatrix} \quad \text{and} \quad \begin{pmatrix} * \\ N_0 \end{pmatrix} B = \begin{pmatrix} * \\ O \end{pmatrix}$$

are row-echelon reductions of A and B, show that the solution space of the linear system

$$\begin{pmatrix} M_0 \\ N_0 \end{pmatrix} X = O$$

is the *intersection of the column spaces of A and B*. Do the analogous thing for two sets of row vectors.

9. Find a basis for the intersection of the column spaces of A and A^t if

$$A = \begin{pmatrix} 1 & 1 & 6 \\ 0 & 1 & 7 \\ 2 & 1 & 5 \end{pmatrix}.$$

10. Suppose the linear system $AX = C$ has a solution. Show how it can be solved by first reducing A^t to row-echelon and then eliminating C^t in $\begin{pmatrix} A^t \\ C^t \end{pmatrix}$. Apply this to $AX = C$ if A is the matrix in Problem 9 and $C = (2, -3, 7)^t$.

11. For Section 6.3, Example 2, show that $M(X^t, Y^t) = (I, MY^t)$ for a suitable invertible M. Hence $M^t = X^{-1}$ and $A = YX^{-1} = (MY^t)^t$. Apply this to Section 6.4, Problem 1(a).

12. In Example 4 enlarge B to an invertible matrix $D = (B, C)$. Set $D^{-1} = \begin{pmatrix} * \\ B' \end{pmatrix}$, where B' is $(q - s) \times q$. Show that the equation $B'X = O$ has exactly $[X_1, \ldots, X_s]$ as its solution space.

13. In Example 4 regard A as the matrix of a sought for linear transformation $\boldsymbol{a}$ from a q-dimensional $\mathbf{V}$ into an r-dimensional $\mathbf{W}$. Let $\mathbf{x}_1, \ldots, \mathbf{x}_s$ be vectors whose coordinate columns are $X_1, \ldots, X_s$ with respect to some coordinate basis $\{\mathbf{u}_1, \ldots, \mathbf{u}_q\}$ of $\mathbf{V}$. Extend this set to a basis $\{\mathbf{x}_1, \ldots, \mathbf{x}_q\}$ of $\mathbf{V}$, with $\mathbf{u}_i = \sum \mathbf{x}_j p_{ji}$. To determine $\boldsymbol{a}$, set $\boldsymbol{a}\mathbf{x}_i = \mathbf{o}$ $(i = 1, \ldots, s)$; $\boldsymbol{a}\mathbf{x}_{s+i} = \mathbf{w}_i$ $(i = 1, \ldots, q - s)$, where $\{\mathbf{w}_1, \ldots, \mathbf{w}_r\}$ is a basis of $\mathbf{W}$. Show that $\boldsymbol{a}$ has a matrix $\operatorname{diag}(O, I_{q-s})P$ with respect to the pair of coordinate bases $\{\mathbf{u}_1, \ldots, \mathbf{u}_q\}$, $\{\mathbf{w}_1, \ldots, \mathbf{w}_r\}$. Find P when $\mathbf{V}$ and $\mathbf{W}$ are column vector spaces and $\mathbf{u}_i$ is the i-th unit column vector, and compare with Problem 12.

7

Invariant Subspaces and Canonical Matrices

7.1 FACTORIZATION OF $|xI - A|$

Throughout this chapter, we restrict our attention to the representations of linear transformations of a vector space.

We can adapt the discussion of characteristic numbers and characteristic vectors in Sections 2.16, 2.17 to any finite-dimensional vector space $\mathbf{V}$. Suppose $\boldsymbol{a}$ is a linear transformation of $\mathbf{V}$. If for a scalar s there is a non-zero vector $\mathbf{u}$ such that

$$\boldsymbol{a}\mathbf{u} = s\mathbf{u},$$

then s is called a *characteristic number of* $\boldsymbol{a}$ and $\mathbf{u}$ is called a *characteristic vector of* $\boldsymbol{a}$ *belonging to* s. With respect to some coordinate basis, let A be the matrix of $\boldsymbol{a}$. We again have the coordinate expression $AU = sU$, or equivalently,

$$(sI - A)U = O,$$

as the matrix representation of the vector equation $\boldsymbol{a}\mathbf{u} = s\mathbf{u}$, or equivalently,

$$(s\boldsymbol{i} - \boldsymbol{a})\mathbf{u} = \mathbf{o}.$$

The *characteristic polynomial of* $\boldsymbol{a}$ is $|xI - A|$ and the characteristic numbers of $\boldsymbol{a}$ are therefore exactly those roots of

$$|xI - A| = 0$$

which lie in the scalar field of $\mathbf{V}$.

However, the characteristic numbers of any $n \times n$ matrix A are, by definition, *all* the n roots of $|xI - A| = 0$ (we count repeated roots). These roots lie in some suitably large field containing the entries of A. The existence of such a field *will be assumed* in our work. When the scalar field of $\mathbf{V}$ is the familiar complex number field, then $\boldsymbol{a}$ and its matrix A have the same characteristic numbers because every complex polynomial factors completely into linear factors.

EXAMPLE 1. We have already seen that a *linear transformation* $\boldsymbol{a}$ of a real vector space may have no characteristic numbers because the characteristic equation $|xI - A| = 0$ may have no real roots. For example, the 2×2 rotation *matrix* has characteristic numbers $e^{\pm i\theta}$, which are real if and only if $\sin\theta = 0$.

For any real matrix A, suppose the characteristic polynomial $|xI - A|$ is factored over the real number field as much as possible. Then from elementary algebra, we know that $|xI - A|$ is a product of linear and quadratic factors with real coefficients. Each factor can be taken with the coefficient of its highest-degree term equal to 1. The latter condition is described by saying that each factor is a ***monic.*** Thus

$$|xI - A| = (x - s_1)(x - s_2)\cdots(x^2 + b_1x + c_1)(x^2 + b_2x + c_2)\cdots,$$

where the coefficients are real, and the quadratic factors have no real zeros. These non-constant factors are called ***irreducible*** over the field of real numbers because none of these factors equals a product of non-constant polynomials of lower degree with real coefficients. Further proper factorization requires resort to imaginary numbers as coefficients.

A non-constant polynomial $f(x)$ with coefficients in a given field is called ***irreducible*** *over this field if and only if it is not the product of two non-constant polynomials with coefficients in the given field.* Otherwise, $f(x)$ is called ***reducible.*** Reducibility clearly depends on the field in which the coefficients are embedded. We shall apply these terms to non-constant polynomials only.

We include the number 1 among the monics, but as before, we do not assign any degree to the constant polynomials. (However, for more extensive work in polynomials than is necessary here, the custom is to assign degree 0 to constant polynomials *other* than the zero polynomial (see Section 1.8, Problem 7)).

EXAMPLE 2. The integral matrix (its entries are integers)

$$A = \begin{pmatrix} 0 & 0 & 2 \\ 1 & 0 & 0 \\ 0 & 1 & 0 \end{pmatrix}$$

has characteristic polynomial $x^3 - 2$. By referring A to the complex number field, we find that its characteristic numbers are the three cube roots of 2, namely, $2^{1/3}$, $\omega 2^{1/3}$, and $\omega^2 2^{1/3}$, where ω is an imaginary cube root of 1. If A is regarded as a representation of a linear transformation $\boldsymbol{a}$ of a rational vector space (that is, the scalar field of the space is the field of rational numbers), then $\boldsymbol{a}$ has no characteristic numbers because the characteristic polynomial $x^3 - 2$ of $\boldsymbol{a}$ is irreducible over the rationals. However, if we choose a real vector space (field of real numbers as scalar field) for the representation $\boldsymbol{a} \leftrightarrow A$, then $2^{1/3}$ is a characteristic number of $\boldsymbol{a}$. In this case,

$$x^3 - 2 = (x^2 + 2^{1/3}x + 2^{2/3})(x - 2^{1/3}),$$

that is, $x^3 - 2$ is reducible over the reals and each of the two factors is irreducible over the reals. With a complex vector space, we would have three characteristic numbers because

$$x^3 - 2 = (x - 2^{1/3})(x - \omega 2^{1/3})(x - \omega^2 2^{1/3});$$

that is, $x^3 - 2$ factors completely over the complex numbers.

When working with the real numbers, we know that an irreducible real polynomial is of degree at most 2, because imaginary roots occur in complex conjugate pairs ($p(r) = 0$ implies $\overline{p(r)} = p(\bar{r}) = 0$). But a polynomial with rational coefficients, considered over the rationals, may be irreducible and of arbitrarily high degree. For instance, $x^n - 2$ can be shown to be irreducible over the rationals for every positive integer n. Note that a polynomial need not have a linear factor in order to be reducible. Thus

$$x^4 - 4 = (x^2 - 2)(x^2 + 2)$$

is a factorization into two quadratic irreducible factors over the rationals, and

$$x^4 + 4x + 4 = (x^2 + 2)^2$$

is a factorization with a repeated quadratic factor which is an irreducible polynomial over the reals as well as over the rationals.

As in the case of the factorization of integers into a product of primes, a *non-constant polynomial can be factored into a product of irreducible polynomials in, essentially, only one way.* If each irreducible factor is adjusted to be a monic (coefficient of highest-degree term equal to 1), then the irreducible factors that occur in the factorization, and their multiplicities, are unique. *We assume these facts.*

EXAMPLE 3. With respect to the rationals,

$$(4x^4 - 1)^2 = 16(x^2 - \tfrac{1}{2})^2(x^2 + \tfrac{1}{2})^2,$$

where the monics $x^2 - \frac{1}{2}$ and $x^2 + \frac{1}{2}$ are irreducible over the rational numbers. These are the only irreducible monic factors possible, and the only possible multiplicities for each is 2.

It can be proved that any field can be embedded in a larger field such that every polynomial with coefficients in the larger field will factor completely into a product of linear factors. *This fact will be assumed.*

EXAMPLE 4. Let

$$|xI - A| = x^n + c_1 x^{n-1} + \cdots + c_n,$$

and suppose $s_1, \ldots, s_n$ are the characteristic numbers of A. Then

$$
\begin{aligned}
-c_1 &= \sum s_i &&= \sum a_{ii}, \\
c_2 &= \sum_{i<j} s_i s_j &&= \sum_{i<j} \begin{vmatrix} a_{ii} & a_{ij} \\ a_{ji} & a_{jj} \end{vmatrix}, \\
-c_3 &= \sum_{i<j<k} s_i s_j s_k &&= \sum_{i<j<k} \begin{vmatrix} a_{ii} & a_{ij} & a_{ik} \\ a_{ji} & a_{jj} & a_{jk} \\ a_{ki} & a_{kj} & a_{kk} \end{vmatrix}, \\
&\vdots && \vdots \\
(-1)^n c_n &= s_1 s_2 \cdots s_n &&= |A|.
\end{aligned}
\tag{1}
$$

Note that we have chosen to write $c_i x^{n-i}$, rather than $c_i x^i$. We shall favor the present style hereafter.

This generalizes the case of Section 2.17, Example 3. Here, the expressions in the middle column are values of the *elementary symmetric functions* of n variables computed for the numbers $s_1, \ldots, s_n$, while those in the last column are the sums of all the like-ordered *principal minors* of A. (See Problem 4.)

EXAMPLE 5. If $f_1(x)$ and $f_2(x)$ are *relatively prime*, which means that they have no non-constant common factor (common divisor) over the given field, then there exist polynomials $q_1(x)$ and $q_2(x)$ with coefficients in the given field such that

$$q_1(x)f_1(x) + q_2(x)f_2(x) = 1.$$

Thus, if $f_1(x) = x^2$ and $f_2(x) = x + 1$, then take $q_1(x) = 1$ and $q_2(x) = 1 - x$ (see Problem 7 below). More generally, suppose $f_1(x)$ and $f_2(x)$ are polynomials such that $f_1(x)f_2(x) \neq 0$ and let $d(x)$ be a *greatest common divisor* of $f_1(x)$ and $f_2(x)$ (it may be a constant). Then there exist polynomials $p_1(x)$ and $p_2(x)$ such that

$$p_1(x)f_1(x) + p_2(x)f_2(x) = d(x),$$

where all coefficients are in the given field. Thus, if $f_1(x) = x^3 + x$ and $f_2(x) = x^2 + ix$, then take $q_1(x) = i$ and $q_2(x) = -ix$. When $d(x)$ is chosen as a monic, then it is unique and is called *the* greatest common divisor. We also choose a monic for the *least common multiple*, so it is unique. These facts and their extension to more than two polynomials are the analogues of the integer case, and we assume their truth for polynomials in x.

PROBLEMS

1. If A and B are square matrices and O is a zero matrix, show that, no matter what the entries are in C,

$$|xI - \operatorname{diag}(A, B)| = \left| xI - \begin{pmatrix} A & O \\ C & B \end{pmatrix} \right| = |xI - A|\,|xI - B|.$$

2. Suppose

$$a(x) = f(x)^h g(x)^k, \quad b(x) = g(x)^m h(x)^n$$

where $f(x)$, $g(x)$, $h(x)$ are irreducible and distinct. If $k \geq m$, find a greatest common divisor and a least common multiple of $a(x)$ and $b(x)$. Extend this process to any two polynomials.

3. Find, in turn, a complex, a real, and a rational polynomial of smallest possible degree whose zeros include $2^{1/3}$ and $i(= \sqrt{-1})$.

4. Use the completely factored form of $|xI - A|$ to get the middle column in Equation (1). To get the right-hand column, write each entry of $xI - A$ as $0 - a_{ij}$ when $i \neq j$ and use the "addition theorem" for determinants (Section 6.7, Example 10).

5. Show that if A and B are $n \times n$, then

$$|xI - A| = |xI - P^{-1}AP|$$

and

$$|xI - AB| = |xI - BA|.$$

6. If an $n \times n$ matrix A has rank r, show that

$$|xI - A| = x^{n-r}(x^r + c_1 x^{r-1} + \cdots + c_r).$$

Show, by example, that c_r need not be zero.

7. Over the rational numbers, find $q_1(x)$ and $q_2(x)$ of Example 5 if $f_1(x) = x^3 - 2$ and $f_2(x) = x^2 + 2$. Show that *the property of being relatively prime does not change when the field of reference is enlarged.*

8. If $f_1(x)$ and $f_2(x)$ are polynomials such that $f_2(x) \neq 0$, then

$$f_1(x) = q(x)f_2(x) + r(x),$$

where $r(x)$ is a constant or has degree less than that of $f_2(x)$, and all coefficients are in a given field containing the coefficients of $f_1(x)$ and $f_2(x)$. The *division algorithm* says that $q(x)$ and $r(x)$ are unique. Prove this uniqueness and apply the algorithm to find the greatest common divisor of $f_1(x)$ and $f_2(x)$ in Problem 7.

9. Suppose

$$\boldsymbol{a} \leftrightarrow A \quad \text{and} \quad |xI - A| = f_1(x)f_2(x),$$

where $f_1(x)$ and $f_2(x)$ are relatively prime non-constant monics. Show that there exist polynomials $e_1(x)$ and $e_2(x)$ such that

$$e_1(\boldsymbol{a}) + e_2(\boldsymbol{a}) = \boldsymbol{i}, \quad e_i(\boldsymbol{a})e_j(\boldsymbol{a}) = \boldsymbol{o} \quad \text{if} \quad i \neq j$$

and $e_i(\boldsymbol{a})^2 = e_i(\boldsymbol{a})$ otherwise. (Use the summands in $q_1(x)f_1(x) + q_2(x)f_2(x) = 1$.)

10. If s is a characteristic number of an $n \times n$ matrix A, show that the number of linearly independent characteristic column vectors belonging to s equals $n - \text{rank}(sI - A)$ and they can be selected with entries in any prescribed field containing s and the entries of A.

11. For a fixed scalar s and an $n \times n$ matrix A with entries in a field containing s, show that there exists an integer t_0, $t_0 \leq n$, such that $(sI - A)^t$ has the same rank for all $t \geq t_0$.

7.2 DIAGONAL AND TRIANGULAR REPRESENTATIONS

The linear transformations of an n-dimensional **V** which have the simplest matrix representations are those which possess n linearly independent characteristic vectors. We have used this fact in our discussion of strains of real 2- and 3-dimensional vector spaces. The existence of n linearly independent characteristic vectors is equivalent to the decomposition

$$\mathbf{V} = [\mathbf{u}_1] \dotplus \cdots \dotplus [\mathbf{u}_n],$$

where each $[\mathbf{u}_i]$ is invariant with respect to the linear transformation under consideration.

Theorem 1. A linear transformation $\boldsymbol{a}$ of an n-dimensional vector space **V** has a diagonal matrix representation if and only if $\boldsymbol{a}$ has n linearly independent characteristic vectors. Let A be any representation of $\boldsymbol{a}$. Then there exists an invertible matrix P with scalar entries (in the scalar field of **V**, that is) such that $P^{-1}AP$ is diagonal, if and only if A has n linearly independent characteristic column vectors with scalar entries.

Proof: That $\boldsymbol{a}$ is represented by $\operatorname{diag}(s_1, \ldots, s_n)$ means there exists a coordinate basis $\{\mathbf{u}_1, \ldots, \mathbf{u}_n\}$ of **V** such that

$$\boldsymbol{a}\mathbf{u}_i = s_i\mathbf{u}_i \quad (i = 1, \ldots, n).$$

That $\boldsymbol{a}$ is represented by both A and $\operatorname{diag}(s_1, \ldots, s_n)$ means

$$P^{-1}AP = \operatorname{diag}(s_1, \ldots, s_n)$$

for some invertible P with scalar entries, or equivalently, $AP = P \operatorname{diag}(s_1, \ldots, s_n)$. The columns of P are obviously n linearly independent characteristic column vectors of A. q.e.d.

EXAMPLE 1. For an arbitrary square matrix we can argue directly as follows: Suppose that an $n \times n$ matrix A has n linearly independent characteristic column vectors $U_1, \ldots, U_n$, and let $s_1, \ldots, s_n$ be the corresponding characteristic numbers. These numbers are the n roots of $|xI - A| = 0$ and they do not change when A is replaced by any similar matrix. The U_i's can be chosen with their entries in any field which contains the s_i's and the entries of A, because each U_i is a solution of $(s_iI - A)U = O$ (see Section 6.8). Define an invertible matrix P by $P = (U_1, \ldots, U_n)$. Then $AP = P \operatorname{diag}(s_1, \ldots, s_n)$, so A is similar to a diagonal matrix with the characteristic numbers of A on the diagonal. *Conversely*, if A is similar to a diagonal matrix, say $P^{-1}AP = \operatorname{diag}(s'_1, \ldots, s'_n)$, then $AP = P \operatorname{diag}(s'_1, \ldots, s'_n)$ and $s'_1, \ldots, s'_n$ are characteristic numbers, so the columns of P constitute a set of n linearly independent characteristic column vectors of A. (Since our definition of similarity of matrices allows the entries of P to be in any field containing the entries of A, we must choose suitable column vector spaces if we want to get these results from the above theorem.)

EXAMPLE 2. Suppose an $n \times n$ matrix A is similar to $\operatorname{diag}(s_1, \ldots, s_n)$ and is similar also to the *upper triangular-block matrix* (Section 6.7, Problem 11)

$$\begin{pmatrix} A_1 & A_3 \\ O & A_2 \end{pmatrix},$$

where A_1 is $r \times r$. Then we know there exists an invertible matrix

$$P = \begin{pmatrix} P_1 & P_2 \\ P_3 & P_4 \end{pmatrix},$$

where P_1 is $r \times r$, such that

$$P\begin{pmatrix} A_1 & A_3 \\ O & A_2 \end{pmatrix} = \operatorname{diag}(s_1, \ldots, s_n)P.$$

Therefore

$$P_1A_1 = \operatorname{diag}(s_1, \ldots, s_r)P_1, \quad P_3A_1 = \operatorname{diag}(s_{r+1}, \ldots, s_n)P_3.$$

Since P is invertible, the columns of $\begin{pmatrix} P_1 \\ P_3 \end{pmatrix}$ are linearly independent, hence there are r linearly independent rows in this $n \times r$ matrix. Use these rows to create an $r \times r$ invertible matrix R. Then

$$RA_1 = \operatorname{diag}(s'_1, \ldots, s'_r)R$$

for some subset of the characteristic numbers. Now set $Q = R^{-1}$ to get the diagonalization of A, namely,

$$Q^{-1}A_1Q = \operatorname{diag}(s'_1, \ldots, s'_r).$$

Similarly, one can show that A_2 can be diagonalized.

Theorem 2. Suppose $\mathbf{u}_1, \ldots, \mathbf{u}_t$ $(t \geq 1)$, are characteristic vectors of a linear transformation $\boldsymbol{a}$ that belong to distinct characteristic numbers $s_1, \ldots, s_t$, respectively. Then the set $\{\mathbf{u}_1, \ldots, \mathbf{u}_t\}$ is linearly independent.

Proof: We are given $\boldsymbol{a}\mathbf{u}_i = s_i\mathbf{u}_i$ and $s_i \neq s_j$ when $i \neq j$. Since a characteristic vector is not zero, the theorem is true when $t = 1$. Consider the case $t > 1$. Suppose the theorem is true for every set of $t - 1$ characteristic vectors of $\boldsymbol{a}$ belonging to distinct characteristic numbers. If a linear dependence $\sum c_i\mathbf{u}_i = \mathbf{o}$ exists for our t vectors, then

$$\boldsymbol{a}\sum c_i\mathbf{u}_i = \sum c_is_i\mathbf{u}_i = \mathbf{o} \quad \text{with some} \quad c_i \neq 0.$$

Since $\sum c_is_t\mathbf{u}_i = \mathbf{o}$, we can write

$$\sum c_i(s_i - s_t)\mathbf{u}_i = \mathbf{o}.$$

But $s_i \neq s_t$ when $i < t$, hence

$$c_1 = c_2 = \cdots = c_{t-1} = 0;$$

and since $\mathbf{u}_t \neq \mathbf{o}$, we must have $c_t = 0$, which is a contradiction of the assumed linear dependence. q.e.d.

Linearly independent characteristic vectors need not belong to distinct characteristic numbers. As an extreme case, every non-zero vector is a characteristic vector of $s\boldsymbol{i}$.

Corollary. If $\boldsymbol{a}$ has n distinct characteristic numbers, where $n = \dim \mathbf{V}$, then $\mathbf{V}$ has a basis consisting of characteristic vectors and $\boldsymbol{a}$ has a representation by a diagonal matrix. If an $n \times n$ matrix A has n distinct characteristic numbers, then A is similar to a diagonal matrix.

Proof: Choose a characteristic vector for each characteristic number and thus form a linearly independent set of n vectors, say $\{\mathbf{u}_1, \ldots, \mathbf{u}_n\}$. Then

$$\mathbf{V} = [\mathbf{u}_1, \ldots, \mathbf{u}_n] = [\mathbf{u}_1] \dotplus \cdots \dotplus [\mathbf{u}_n],$$

with each $[\mathbf{u}_i]$ invariant. Apply Theorem 1. As for the matrix A, consider it as the matrix of a linear transformation of a vector space $\mathbf{V}$ whose scalars include the characteristic numbers of A. q.e.d.

With respect to a linear transformation $\boldsymbol{a}$ of $\mathbf{V}$, suppose $\mathbf{V}_0$ is an *invariant subspace*. Let

$$\{\mathbf{v}_1, \ldots, \mathbf{v}_r, \mathbf{v}_{r+1}, \ldots, \mathbf{v}_n\}$$

be a coordinate basis of $\mathbf{V}$, where

$$\mathbf{V}_0 = [\mathbf{v}_1, \ldots, \mathbf{v}_r] \quad \text{and} \quad \mathbf{V}/\mathbf{V}_0 = [\bar{\mathbf{v}}_{r+1}, \ldots, \bar{\mathbf{v}}_n];$$

and let $A = (a_{ij})$ be the representation of $\boldsymbol{a}$ with respect to this coordinate basis. Recall that $\boldsymbol{a} \mid \mathbf{V}_0$ denotes the *restriction of* $\boldsymbol{a}$ *to* $\mathbf{V}_0$ (the linear transformation induced in $\mathbf{V}_0$ by $\boldsymbol{a}$). Then, from

$$\boldsymbol{a}\mathbf{v}_i = \sum_1^r \mathbf{v}_j a_{ji} \quad (i = 1, \ldots, r),$$

we get a representation of $\boldsymbol{a} \mid \mathbf{V}_0$ by an $r \times r$ matrix, say A_1, which is the *upper left-hand corner of* A. Also, recall that $\bar{\boldsymbol{a}}$ denotes the factor linear transformation of $\mathbf{V}/\mathbf{V}_0$. Then, from

$$\bar{\boldsymbol{a}}\bar{\mathbf{v}}_i = \overline{\boldsymbol{a}\mathbf{v}_i} = \overline{\sum_1^r \mathbf{v}_j a_{ji} + \sum_{r+1}^n \mathbf{v}_j a_{ji}} = \sum_{r+1}^n \bar{\mathbf{v}}_j a_{ji} \quad (i = r+1, \ldots, n),$$

we get a representation of $\bar{\boldsymbol{a}}$ by an $(n - r) \times (n - r)$ matrix, say A_2, which is the *lower right-hand corner of* A. The representation A, therefore, has the upper triangular-block (Section 6.7, Problem 11) form

$$A = \begin{pmatrix} A_1 & * \\ O & A_2 \end{pmatrix}, \tag{2}$$

where as usual, the columns of A are the coordinate columns of the image vectors, and the asterisk is noncommital. By interchanging the vectors in a basis of $\mathbf{V}_0$ with the representatives of the basis of $\mathbf{V}/\mathbf{V}_0$, we get a lower triangular-block form.

Theorem 3. If $\mathbf{V}_0$ is an invariant subspace of $\mathbf{V}$ with respect to a linear transformation $\boldsymbol{a}$, then the characteristic vectors and numbers of $\boldsymbol{a} \mid \mathbf{V}_0$ are also characteristic vectors and numbers of $\boldsymbol{a}$, and the characteristic numbers of $\bar{\boldsymbol{a}}$ are characteristic numbers of $\boldsymbol{a}$. Every characteristic number of $\boldsymbol{a}$ is a characteristic number of $\boldsymbol{a} \mid \mathbf{V}_0$ or $\bar{\boldsymbol{a}}$, at least, with repetitions counted.

Proof: We can represent A as in Equation (2) above where A_1 is the matrix of $\boldsymbol{a} \mid \mathbf{V}_0$ and A_2 is the matrix of $\bar{\boldsymbol{a}}$. Then

$$|xI - A| = |xI - A_1|\,|xI - A_2|.$$

Hence all the characteristic numbers of $\boldsymbol{a}$ are among the roots of $|xI - A_1| = 0$ and $|xI - A_2| = 0$; and because $\mathbf{V}$, $\mathbf{V}_0$, $\mathbf{V}/\mathbf{V}_0$ have the same scalar field, the characteristic numbers of $\boldsymbol{a} \mid \mathbf{V}_0$ and $\bar{\boldsymbol{a}}$ are also characteristic numbers of $\boldsymbol{a}$, namely, those roots of $|xI - A_1| = 0$ and $|xI - A_2| = 0$ which lie in this scalar field. Since a characteristic vector of $\boldsymbol{a} \mid \mathbf{V}_0$ is a vector in $\mathbf{V}$, it is a characteristic vector of $\boldsymbol{a}$. q.e.d.

EXAMPLE 3. Suppose $\boldsymbol{a}$ is a linear transformation of $\mathbf{V}$. Let $\mathbf{u}$ be a nonzero vector in $\mathbf{V}$ and set

$$\mathbf{V}_0 = [\mathbf{u}, \boldsymbol{a}\mathbf{u}, \ldots, \boldsymbol{a}^{p-1}\mathbf{u}],$$

where p is such that $\boldsymbol{a}^p\mathbf{u}$ is the first vector in the sequence $\mathbf{u}, \boldsymbol{a}\mathbf{u}, \ldots$ which is linearly dependent on its predecessors:

$$\boldsymbol{a}^p\mathbf{u} + c_1\boldsymbol{a}^{p-1}\mathbf{u} + c_2\boldsymbol{a}^{p-2}\mathbf{u} + \cdots + c_p\mathbf{u} = \mathbf{o}.$$

Then $\mathbf{V}_0$ is an invariant subspace and $\dim \mathbf{V}_0 = p$. With respect to $\{\mathbf{u}, \ldots, \boldsymbol{a}^{p-1}\mathbf{u}\}$ as coordinate basis of $\mathbf{V}_0$, $\boldsymbol{a} \mid \mathbf{V}_0$ has a matrix

$$A_1 = \begin{pmatrix} 0 & & & & & -c_p \\ 1 & 0 & & & & \cdot \\ & 1 & \cdot & & & \cdot \\ & & & \cdot & & \cdot \\ & & & \cdot & 0 & -c_2 \\ & & & & 1 & -c_1 \end{pmatrix}. \tag{3}$$

In Equation (3), all entries which are not in the last column and not on the first "sub-diagonal" are equal to zero.

If we extend this coordinate basis of $\mathbf{V}_0$ to a coordinate basis of $\mathbf{V}$, then $\boldsymbol{a}$ can be represented by the upper triangular-block matrix of Equation (2). The *characteristic polynomial* $|xI - A_1|$ of A_1 turns out to be

$$x^p + c_1x^{p-1} + \cdots + c_p.$$

EXAMPLE 4. Let $\mathbf{V}$ be an n-dimensional real vector space and $\boldsymbol{a}$ a linear transformation of $\mathbf{V}$. Then, let us show that the characteristic vectors of $\boldsymbol{a}$ always furnish a basis of $\mathbf{V}$, and an orthonormal basis of n-dimensional real column vector space, *if $\boldsymbol{a}$ can be represented by a symmetric* (real) *matrix A*,

$$A = A^t = A^c.$$

Suppose s is a zero of the characteristic polynomial of $\boldsymbol{a}$. Then $AU = sU$ for some $U \neq O$. But

$$(U^*AU)^* = (sU^*U)^* = \bar{s}U^*U, \quad \text{and} \quad (U^*AU)^* = U^*AU = sU^*U,$$

where

$$A^* = A^{ct}.$$

Therefore, $s = \bar{s}$, so *all the characteristic numbers of A are real.* Hence $\boldsymbol{a}$ has n real characteristic numbers. Denote s by s_1 and U by U_1, where we can assume that U_1 is a *real* normalized characteristic column vector belonging to s_1, because s_1 is real. Now, complete U_1 to an orthonormal coordinate basis $\{U_1, \ldots, U_n\}$ of the real vector space of $n \times 1$ real column vectors. Denote by P the real orthogonal matrix $P = (U_1, \ldots, U_n)$. From $AU_1 = s_1U_1$ it follows that, for some real matrix L and real matrix B,

$$AP = P\begin{pmatrix} s_1 & L \\ O & B \end{pmatrix}.$$

But $P^{-1} = P^t$, so

$$\begin{pmatrix} s_1 & L \\ O & B \end{pmatrix} = P^tAP = (P^tAP)^t = \begin{pmatrix} s_1 & O \\ L^t & B^t \end{pmatrix}.$$

Thus $L = O$ and $B = B^t$. This suggests that A can be diagonalized if we continue the process. It is trivially true that a real 1×1 matrix can be diagonalized by a similarity using a real orthogonal matrix. Assume it is true for $(n-1) \times (n-1)$ real symmetric matrices; hence there exists a real orthogonal matrix Q such that

$$Q^tBQ = \operatorname{diag}(s_2, \ldots, s_n),$$

where $s_2, \ldots, s_n$ are the other characteristic numbers of A. Set $R = \operatorname{diag}(1, Q)$ and $T = PR$. Then T is real orthogonal and

$$T^tAT = (PR)^tA(PR) = \operatorname{diag}(s_1, \ldots, s_n).$$

Thus, *every real symmetric matrix is similar to a diagonal matrix and is connected to it by a real orthogonal matrix* T. The columns of the latter matrix are *orthonormal characteristic column vectors of* A, and because the s_i's are real, these vectors are coordinate columns of characteristic vectors of the linear transformation $\boldsymbol{a}$ which A represents.

EXAMPLE 5. If the argument in Example 4 is varied slightly, the result is that *any complex matrix* A *such that* $A = A^*$ *is also similar to a real diagonal matrix and the connecting matrix can be chosen unitary.* Thus,

$$P^*AP = \operatorname{diag}(s_1, \ldots, s_n), \quad \text{where } P^*P = I$$

and $s_1, \ldots, s_n$ are real characteristic numbers of A. *A matrix* A *is called* ***hermitian*** *if and only if it has the property*

$$A = A^*.$$

We see that a *real symmetric matrix* is the same thing as a *real hermitian matrix*. The column vectors of P are *orthonormal characteristic column vectors of* A and are coordinate columns of characteristic vectors of any linear transformation represented by A.

EXAMPLE 6. Another modification of the argument in Example 4 will show that *any* $n \times n$ *complex matrix* A *is similar to an upper* (and lower, too) *triangular matrix and the connecting matrix can be chosen unitary.* For, begin with any characteristic number s_1 and corresponding vector U_1. Extend U_1 to an orthonormal basis and construct P from this basis. Then

$$P^*AP = \begin{pmatrix} s_1 & L \\ O & B \end{pmatrix}.$$

Then make the appropriate induction assumption on $(n - 1) \times (n - 1)$ complex matrices, so there exists a unitary $(n - 1) \times (n - 1)$ matrix Q such that Q^*BQ is upper triangular. Now, with $R = \operatorname{diag}(1, Q)$, and $T = PR$, we again find that T is unitary and T^*AT is upper triangular. This is known as the ***Schur canonical form*** of A:

$$T^*AT = \begin{pmatrix} s_1 & & * \\ & \ddots & \\ 0 & & s_n \end{pmatrix}, \quad T^*T = I. \tag{4}$$

The 0 indicates that all sub-diagonal entries are equal to 0.

EXAMPLE 7. Suppose a linear transformation $\boldsymbol{a}$ of an n-dimensional $\mathbf{V}$ has n characteristic numbers, that is, *its characteristic polynomial factors completely* over the scalar field of $\mathbf{V}$. Then $\boldsymbol{a}$ can be represented by (is similar to) an *upper* (or lower, if desired) *triangular matrix*. For, assume this is true in the $(n - 1)$-dimensional case. Let $\boldsymbol{a}\mathbf{u}_1 = s_1\mathbf{u}_1$. When $n > 1$, we can represent $\boldsymbol{a}$ by

$$A = \begin{pmatrix} s_1 & L \\ O & B \end{pmatrix},$$

where B represents the factor linear transformation $\bar{\boldsymbol{a}}$ of the $(n - 1)$-dimensional $\mathbf{V}/[\mathbf{u}_1]$, and the characteristic numbers of $\bar{\boldsymbol{a}}$ are the remaining characteristic numbers of $\boldsymbol{a}$. Hence we can represent A by a new matrix in which B is replaced by an upper triangular matrix reflecting the choice of a suitable coordinate basis in $\mathbf{V}/[\mathbf{u}_1]$. Since the case $n = 1$ is obvious, the desired result follows by induction.

PROBLEMS

1. For a hermitian matrix H show that: (a) H has real diagonal entries, (b) $|H|$ is real, (c) each principal minor of H is real because it is formed from a hermitian matrix, (d) the hermitian form X^*HX satisfies $X^*HX \geq 0$ if and only if all characteristic numbers of H are non-negative; $X^*HX > 0$ if and only if all characteristic numbers of H are positive.
2. For a unitary matrix show that: (a) its characteristic numbers and determinant have absolute value 1, (b) if it is real orthogonal its imaginary characteristic numbers occur in complex conjugate pairs and its determinant is ± 1.
3. Prove that each of the following matrices are diagonal and describe the diagonal entries: (a) A is unitary and triangular, (b) A is triangular and hermitian.
4. In Example 2, show that the columns of Q give rise to characteristic column vectors of A. Show how to diagonalize A_2.
5. If $\mathbf{V}_0$ is an invariant subspace of $\mathbf{V}$ with respect to a linear transformation $\boldsymbol{a}$, show that the restriction of $\boldsymbol{a}$ to $\mathbf{V}_0$ is a linear transformation of $\mathbf{V}_0$ and has the property
$$(\boldsymbol{a} \mid \mathbf{V}_0)^i = \boldsymbol{a}^i \mid \mathbf{V}_0 \quad (i \geq 0).$$
6. If a linear transformation $\boldsymbol{a}$ can be represented by a diagonal matrix, show that the restriction of $\boldsymbol{a}$ to any invariant subspace can also be represented by a diagonal matrix (see Equation (2) and Example 2).
7. If a complex matrix A is such that $AA^* = A^*A$ (***normal***), show that it is unitarily similar to a diagonal matrix (see Equation (4)).
8. Show that if a hermitian matrix H has no negative characteristic numbers, then it equals the square of a hermitian matrix: $H = K^2$ with $K = K^*$. Show that this implies $X^*HX \geq 0$. Apply these facts to a real symmetric matrix.
9. If S is real symmetric and P is positive definite real symmetric, show that SP has all real characteristic numbers. (Try $P = Q^2$.)
10. Let A be real. From the fact that $A^tA = M^2$ for some real symmetric M, show that $A = QM$ for some real orthogonal Q.

11. If A is an $n \times n$ real matrix such that $A = -A^t$ (real skew-symmetric), show that when n is odd, then $|A| = 0$ and the characteristic numbers are zero or pure imaginary.

12. Compare the characteristic numbers of: (a) AB and BA, (b) AA^t and A^tA for any real rectangular A.

13. Show that a real quadratic form X^tAX is positive definite if and only if the coefficients of the characteristic polynomial $|xI - A|$ have alternating signs.

14. If A is complex $n \times n$, let $s_1, \ldots, s_n$ be its characteristic numbers and let $t_1, \ldots, t_n$ be the characteristic numbers of A^*A.

(a) If $A = A^*$ (hermitian), show that

$$s_i^2 = t_{k_i} \quad (i = 1, \ldots, n).$$

(b) Whether or not A is hermitian, show that

$$\min_j t_j \leq |s_i|^2 \leq \max_j t_j \quad (i = 1, \ldots, n).$$

15. For a complex matrix $A = (a_{ij})$, show that any characteristic number s satisfies:

$$|s| \leq \max_j \sum_s |a_{sj}|,$$

$$|s| \leq \max_i \sum_s |a_{is}|.$$

16. If A, B, C, D are commutative lower triangular (or all upper triangular) $n \times n$ matrices, show that

$$\begin{vmatrix} A & B \\ C & D \end{vmatrix} = |AD - BC|.$$

17. If A_1, A_2 are invertible and $A = \operatorname{diag}(A_1, A_2)$ is $n \times n$, show that an n-dimensional column vector space on which A represents a linear transformation is a direct sum of the null-spaces of $\operatorname{diag}(A_1, O)$ and $\operatorname{diag}(O, A_2)$, respectively. (Null-space of a matrix A is the solution space of $AX = O$.)

18. If $A = \begin{pmatrix} O & A_3 \\ O & A_2 \end{pmatrix}$ and $P = \begin{pmatrix} I & A_3 \\ O & A_2 \end{pmatrix}$, with A_2 invertible, show that $P^{-1}AP = \operatorname{diag}(O, A_2)$.

7.3 ROOT SPACES

The triangular reduction achieved in Section 7.2, Example 7, can be improved. Suppose, again, that the characteristic polynomial of $\boldsymbol{a}$ factors completely into linear factors over the scalar field. Then we can show that $\mathbf{V}$ is the direct sum of certain invariant subspaces, one for each distinct characteristic number, such that the restriction of $\boldsymbol{a}$ to any of these subspaces has only one characteristic number and is represented by a triangular matrix with this characteristic number repeated along its diagonal (Equations (8), (9) below).

Theorem 4. Suppose the characteristic polynomial of a linear transformation $\boldsymbol{a}$ of a vector space $\mathbf{V}$ factors completely into linear factors over the scalar field of $\mathbf{V}$. Let $s_1, \ldots, s_t$ be all the distinct characteristic numbers of $\boldsymbol{a}$. Then $\mathbf{V}$ is a direct sum of certain invariant subspaces, called ***root spaces***,

$$\mathbf{V} = \mathbf{R}_1 \dotplus \cdots \dotplus \mathbf{R}_t,$$

such that for each i, $\mathbf{R}_i$ has a basis $\{\mathbf{u}_{i1}, \ldots, \mathbf{u}_{in_i}\}$ with the property:

$$\boldsymbol{a}\mathbf{u}_{ik} = s_i\mathbf{u}_{ik} + \sum_1^{k-1} \mathbf{u}_{ir}a^i_{rk} \quad (k = 1, \ldots, n_i). \tag{5}$$

Furthermore,

$$\mathbf{R}_i = \{\mathbf{v} \mid (s_i\boldsymbol{i} - \boldsymbol{a})^{n_i}\mathbf{v} = \mathbf{o}\}. \tag{6}$$

Proof: Let us prove this by induction on dim $\mathbf{V}$. The result is obvious for dim $\mathbf{V} = 1$. Assume it is true with respect to such linear transformations when dim $\mathbf{V} = n - 1$. Now, suppose that dim $\mathbf{V} = n$ and that $\mathbf{u}$ is a characteristic vector of a linear transformation $\boldsymbol{a}$ of $\mathbf{V}$ belonging to a characteristic number s_1. Then dim $\mathbf{V}/[\mathbf{u}] = n - 1$ and the factor linear transformation $\bar{\boldsymbol{a}}$ has, as its characteristic numbers, a subset of those of $\boldsymbol{a}$. Let t' be the number of distinct characteristic numbers of $\bar{\boldsymbol{a}}$, so $t' = t - 1$ or t. Apply the induction hypothesis to $\mathbf{V}/[\mathbf{u}]$ and $\bar{\boldsymbol{a}}$. Hence,

$$\mathbf{V}/[\mathbf{u}] = \mathbf{R}_1 \dotplus \cdots \dotplus \mathbf{R}_{t'},$$

where, by the induction hypothesis, each invariant subspace $\mathbf{R}_i$ has a basis of cosets $\bar{\mathbf{u}}_{ik}$ $(i = 1, \ldots, t';\ k = 1, \ldots, n_i)$, such that $\sum n_i = n - 1$ and, for unique scalars a^i_{rk},

$$\bar{\boldsymbol{a}}\bar{\mathbf{u}}_{ik} = s'_i\bar{\mathbf{u}}_{ik} + \sum_1^{k-1} \bar{\mathbf{u}}_{ir}a^i_{rk} \quad (s'_i = \text{a characteristic number of } \bar{\boldsymbol{a}}).$$

In terms of the indicated representative $\mathbf{u}_{ik}$ of the coset $\bar{\mathbf{u}}_{ik}$, this means that for each pair i, k,

$$\boldsymbol{a}\mathbf{u}_{ik} = s'_i\mathbf{u}_{ik} + \sum_1^{k-1} \mathbf{u}_{ir}a^i_{rk} + b_{ik}\mathbf{u} \quad (\boldsymbol{a}\mathbf{u} = s_1\mathbf{u}),$$

for some scalar b_{ik}. Now, choose another set of representatives for a new basis of $\mathbf{R}_i$ by the formula

$$\mathbf{u}'_{ik} = \mathbf{u}_{ik} + c_{ik}\mathbf{u},$$

where $c_{ik} = 0$ if $s'_i = s_1$, and

$$\sum_1^{k-1} c_{ir}a^i_{rk} + (s'_i - s_1)c_{ik} = b_{ik} \quad (k = 1, \ldots, n_i), \quad \text{if} \quad s'_i \neq s_1. \tag{7}$$

Equations (7) are suggested when one attempts to choose constants c_{ik} such that Equation (5) will be satisfied by the modified representatives $\mathbf{u}'_{ik}$. When $s'_i \neq s_1$, then we can solve Equation (7) recursively for the constants c_{ik} ($i = 1, \ldots, t'$; $k = 1, \ldots, n_i$). Furthermore, without solving explicitly, we readily verify that

$$\boldsymbol{a}\mathbf{u}'_{ik} = s'_i\mathbf{u}'_{ik} + \sum_{1}^{k-1} \mathbf{u}'_{ir}a^i_{rk} \quad (k = 1, \ldots, n_i).$$

In this case, $[\mathbf{u}'_{i1}, \ldots, \mathbf{u}'_{in_i}]$ is an invariant subspace of $\mathbf{V}$, of dimension n_i.

If $s_1 = s'_j$ for some j, $1 \leq j \leq t'$, then adjoin the vector $\mathbf{u}$ to the set $\{\mathbf{u}'_{jk} | k = 1, \ldots, n_j\}$, and denote by $\mathbf{R}'_1$ the invariant subspace that the enlarged set generates; but if $s_1 \neq s'_j$ for any j, $1 \leq j \leq t'$, set $\mathbf{R}'_1 = [\mathbf{u}]$. Now, set $\mathbf{R}'_2 = [\{\mathbf{u}'_{ik} | k = 1, \ldots, n_i\}]$ if $s'_i = s_2$, and so forth. The spaces $\mathbf{R}'_1, \ldots, \mathbf{R}'_t$ add up to the desired direct sum expression for $\mathbf{V}$, because their bases satisfy Equation (5) and constitute a partition of the basis $\{\mathbf{u}, \ldots, \mathbf{u}'_{ij}, \ldots\}$ of $\mathbf{V}$.

To show that Equation (6) holds, assume a root space decomposition of $\mathbf{V}$ and take $\{\mathbf{u}_{11}, \ldots, \mathbf{u}_{1n_1}; \mathbf{u}_{21}, \ldots\}$, in this order, as a coordinate basis of $\mathbf{V}$. Let us proceed in a way that uses a matrix representation of $\boldsymbol{a}$. Note that, with respect to this special coordinate basis, $\boldsymbol{a}$ has a matrix

$$\operatorname{diag}(s_1 I + T_1, \ldots, s_i I + T_i, \ldots),$$

where T_i is a strictly (zeros on the diagonal) upper triangular $n_i \times n_i$ matrix whose n_i-th power is O, and each I is a suitable identity matrix. Hence the matrix of $s_i\boldsymbol{i} - \boldsymbol{a}$, with respect to this coordinate basis, has invertible diagonal blocks *except for the i-th one*, whose n_i-th power is certainly O. Therefore

$$(s_i\boldsymbol{i} - \boldsymbol{a})^{n_i}\mathbf{v} = \mathbf{o}$$

if and only if $\mathbf{v}$ is a vector in $\mathbf{R}_i$. (Recall that the columns of a representation give the coordinates of the images of basis vectors.) q.e.d.

Corollary. When the scalar field of an n-dimensional $\mathbf{V}$ includes all the n roots of the characteristic equation of a linear transformation $\boldsymbol{a}$ of $\mathbf{V}$, then $\boldsymbol{a}$ can be represented by a matrix

$$A = \operatorname{diag}(A_1, \ldots, A_t), \quad A_i = s_i I + T_i, \tag{8}$$

where T_i is strictly upper triangular ("strictly" means that its diagonal entries are all zeros), and $\{s_1, \ldots, s_t\}$ is the set of all the distinct characteristic numbers of $\boldsymbol{a}$. So A_i is an $n_i \times n_i$ matrix of the form

$$A_i = \begin{pmatrix} s_i & & & * \\ & s_i & & \\ & & \ddots & \\ 0 & & & s_i \end{pmatrix} = s_i I + T_i, \quad n_i = \dim \mathbf{R}_i. \tag{9}$$

Proof: This follows from the last paragraph in the proof of Theorem 4. q.e.d.

If a linear transformation $\boldsymbol{b}$ *has the property that* $\boldsymbol{b}^k = \boldsymbol{o}$ *for some positive integer* k, *then* $\boldsymbol{b}$ *is called* ***nilpotent.*** The same term is applied to a matrix. Thus in Equation (9), T_i is *nilpotent* because its n_i-th power equals the $n_i \times n_i$ zero matrix. The linear transformation defined by $\boldsymbol{a} \mid \mathbf{R}_i$, that is, the restriction of $\boldsymbol{a}$ to $\mathbf{R}_i$, is represented by A_i, and $(s_i\boldsymbol{i} - \boldsymbol{a}) \mid \mathbf{R}_i$ *is a nilpotent linear transformation of* $\mathbf{R}_i$ because it is represented by $-T_i$. ($\boldsymbol{i}$ is the identity linear transformation on whatever space is required by the context. We shall use the symbol $\boldsymbol{o}$ and the symbols I and O in this same way when the dimension is obvious.)

EXAMPLE 1. Suppose there exists a positive integer k for which $\boldsymbol{b}^k = \boldsymbol{o}$, but $\boldsymbol{b}^{k-1} \neq \boldsymbol{o}$ $(k > 0)$. The integer k is called the ***index*** (*of nilpotency*) of $\boldsymbol{b}$, and we say that $\boldsymbol{b}$ is nilpotent of index k. The same terms are applied to a matrix. Then there exists a vector $\mathbf{v}$, $\mathbf{v} \neq \mathbf{o}$, such that $\boldsymbol{b}^{k-1}\mathbf{v} \neq \mathbf{o}$. Consider the set $\{\boldsymbol{b}^{k-1}\mathbf{v}, \boldsymbol{b}^{k-2}\mathbf{v}, \ldots, \mathbf{v}\}$. If

$$\sum_{0}^{k-1} c_i \boldsymbol{b}^i \mathbf{v} = \mathbf{o}$$

is a linear dependence, then there is a j such that

$$c_0 = \cdots = c_{j-1} = 0 \quad \text{but} \quad c_j \neq 0.$$

This implies

$$\boldsymbol{b}^{k-j-1} \sum c_i \boldsymbol{b}^i \mathbf{v} = c_j \boldsymbol{b}^{k-1} \mathbf{v} = \mathbf{o},$$

which is a contradiction. Hence the set is linearly independent. If we use it *in the given order* as a coordinate basis for the invariant subspace $\mathbf{V}_0 = [\boldsymbol{b}^{k-1}\mathbf{v}, \boldsymbol{b}^{k-2}\mathbf{v}, \ldots, \mathbf{v}]$, then the restriction, $\boldsymbol{b} \mid \mathbf{V}_0$, of $\boldsymbol{b}$ to $\mathbf{V}_0$, is represented by the $k \times k$ nilpotent matrix

$$\begin{pmatrix} 0 & 1 & & & \\ & 0 & 1 & & \\ & & \ddots & \ddots & \\ & & & 0 & 1 \\ & & & & 0 \end{pmatrix} \tag{10}$$

which has zeros everywhere except for a super-diagonal stripe of 1's, and has index k.

EXAMPLE 2. If $\boldsymbol{b}$ is nilpotent of index k, as in Example 1, then $s\boldsymbol{i} + \boldsymbol{b}$ is invertible for any non-zero scalar s. We can see directly from the factorization of $s^k\boldsymbol{i} - (-\boldsymbol{b})^k$, that

$$s^k\boldsymbol{i} = (s\boldsymbol{i} + \boldsymbol{b})(s^{k-1}\boldsymbol{i} - s^{k-2}\boldsymbol{b} + \cdots + (-1)^{k-1}\boldsymbol{b}^{k-1}),$$

where $1/s^k$ times the second factor is, therefore, the inverse of the first.

EXAMPLE 3. With $\mathbf{V}$ and $\boldsymbol{a}$ as in Theorem 4, let s_k be a characteristic number and

$$\mathbf{W} = \{\mathbf{v} \mid (s_k\boldsymbol{i} - \boldsymbol{a})^t\mathbf{v} = \mathbf{o} \quad \text{for some} \quad t \geq 0\}.$$

By Equation (6), $\mathbf{W}$ contains $\mathbf{R}_k$. By the Corollary of Theorem 4, we also see that

$$\text{rank}(s_k\boldsymbol{i} - \boldsymbol{a})^{n_k} = \text{rank}\,(s_k\boldsymbol{i} - \boldsymbol{a})^t, \quad \text{when} \quad t \geq n_k.$$

Hence,

$$\mathbf{W} = \mathbf{R}_k.$$

The condition on $\mathbf{V}$ at the beginning of the statement of the Corollary is equivalent to that at the beginning of Theorem 4. We shall often abbreviate it to the less precise version: The scalar field contains the roots of the characteristic equation. The problems of Sections 7.3–7.5 should be worked in such a field.

PROBLEMS

1. A linear transformation on a 3-dimensional $\mathbf{V}$ is specified on a basis $\{\mathbf{u}, \mathbf{v}, \mathbf{w}\}$ by $\boldsymbol{a}\mathbf{u} = \mathbf{u}$, $\boldsymbol{a}\mathbf{v} = 2\mathbf{u} + \mathbf{v} - \mathbf{w}$, $\boldsymbol{a}\mathbf{w} = 2\mathbf{w}$. Find its root spaces and its representation in the form of Equation (8).
2. If $\boldsymbol{b}$ is a nilpotent linear transformation of index $k > 0$, show that its rank is at least $k - 1$. If $k = \dim \mathbf{V}$, show that $\boldsymbol{b}$ has only one linearly independent characteristic vector.
3. If for a linear transformation $\boldsymbol{a}$ it is true that rank $\boldsymbol{a}^t$ = rank $\boldsymbol{a}^{t+1}$, then show that rank $\boldsymbol{a}^{t+k}$ = rank $\boldsymbol{a}^t$ for all $k \geq 0$.
4. Let $\boldsymbol{a}$ be a linear transformation of vector space $\mathbf{V}$. Define an invariant subspace $\mathbf{V}_1 = \{\mathbf{v} \mid \boldsymbol{a}^j\mathbf{v} = \mathbf{o} \text{ for some } j \geq 0\}$. Show that $\mathbf{V}$ is a direct sum $\mathbf{V}_1 \dotplus \mathbf{V}_2$ of invariant subspaces such that $\boldsymbol{a} \mid \mathbf{V}_1$ is nilpotent and $\boldsymbol{a} \mid \mathbf{V}_2$ is invertible.
5. Let $\boldsymbol{a}$ be a linear transformation of a complex vector space, and let $s_1, \ldots, s_t$ be its distinct characteristic numbers. Use Theorem 4 to show the existence of t linear transformations $\{\boldsymbol{e}_1, \ldots, \boldsymbol{e}_t\}$ such that:
$$\boldsymbol{e}_1 + \cdots + \boldsymbol{e}_t = \boldsymbol{i}, \quad \boldsymbol{e}_i\boldsymbol{a} = \boldsymbol{a}\boldsymbol{e}_i, \quad \boldsymbol{e}_i^2 = \boldsymbol{e}_i, \quad \boldsymbol{e}_i\boldsymbol{e}_j = \boldsymbol{o} \quad \text{if} \quad i \neq j,$$
and rank $\boldsymbol{e}_i = n_i$ = multiplicity of s_i.
6. Let $\mathbf{V}_0$ be an invariant subspace of a vector space to which Theorem 4 applies. If any vector $\mathbf{v}$ is expressed as $\mathbf{v} = \sum \mathbf{v}_j$, $\mathbf{v}_j$ in $\mathbf{R}_j$, and if we set
$$\boldsymbol{a}'_i = \prod_{j \neq i} (s_j\boldsymbol{i} - \boldsymbol{a})^{n_i},$$
show that $\boldsymbol{a}'_i\mathbf{v} = \boldsymbol{a}'_i\mathbf{v}_i$, and that $\mathbf{V}_0$ is a direct sum of invariant subspaces of the root spaces $\{\mathbf{R}_i\}$.

7.4 JORDAN MATRIX

The decomposition of a vector space $\mathbf{V}$, with respect to a linear transformation $\boldsymbol{a}$ of $\mathbf{V}$, into the root spaces described in Section 7.3 yields, for each invariant direct summand $\mathbf{R}_i$, an induced linear transformation $\boldsymbol{a}_i = \boldsymbol{a} \mid \mathbf{R}_i$, and a corresponding induced nilpotent linear transformation $\boldsymbol{b}_i = \boldsymbol{a}_i - s_i\boldsymbol{i}$ of $\mathbf{R}_i$ with index at most n_i ($\boldsymbol{i} = \boldsymbol{i} \mid \mathbf{R}_i$). These facts can be used to further simplify the upper triangular matrix representation A_i of $\boldsymbol{a}_i$ by choosing a coordinate basis adapted to a decomposition of $\mathbf{R}_i$ *with respect to* the nilpotent linear transformation $\boldsymbol{b}_i$ into certain invariant subspaces described below. We shall use the fact that $\boldsymbol{a}_i$ and $\boldsymbol{b}_i$ have the *same invariant subspaces.* Since the characteristic polynomial of a nilpotent linear transformation of $\mathbf{V}$ is $x^n = 0$, the roots of its characteristic equation are certainly in the field of scalars of $\mathbf{V}$. Hence the following theorem holds for any vector space. Here, we shall use the notation $\supset$ to mean "contains"; thus, $\mathbf{V} \supset \mathbf{V}_1$ *means that every vector in* $\mathbf{V}_1$ *is also in* $\mathbf{V}$, that is, $\mathbf{V}_1$ is a subset.

Theorem 5. Let $\boldsymbol{b}$ be a nilpotent linear transformation of index k of a vector space $\mathbf{V}$. For each integer i, $0 \leq i \leq k$, define a subspace $\mathbf{V}_i$ of $\mathbf{V}$ by

$$\mathbf{V}_i = \{\mathbf{u} \mid \boldsymbol{b}^{k-i}\mathbf{u} = \mathbf{o}\}.$$

Then:

(a) $\mathbf{V} = \mathbf{V}_0 \supset \mathbf{V}_1 \supset \cdots \supset \mathbf{V}_k = \{\mathbf{o}\}$, each $\mathbf{V}_i$ is an invariant subspace of $\mathbf{V}$, and $\mathbf{V}_{i-1} \neq \mathbf{V}_i \quad (i = 1, \ldots, k)$.

(b) If $\{\mathbf{v}_1, \ldots, \mathbf{v}_r\}$ is a subset of $\mathbf{V}_i$ such that $\{\bar{\mathbf{v}}_1, \ldots, \bar{\mathbf{v}}_r\}$ is a linearly independent subset of $\mathbf{V}_i/\mathbf{V}_{i+1}$, then $\{\overline{\boldsymbol{b}\mathbf{v}}_1, \ldots, \overline{\boldsymbol{b}\mathbf{v}}_r\}$ is a linearly independent subset of $\mathbf{V}_{i+1}/\mathbf{V}_{i+2} \quad (i = 0, \ldots, k-2)$.

Proof: (a) Since $\boldsymbol{b}^{k-1} \neq \boldsymbol{o}$, there exists a non-zero vector $\mathbf{v}$ such that $\boldsymbol{b}^{k-1}\mathbf{v} \neq \mathbf{o}$. Hence $\boldsymbol{b}^{i-1}\mathbf{v} \neq \mathbf{o}$ for $i = 1, \ldots, k$. If $\boldsymbol{b}^{i-1}\mathbf{v}$ is in $\mathbf{V}_i$, then

$$\mathbf{o} = \boldsymbol{b}^{k-i}(\boldsymbol{b}^{i-1}\mathbf{v}) = \boldsymbol{b}^{k-1}\mathbf{v},$$

a contradiction. So $\boldsymbol{b}^{i-1}\mathbf{v}$ is not in $\mathbf{V}_i$. But $\boldsymbol{b}^{i-1}\mathbf{v}$ is in $\mathbf{V}_{i-1}$ because

$$\boldsymbol{b}^{k-(i-1)}\boldsymbol{b}^{i-1}\mathbf{v} = \boldsymbol{b}^k\mathbf{v} = \mathbf{o}.$$

Hence $\mathbf{V}_{i-1} \neq \mathbf{V}_i$.

(b) Let $\{\bar{\mathbf{v}}_1, \ldots, \bar{\mathbf{v}}_r\}$ be a linearly independent subset of $\mathbf{V}_i/\mathbf{V}_{i+1}$. Then $\{\mathbf{v}_1, \ldots, \mathbf{v}_r\}$ is linearly independent in $\mathbf{V}_i$. Suppose $\sum c_i\overline{\boldsymbol{b}\mathbf{v}}_i = \bar{\mathbf{o}}$ is a linear dependence on the subset $\{\overline{\boldsymbol{b}\mathbf{v}}_1, \ldots, \overline{\boldsymbol{b}\mathbf{v}}_r\}$ of $\mathbf{V}_{i+1}/\mathbf{V}_{i+2}$. Then $\boldsymbol{b}(\sum c_i\mathbf{v}_i)$ is an element of $\mathbf{V}_{i+2}$ and $\sum c_i\mathbf{v}_i$ is a non-zero vector which is in $\mathbf{V}_i$ but not in $\mathbf{V}_{i+1}$. Hence

$$\mathbf{o} = \boldsymbol{b}^{k-(i+2)}\boldsymbol{b}(\textstyle\sum c_i\mathbf{v}_i) = \boldsymbol{b}^{k-(i+1)}(\textstyle\sum c_i\mathbf{v}_i) \neq \mathbf{o},$$

which is a contradiction. Therefore $\{\overline{\boldsymbol{b}\mathbf{v}}_1, \ldots, \overline{\boldsymbol{b}\mathbf{v}}_r\}$ is a linearly independent subset of $\mathbf{V}_{i+1}/\mathbf{V}_{i+2}$. q.e.d.

We now select a special basis of the vector space $\mathbf{V}$ of Theorem 5 by choosing bases of the factor spaces $\mathbf{V}_0/\mathbf{V}_1, \ldots, \mathbf{V}_{k-1}/\mathbf{V}_k$, in turn as follows:

In $\mathbf{V}_0/\mathbf{V}_1$ take any basis $\{\bar{\mathbf{v}}_{11}, \ldots, \bar{\mathbf{v}}_{1p_1}\}$ and set $\mathbf{W}_1 = [\mathbf{v}_{11}, \ldots, \mathbf{v}_{1p_1}]$.
In $\mathbf{V}_1/\mathbf{V}_2$ take $\{\overline{b\mathbf{v}}_{11}, \ldots, \overline{b\mathbf{v}}_{1p_1}; \bar{\mathbf{v}}_{21}, \ldots, \bar{\mathbf{v}}_{2p_2}\}$ as a basis and set $\mathbf{W}_2 = [\mathbf{v}_{21}, \ldots, \mathbf{v}_{2p_2}]$.

$\vdots$

In $\mathbf{V}_{k-1}/\mathbf{V}_k$ take $\{\overline{b^{k-1}\mathbf{v}}_{11}, \ldots, \overline{b^{k-1}\mathbf{v}}_{1p_1}; \overline{b^{k-2}\mathbf{v}}_{21}, \ldots, \overline{b^{k-2}\mathbf{v}}_{2p_2}; \ldots; \bar{\mathbf{v}}_{k1}, \ldots, \bar{\mathbf{v}}_{kp_k}\}$ as a basis and set $\mathbf{W}_k = [\mathbf{v}_{k1}, \ldots, \mathbf{v}_{kp_k}]$.

Thus, at each step, by supplementing when necessary the basis transmitted from the previous step, we create a collection of subspaces $\mathbf{W}_1, \ldots, \mathbf{W}_k$ *of* $\mathbf{V}$ (some of which may be $\{\mathbf{o}\}$) such that

$$\begin{aligned} \mathbf{V} = \mathbf{W}_1 \dotplus (b\mathbf{W}_1 \dotplus \mathbf{W}_2) \dotplus (b^2\mathbf{W}_1 \dotplus b\mathbf{W}_2 \dotplus \mathbf{W}_3) \dotplus \cdots \\ \dotplus (b^{k-1}\mathbf{W}_1 \dotplus \cdots \dotplus \mathbf{W}_k), \\ \mathbf{W}_i = [\mathbf{v}_{i1}, \ldots, \mathbf{v}_{ip_i}] \quad (i = 1, \ldots, k). \end{aligned} \tag{11}$$

Although $p_1 > 0$ if $\mathbf{V} \neq \{\mathbf{o}\}$, *some or all of the other* p_i*'s may be zero.*

EXAMPLE 1. Let b be a nilpotent linear transformation of index 3 and rank 3 of a 5-dimensional vector space $\mathbf{V}$. Hence, $\mathbf{V}_2 = \{\mathbf{u} \mid b\mathbf{u} = \mathbf{o}\}$ and $\dim \mathbf{V}_2 = 2$. If $\dim \mathbf{V}_1/\mathbf{V}_2 = 1$, then $\dim \mathbf{V}_0/\mathbf{V}_1 = 1$, which contradicts $\dim \mathbf{V} = 5$. Therefore, $\dim \mathbf{V}_1/\mathbf{V}_2 = 2$ and $\dim \mathbf{V}_0/\mathbf{V}_1 = 1$. So we have

$$\mathbf{V}_0/\mathbf{V}_1 = [\bar{\mathbf{v}}_{11}], \quad \mathbf{V}_1/\mathbf{V}_2 = [\overline{b\mathbf{v}}_{11}, \bar{\mathbf{v}}_{21}], \quad \mathbf{V}_2/\mathbf{V}_3 = [\overline{b^2\mathbf{v}}_{11}, \overline{b\mathbf{v}}_{21}],$$
$$p_1 = 1, \quad p_2 = 1, \quad p_3 = 0.$$

If $\mathbf{v}_{ij} \neq \mathbf{o}$, where $\mathbf{v}_{ij}$ is one of the vectors in the above construction, then the subspace $\mathbf{W}_{ij}$ defined by

$$\mathbf{W}_{ij} = [b^{k-i}\mathbf{v}_{ij}, \; b^{k-i-1}\mathbf{v}_{ij}, \ldots, \mathbf{v}_{ij}] \tag{12}$$

is invariant (because $b^{k-i+1}\mathbf{v}_{ij} = \mathbf{o}$), and $\dim \mathbf{W}_{ij} = k - i + 1$. We can use this basis *in the given order* as a coordinate basis for $\mathbf{W}_{ij}$. Then $b \mid \mathbf{W}_{ij}$ is represented by a $(k - i + 1) \times (k - i + 1)$ nilpotent matrix, of index $k - i + 1$,

$$b \mid \mathbf{W}_{ij} \leftrightarrow N_{ij} = \begin{pmatrix} 0 & 1 & & & \\ & 0 & 1 & & \\ & & \ddots & \ddots & \\ & & & 0 & 1 \\ & & & & 0 \end{pmatrix}, \tag{13}$$

where the only non-zero entries are the 1's indicated on the first super-diagonal. Since $\mathbf{V}$ is a direct sum of such invariant subspaces, we can represent b by a diagonal-block matrix,

$$b \leftrightarrow \operatorname{diag}(\ldots, N_{ij}, \ldots) \quad (i = 1, \ldots, k; \; j = 1, \ldots, p_i). \tag{14}$$

The number of N_{ij}*'s actually present for a fixed i is therefore* p_i, hence a total of

$\sum_{i=1}^{k} p_i$ blocks altogether. *The number of rows* in N_{1j} *equals* k, hence equals the index of $\boldsymbol{b}$. Finally, $\dim \mathbf{V} = \sum_{i=1}^{k} (k - i + 1)p_i$.

EXAMPLE 2. In Example 1, $\mathbf{W}_{11} = [\boldsymbol{b}^2\mathbf{v}_{11}, \boldsymbol{b}\mathbf{v}_{11}, \mathbf{v}_{11}]$ and $\mathbf{W}_{21} = [\boldsymbol{b}\mathbf{v}_{21}, \mathbf{v}_{21}]$ are the only subspaces of the type in Equation (12). Hence,

$$\boldsymbol{b} \leftrightarrow \text{diag}(N_{11}, N_{21}),$$

where

$$N_{11} = \begin{pmatrix} 0 & 1 & 0 \\ 0 & 0 & 1 \\ 0 & 0 & 0 \end{pmatrix} \quad \text{and} \quad N_{21} = \begin{pmatrix} 0 & 1 \\ 0 & 0 \end{pmatrix}.$$

We can apply these facts to the nilpotent linear transformation $\boldsymbol{b}_i = \boldsymbol{a}_i - s_i\boldsymbol{i}$ of $\mathbf{R}_i$, $i = 1, \ldots, t$, where $\boldsymbol{a}_i = \boldsymbol{a} \mid \mathbf{R}_i$ and $\mathbf{R}_i$ is the i-th root space of Section 7.3. Denote the index of $\boldsymbol{b}_i$ by k_i. *The decomposition in Equation* (11) *is applicable to* $\mathbf{R}_i$ *in place of* $\mathbf{V}$. Each $\mathbf{R}_i$ gives rise to a set of invariant subspaces which we distinguish by the notation

$$\mathbf{W}_{mn}(s_i) \quad (i = 1, \ldots, t;\ m = 1, \ldots, k_i;\ n = 1, \ldots, p_{im}).$$

We see that $k_i \leq n_i$, that is, $\boldsymbol{b}_i$ is a nilpotent linear transformation of index at most n_i. If we represent $\boldsymbol{b}_i$ in the same way as $\boldsymbol{b}$ in (14) above, then $\boldsymbol{a}_i = s_i\boldsymbol{i} + \boldsymbol{b}_i$ will be represented, with respect to this kind of coordinate basis of $\mathbf{R}_i$, by

$$\text{diag}(\ldots, s_iI + N_{mn}(s_i), \ldots).$$

The typical diagonal block that occurs here is called a ***Jordan Block.*** More explicitly, we have for each allowable pair i, m, a collection of p_{im} blocks of type

$$\boldsymbol{a} \mid \mathbf{W}_{mn}(s_i) \leftrightarrow s_iI + N_{mn}(s_i) = \begin{pmatrix} s_i & 1 & & & & \\ & s_i & 1 & & & \\ & & \cdot & & & \\ & & & \cdot & & \\ & & & & \cdot & 1 \\ & & & & & s_i \end{pmatrix} = \text{a Jordan Block with } k_i - m + 1 \text{ rows.} \tag{15}$$

Here s_i is one of the distinct characteristic numbers of $\boldsymbol{a}$, and $N_{mn}(s_i)$ is a matrix of the type in Equation (13). Finally, $\dim \mathbf{R}_i = \sum_{m=1}^{k_i} (k_i - m + 1)p_{im}$.

If we choose the basis of each root space $\mathbf{R}_i$ in this way, then instead of $\text{diag}(A_1, \ldots, A_t)$ as given in Section 7.3, Equations (8) and (9), we get a diagonal-block matrix with Jordan Blocks on the diagonal:

$$\boldsymbol{a} \leftrightarrow \text{diag}(\ldots, s_iI + N_{mn}(s_i), \ldots). \tag{16}$$

This representation of $\boldsymbol{a}$, or any one of the similar matrices resulting from any permutation of the Jordan Blocks in this representation, is called a *Jordan Matrix Representation* of $\boldsymbol{a}$. Suppose the distinct characteristic numbers of $\boldsymbol{a}$ are labeled $s_1, \ldots, s_t$. Now, if the Jordan Blocks corresponding to s_1 are listed on the diagonal *in order of decreasing size* before the Jordan Blocks corresponding to s_2, and so forth, then the Jordan Matrix is called a *Jordan Canonical Matrix.* Every representation of $\boldsymbol{a}$ is similar to a unique (Theorem 6 below) Jordan Canonical Matrix; or, putting it another way, among all linear transformations similar to $\boldsymbol{a}$, exactly one is represented (with respect to a fixed basis) by a Jordan Canonical Matrix. This assumes that the scalar field of $\mathbf{V}$ contains all the roots of the characteristic equation of $\boldsymbol{a}$, and that these roots have preassigned labels.

EXAMPLE 3. The simplest Jordan Block is a 1×1 matrix; the next simplest is the type in Section 2.18, Case (b′), and Section 3.7. In n-dimensional space, a nilpotent linear transformation $\boldsymbol{b}$ of index n must have a representation by an $n \times n$ matrix of the type in Equation (13), because N_{11} has the number of its rows equal to the index of $\boldsymbol{b}$. As an illustration, suppose $n = 3$ and define a nilpotent linear transformation $\boldsymbol{b}$ of a 3-tuple vector space by $\boldsymbol{b}(x, y, z) = (y, z, 0)$. Then

$$\mathbf{V}_1 = [(x, y, 0)], \quad \mathbf{V}_2 = [(x, 0, 0)], \quad \mathbf{V} = \mathbf{V}_0 \supset \mathbf{V}_1 \supset \mathbf{V}_2 \supset \mathbf{V}_3 = \{\mathbf{o}\},$$
$$\mathbf{v}_{11} = (0, 0, 1), \quad \boldsymbol{b}\mathbf{v}_{11} = (0, 1, 0), \quad \boldsymbol{b}^2\mathbf{v}_{11} = (1, 0, 0).$$

So there exists only one $\mathbf{W}_{ij}$, namely, $\mathbf{W}_{11} = [\boldsymbol{b}^2\mathbf{v}_{11}, \boldsymbol{b}\mathbf{v}_{11}, \mathbf{v}_{11}]$. Therefore, $\boldsymbol{b}$, and in general, $s\boldsymbol{i} + \boldsymbol{b}$ are represented, respectively by

$$\begin{pmatrix} 0 & 1 & 0 \\ 0 & 0 & 1 \\ 0 & 0 & 0 \end{pmatrix} \quad \text{and} \quad \begin{pmatrix} s & 1 & 0 \\ 0 & s & 1 \\ 0 & 0 & s \end{pmatrix}.$$

Theorem 6. The representation of a nilpotent linear transformation $\boldsymbol{b}$ by a diagonal-block matrix of the type,

$$\boldsymbol{b} \leftrightarrow M = \operatorname{diag}(M_1, \ldots, M_s),$$

such that each M_f is a nilpotent $t_f \times t_f$ matrix of the type in Equation (13) and $t_f \geq t_{f+1}$, is uniquely determined by $\boldsymbol{b}$.

Proof: Suppose $M' = \operatorname{diag}(M'_1, \ldots, M'_{s'})$ is another such representation, so each M'_f is a nilpotent $t'_f \times t'_f$ matrix of the type in Equation (13). Then $t_1 = t'_1 = k$, where k is the index of $\boldsymbol{b}$. Let l be the first subscript such that $t_l \neq t'_l$, and suppose that $t_l < t'_l$. Hence, $t_{l-1} > t_l$. Set $p = t_l$. Comparing M^p with M'^p, we find that $M_f^p = M_f'^p \neq O$ for $f = 1, \ldots, l-1$, and $M_l'^p \neq O$. But $M_f^p = 0$ for $f = l, \ldots, s$. Hence

$$\operatorname{rank} M'^p - \operatorname{rank} M^p \geq \operatorname{rank} M_l'^p > 0.$$

However, M^p and M'^p both represent $\boldsymbol{b}^p$, hence they must have the same rank.

This contradiction implies $t_l = t'_l$. So $t_f = t'_f$ for values of f up to the smaller of the integers s and s'. Since M and M' are matrices of same size, $s = s'$. q.e.d.

Corollary. The representation of a linear transformation $\boldsymbol{a}$ by a Jordan Matrix is unique except for the order in which the diagonal blocks occur.

Proof: Given two representations A and A' of $\boldsymbol{a}$ by Jordan Matrices, we can derive from A and A', by permutations of the Jordan Blocks, two Jordan Matrices B and B', B similar to A and B' similar to A', in which Jordan Blocks with the same characteristic numbers are contiguous. In each of the two representations B and B', the sequence of Jordan Blocks with the same characteristic number s_i defines an $n_i \times n_i$ submatrix which represents $\boldsymbol{a}_i$ on the root space $\mathbf{R}_i$. Hence we have two diagonal-block representations of the nilpotent linear transformation $\boldsymbol{b}_i = \boldsymbol{a}_i - s_i\boldsymbol{i}$ on $\mathbf{R}_i$, say

$$\operatorname{diag}(N_{11}(s_i), \ldots) \leftrightarrow \boldsymbol{b}_i \leftrightarrow \operatorname{diag}(N'_{11}(s_i), \ldots).$$

By Theorem 6, these are identical except for order of the blocks along the diagonal. q.e.d.

EXAMPLE 4. Two linear transformations $\boldsymbol{a}$ and $\boldsymbol{b}$ are similar if and only if

$$\operatorname{rank}(s\boldsymbol{i} - \boldsymbol{a})^j = \operatorname{rank}(s\boldsymbol{i} - \boldsymbol{b})^j$$

for every scalar s and every $j > 0$. Actually, one need check for characteristic numbers only, and j need range only as far as the multiplicity of the characteristic number. For, suppose $\boldsymbol{a}$ and $\boldsymbol{b}$ are similar, say $\boldsymbol{b} = \boldsymbol{p}^{-1}\boldsymbol{a}\boldsymbol{p}$. Then

$$(s\boldsymbol{i} - \boldsymbol{b})^j = \boldsymbol{p}^{-1}(s\boldsymbol{i} - \boldsymbol{a})^j\boldsymbol{p}.$$

Since similar linear transformations are certainly equivalent, we have that for every $j \geq 0$,

$$\operatorname{rank}(s\boldsymbol{i} - \boldsymbol{a})^j = \operatorname{rank}(s\boldsymbol{i} - \boldsymbol{b})^j.$$

(The same applies to any two representing matrices.) On the other hand, assumption of the equality of these ranks for every s and j implies that $\boldsymbol{a}$ and $\boldsymbol{b}$ have the same distinct characteristic numbers, for only when s equals a characteristic number does the rank of $s\boldsymbol{i} - \boldsymbol{a}$ (and $s\boldsymbol{i} - \boldsymbol{b}$) drop from full. Consider Jordan Matrices for $\boldsymbol{a}$ and $\boldsymbol{b}$, using the notation $N_{mn}(s_i)$ in reference to $\boldsymbol{a}$ and $N'_{mn}(s_i)$ in reference to $\boldsymbol{b}$. Then

$$\operatorname{rank}(s_i\boldsymbol{i} - \boldsymbol{a})^j = \operatorname{rank}(s_i\boldsymbol{i} - \boldsymbol{b})^j$$

implies

$$\operatorname{rank}\ \operatorname{diag}(\ldots, N_{mn}(s_i)^j, \ldots) = \operatorname{rank}\ \operatorname{diag}(\ldots, N'_{mn}(s_i)^j, \ldots),$$

where we indicate only the nilpotent blocks; the others are invertible. Since this is true for every i and j, one can show that these nilpotent blocks are the same except for order, hence $\boldsymbol{a}$ and $\boldsymbol{b}$ are similar.

PROBLEMS

1. Show that a Jordan Block has only one linearly independent characteristic column vector.
2. Show that a Jordan Block is not similar to a diagonal matrix unless it is 1×1.
3. Show that $\boldsymbol{a}^2$ need not have the same number of Jordan Blocks as $\boldsymbol{a}$ in the Jordan Matrix.
4. Show that a linear transformation $\boldsymbol{a}$ has a diagonal representation if and only if

$$\text{rank}(s_i\boldsymbol{i} - \boldsymbol{a}) = \text{rank}(s_i\boldsymbol{i} - \boldsymbol{a})^2$$

for every characteristic number s_i.

5. Classify the possible kinds of 2×2 and 3×3 Jordan Canonical Matrices in terms of distinct characteristic numbers and their multiplicities.

7.5 PROPERTIES OF THE JORDAN BLOCK

The typical Jordan Block is of the form

$$J = sI + N,$$

where s is the characteristic number of J and N has non-zero entries only on the first super-diagonal stripe, whereon it has 1's. Let us consider a few more properties of J.

EXAMPLE 1. By reversing the order of the coordinate basis chosen for the invariant subspace $\mathbf{W}_{ij}$ of Section 7.4, Equation (12), we find that the Jordan Block $J = sI + N_{ij}$ which represents $s\boldsymbol{i} + \boldsymbol{b} \mid \mathbf{W}_{ij}$ is similar to its transpose, J^t. This applies to any Jordan Matrix. Hence, any square matrix is similar to its transpose (see Section 7.13, Problem 7).

EXAMPLE 2. If $p(x) = \sum b_i x^i$, then the polynomial $p(J)$ can be expanded by using a "binomial theorem" on each term $b_i(sI + N)^i$. The result is that

$$p(J) = p(s)I + p'(s)N + (1/2!)p''(s)N^2 + \cdots,$$

where the primes indicate derivatives and the sum terminates because N is nilpotent. If J is $n \times n$, then J has a characteristic polynomial $(x - s)^n$. Indeed, setting $p(x) = (x - s)^n$, we can check in the above expansion that $p(J) = O$, as it should be.

EXAMPLE 3. Consider a k-dimensional vector space $\mathbf{V}$ on which $\boldsymbol{a} = s\boldsymbol{i} + \boldsymbol{b}$ is a linear transformation represented by a $k \times k$ Jordan Block J. Then $p_1 = 1, p_2 = \cdots = 0$, and $\mathbf{V} = \mathbf{W}_{11}$ (Equation (12)). Set $\mathbf{v} = \mathbf{v}_{11}$ and define the following subspaces of $\mathbf{W}_{11}$:

$$\mathbf{V}_i = [\boldsymbol{b}^{k-1}\mathbf{v}, \ldots, \boldsymbol{b}^{i+1}\mathbf{v}, \boldsymbol{b}^i\mathbf{v}] \quad (i = 0, 1, \ldots, k - 1).$$

Let us use the symbol $\subset$ to mean "contained in." We have already used the symbol $\supset$ to mean "contains." A vertical stroke through either symbol means its denial. Then $\mathbf{V}_i$ is an invariant subspace with respect to $\boldsymbol{a}$ and with respect to $\boldsymbol{b} = \boldsymbol{a} - s\boldsymbol{i}$, and

$$\mathbf{V} = \mathbf{V}_0 \supset \mathbf{V}_1 \supset \cdots \supset \mathbf{V}_{k-1} \supset \mathbf{V}_k = \{\mathbf{o}\}.$$

Now, let $\mathbf{W}$ be any *invariant subspace* of $\mathbf{V}$, other than $\mathbf{V}$ and $\{\mathbf{o}\}$. Choose i such that $\mathbf{V}_i \subset \mathbf{W}$, but $\mathbf{V}_{i-1} \not\subset \mathbf{W}$ (that is, $\mathbf{V}_i$ is a subset of $\mathbf{W}$, but $\mathbf{V}_{i-1}$ is not). If $\mathbf{W} \neq \mathbf{V}_i$, then let $\mathbf{w}$ be a vector in $\mathbf{W}$, but not in $\mathbf{V}_i$. We can write

$$\mathbf{w} = (c_j \boldsymbol{b}^j + c_{j+1} \boldsymbol{b}^{j+1} + \cdots)\mathbf{v}, \quad \text{for some} \quad c_j \neq 0.$$

If $j < i$, then

$$\boldsymbol{b}^{i-j-1}\mathbf{w} = (c_j \boldsymbol{b}^{i-1} + c_{j+1}\boldsymbol{b}^i + \cdots)\mathbf{v}$$

implies $\boldsymbol{b}^{i-1}\mathbf{v}$ is in $\mathbf{W}$. But

$$\left[\overline{\boldsymbol{b}^{i-1}\mathbf{v}}\right] = \mathbf{V}_{i-1}/\mathbf{V}_i,$$

hence $\mathbf{V}_{i-1} \subset \mathbf{W}$, contrary to assumption. Therefore, $j \geq i$ and $\mathbf{w}$ is in $\mathbf{V}_i$. Since $\mathbf{w}$ was any choice of a vector in $\mathbf{W}$ not in $\mathbf{V}_i$, we have $\mathbf{W} = \mathbf{V}_i$. The conclusion is that *the* $\mathbf{V}_i$*'s are the only invariant subspaces in* $\mathbf{V}$. Also, $\mathbf{V}$ *is indecomposable with respect to* $\boldsymbol{a}$, that is, $\mathbf{V} \neq \mathbf{W} \dotplus \mathbf{W}'$ with $\mathbf{W}$ and $\mathbf{W}'$ non-zero invariant subspaces. For if it were, then $\mathbf{W} = \mathbf{V}_i$ and $\mathbf{W}' = \mathbf{V}_j$ for some i and j. This is impossible since either $\mathbf{V}_i \subset \mathbf{V}_j$ or $\mathbf{V}_j \subset \mathbf{V}_i$.

PROBLEMS

1. If $c \neq 0$, find P such that

$$P^{-1}\begin{pmatrix} 1 & c \\ 0 & 1 \end{pmatrix} P = \begin{pmatrix} 1 & 1 \\ 0 & 1 \end{pmatrix},$$

and find Q such that

$$Q^{-1}\begin{pmatrix} 1 & c \\ 0 & 1 \end{pmatrix} Q = \begin{pmatrix} 1 & 0 \\ c & 1 \end{pmatrix}.$$

2. Let J be a Jordan Block $sI + N$. (a) Show that J is similar to $sI + cN$ for any *non-zero* scalar c. (b) Find an invertible matrix which transforms J into $sI + N^t$ (see Example 2). (c) Show that J is not similar to a diagonal-block matrix having more than one Jordan Block on its diagonal.

3. If J is a Jordan Block, show that $J^n = I$ for some $n > 0$, if and only if J is the 1×1 identity matrix.

4. If $\boldsymbol{a}^2 = \boldsymbol{i}$, show that $\boldsymbol{a}$ can be represented by a diagonal matrix. Discuss the case $\boldsymbol{a}^n = \boldsymbol{i}$.

5. Let $J_1, \ldots, J_t$ be Jordan Blocks of the same size, but *not similar*. (a) Show that $J_iB = BJ_j$ implies $B = O$ if $i \neq j$. (b) Find the structure of B if $J_iB = BJ_i$.

6. If $J_1, \ldots, J_t$ are Jordan Blocks with *different* characteristic numbers, and if $J_1', \ldots, J_t'$ is a permutation of these blocks, discuss the structure of an invertible P such that

$$P\,\mathrm{diag}(J_1', \ldots, J_t') = \mathrm{diag}(J_1, \ldots, J_t)P.$$

7. If A is a real matrix, show that its conjugate pairs of imaginary characteristic numbers correspond to conjugate pairs of Jordan Blocks in a Jordan Canonical Representation.

8. If $A = \begin{pmatrix} a & b \\ -b & a \end{pmatrix}$, where a and b are real, $b \neq 0$, find invertible matrices P and Q such that

$$P^{-1}AP = \mathrm{diag}(s, \bar{s}) \quad \text{and} \quad Q^{-1}\,\mathrm{diag}(s, \bar{s})Q = \begin{pmatrix} 0 & -s\bar{s} \\ 1 & s + \bar{s} \end{pmatrix}.$$

9. If A is the matrix of Problem 8, $S = \begin{pmatrix} s & 1 \\ 0 & s \end{pmatrix}$, and I the 2×2 identity matrix, show that

$$\begin{pmatrix} A & I \\ O & A \end{pmatrix} \quad \text{is similar to} \quad \mathrm{diag}(S, \bar{S}).$$

10. Suppose a linear transformation $\boldsymbol{a}$ of a $2k$-dimensional complex $\mathbf{V}$ is represented by

$$\mathrm{diag}(sI + N, \bar{s}I + N), \quad \text{where} \quad s = a + ib \quad (a \text{ and } b \text{ real, } b \neq 0).$$

Show that there exists a coordinate basis with respect to which $\boldsymbol{a}$ is represented by

$$\begin{pmatrix} A & I & & \\ & \ddots & \ddots & \\ & & \ddots & I \\ & & & A \end{pmatrix},$$

where A is the 2×2 matrix of Problem 8.

11. Show that if $\boldsymbol{a}$ is an invertible linear transformation, then $\boldsymbol{a}^{-1}$ has the same invariant subspaces as $\boldsymbol{a}$. Compare a Jordan Canonical Matrix of $\boldsymbol{a}^{-1}$ with that of $\boldsymbol{a}$.

7.6 CYCLIC SUBSPACES AND THE MINIMAL POLYNOMIAL OF A VECTOR

A subspace $\mathbf{W}$ *of a vector space* $\mathbf{V}$ *is called* **cyclic** *with respect to a linear transformation* $\boldsymbol{a}$ *of* $\mathbf{V}$ *if and only if there is a non-zero vector* $\mathbf{w}$ *in* $\mathbf{W}$ *such that*

$$\mathbf{W} = [\mathbf{w}, \boldsymbol{a}\mathbf{w}, \boldsymbol{a}^2\mathbf{w}, \boldsymbol{a}^3\mathbf{w}, \ldots].$$

It is convenient to denote such a space by $[\mathbf{w};\ \boldsymbol{a}]$. Hence we have

$$\mathbf{W} = [\mathbf{w};\ \boldsymbol{a}] = \{\mathbf{u} \mid \mathbf{u} = h(\boldsymbol{a})\mathbf{w},\ h(x) \text{ a polynomial with coefficients in the scalar field of } \mathbf{V}\}.$$

A cyclic subspace is clearly invariant. Also, because **V** is finite-dimensional, $[\mathbf{w};\ \boldsymbol{a}]$ is finite-dimensional. Hence, there is a smallest positive integer p for which

$$\boldsymbol{a}^p\mathbf{w} + \sum_1^p c_i\boldsymbol{a}^{p-i}\mathbf{w} = \mathbf{o}, \tag{17}$$

where the coefficients are in the scalar field of **V** (as will be assumed for the coefficients of all polynomials hereafter considered). We see that $p = \dim[\mathbf{w};\ \boldsymbol{a}]$.

EXAMPLE 1. The non-zero subspaces among the subspaces $\mathbf{W}_{ij} = [\mathbf{v}_{ij};\ \boldsymbol{b}]$ in Section 7.4, Equation (12), are cyclic with respect to the nilpotent linear transformation $\boldsymbol{b}$, and although they happen to be indecomposable (Section 7.5, Example 3), this is not usually so for a cyclic space. For instance, if $\boldsymbol{a}$ is a linear transformation of a 2-dimensional vector space for which there exist two linearly independent characteristic vectors $\mathbf{u}_1$, $\mathbf{u}_2$ with *unequal* characteristic numbers s_1, s_2, then **V** itself is cyclic and, at the same time, **V** is the direct sum of two cyclic subspaces. For if we set $\mathbf{v} = \mathbf{u}_1 + \mathbf{u}_2$, then $\mathbf{v} \neq \mathbf{o}$, $\boldsymbol{a}\mathbf{v} = s_1\mathbf{u}_1 + s_2\mathbf{u}_2$, and $\{\mathbf{v}, \boldsymbol{a}\mathbf{v}\}$ is a basis. But $\{\mathbf{u}_1, \mathbf{u}_2\}$ is also a basis. Therefore,

$$\mathbf{V} = [\mathbf{v};\ \boldsymbol{a}] = [\mathbf{u}_1] \dot{+} [\mathbf{u}_2].$$

($[\mathbf{u};\ \boldsymbol{a}] = [\mathbf{u}]$ if and only if **u** is a characteristic vector or **o**.)

If we set

$$\phi(x) = x^p + \sum_1^p c_i x^{p-i},$$

then the linear dependence of Equation (17) *for the non-zero vector* **w** can be expressed by

$$\phi(\boldsymbol{a})\mathbf{w} = \mathbf{o}.$$

Now, consider the set

$$\{g(x) \mid g(\boldsymbol{a})\mathbf{w} = \mathbf{o}\} \tag{18}$$

of polynomials $g(x)$ such that $g(\boldsymbol{a})$ "annihilates" **w**. In this set there are polynomials of least possible degree, *including the monic* $\phi(x)$. *We call* $\phi(x)$ *the* ***minimal polynomial*** *of* **w**, because by Theorem 7 below, $\phi(x)$ is the *only monic* of least degree in the set (18).

Since every non-zero vector **w** gives rise to a cyclic subspace $[\mathbf{w};\boldsymbol{a}]$, there is a minimal polynomial associated with **w** and its degree is a positive integer p, where $p = \dim[\mathbf{w};\ \boldsymbol{a}]$. (Recall that we have not assigned any degree to constant polynomials.)

Theorem 7. With respect to a linear transformation $\boldsymbol{a}$, the minimal polynomial $\phi(x)$ of a non-zero vector **w** divides every polynomial $g(x)$ which has the property $g(\boldsymbol{a})\mathbf{w} = \mathbf{o}$. $\phi(x)$ is the only monic in the set (18).

Proof: By the division algorithm for polynomials, Section 7.1, Problem 8, there exists a unique polynomial $q(x)$, and a unique polynomial $r(x)$ of degree less than that of $\phi(x)$, or equal to a constant, such that

$$g(x) = q(x)\phi(x) + r(x).$$

This implies

$$g(\boldsymbol{a}) = q(\boldsymbol{a})\phi(\boldsymbol{a}) + r(\boldsymbol{a}),$$

from which it follows that

$$\mathbf{o} = g(\boldsymbol{a})\mathbf{w} = r(\boldsymbol{a})\mathbf{w}.$$

If $r(x) \neq 0$, then we contradict the fact that $\phi(x)$ is the minimal polynomial of $\mathbf{w}$. Hence $g(x) = q(x)\phi(x)$. In particular, when the degree of $g(x)$ equals the degree of $\phi(x)$, then $q(x)$ is a constant that has to equal 1 if $g(x)$ is a monic. Therefore, if $g(x)$ is a monic of the same degree as $\phi(x)$, then $g(x) = \phi(x)$. q.e.d.

EXAMPLE 2. The minimal polynomial of $\mathbf{v}_{ij}$ in the non-zero subspace $\mathbf{W}_{ij} = [\mathbf{v}_{ij};\ \boldsymbol{b}]$ is x^{k-i+1}. If s is any scalar, then

$$[\mathbf{v}_{ij};\ s\boldsymbol{i} + \boldsymbol{b}] = [\mathbf{v}_{ij};\ \boldsymbol{b}]$$

and the minimal polynomial of $\mathbf{v}_{ij}$ with respect to $s\boldsymbol{i} + \boldsymbol{b}$ is $(x - s)^{k-i+1}$.

EXAMPLE 3. If $\dim[\mathbf{w};\ \boldsymbol{a}] = p$ and

$$\boldsymbol{a}^p + \sum c_i \boldsymbol{a}^{p-i} = \boldsymbol{o},$$

as in Equation (17) above, we may choose $\{\mathbf{w}, \boldsymbol{a}\mathbf{w}, \ldots, \boldsymbol{a}^{p-1}\mathbf{w}\}$ as a coordinate basis of $[\mathbf{w};\ \boldsymbol{a}]$. Then we can represent the restriction $\boldsymbol{a} \mid [\mathbf{w};\ \boldsymbol{a}]$ by the $p \times p$ matrix

$$\begin{pmatrix} 0 & & & & -c_p \\ 1 & 0 & & & \cdot \\ & 1 & \ddots & & \cdot \\ & & \ddots & & \cdot \\ & & & 0 & -c_2 \\ & & & 1 & -c_1 \end{pmatrix}.$$

If we reverse the order of the vectors in this coordinate basis, we get the transposed matrix.

PROBLEMS

1. (a) If $A = \begin{pmatrix} 3 & -2 \\ 2 & -1 \end{pmatrix}$, find the minimal polynomial of the unit column vector $E_1 = (1, 0)^t$ with respect to the linear transformation of column vector space defined by $\boldsymbol{a}U = AU$.

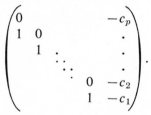

(b) If $A = \begin{pmatrix} 0 & 1 & 0 \\ 0 & 0 & 1 \\ 0 & 0 & 0 \end{pmatrix}$, find the minimal polynomials of the unit column vectors $E_1 = (1, 0, 0)^t$ and $E_3 = (0, 0, 1)^t$ with respect to the linear transformation defined by $\boldsymbol{a}U = AU$.

2. Let $\mathbf{w} \neq \mathbf{o}$ and let $\mathbf{W}$ be a proper ($\neq[\mathbf{w}; \boldsymbol{a}]$) non-zero invariant subspace of $[\mathbf{w}; \boldsymbol{a}]$. Show that there exists a least-degree polynomial $h(x)$ such that $h(\boldsymbol{a})\mathbf{w}$ is in $\mathbf{W}$, hence $\mathbf{W}$ is cyclic and equal to $[h(\boldsymbol{a})\mathbf{w}; \boldsymbol{a}]$.

3. In Problem 2, show that the minimal polynomial of $h(\boldsymbol{a})\mathbf{w}$ is a divisor of the minimal polynomial of $\mathbf{w}$, and that this divisor uniquely determines an invariant subspace of $[\mathbf{w}; \boldsymbol{a}]$.

7.7 MINIMAL POLYNOMIAL OF AN INVARIANT SUBSPACE

Let $\{\mathbf{u}_1, \ldots, \mathbf{u}_{n'}\}$ be a basis of a non-zero invariant subspace $\mathbf{V}'$ of the vector space $\mathbf{V}$, and let $\{\phi_1(x), \ldots, \phi_{n'}(x)\}$ be the minimal polynomials of these basis vectors in the order listed. As usual, our discussion is relative to some fixed linear transformation $\boldsymbol{a}$ of $\mathbf{V}$. Denote by $\psi(x)$ *the least common multiple of* $\{\phi_1(x), \ldots, \phi_{n'}(x)\}$, which means:

1. $\psi(x)$ is a monic and $\phi_i(x) \mid \psi(x)$ for each i, where the symbol "|" means "divides," and it is understood that the quotient has coefficients in the given scalar field.
2. If $g(x)$ is a polynomial such that $\phi_i(x) \mid g(x)$ for each i, then $\psi(x) \mid g(x)$.

If $h(x)$ is a polynomial such that $h(\boldsymbol{a})\mathbf{v} = \mathbf{o}$ for every vector $\mathbf{v}$ in the subspace $\mathbf{V}'$, we shall denote this property by either

$$h(\boldsymbol{a})\mathbf{V}' = \{\mathbf{o}\} \quad \text{or} \quad h(\boldsymbol{a}) \mid \mathbf{V}' = \boldsymbol{o}.$$

$\psi(x)$ is such a polynomial, and $\psi(x)$ *is called the* ***minimal polynomial*** *of* $\mathbf{V}'$ because Theorem 8 below characterizes $\psi(x)$ independently of how $\mathbf{V}'$ is generated.

Theorem 8. Let $\mathbf{V}'$ be a non-zero invariant subspace of $\mathbf{V}$, and let $\psi(x)$ be the least common multiple of the minimal polynomials of the vectors in a basis of $\mathbf{V}'$. Then $\psi(\boldsymbol{a})\mathbf{V}' = \{\mathbf{o}\}$, and if $h(x)$ is any polynomial with scalar coefficients such that $h(\boldsymbol{a})\mathbf{V}' = \{\mathbf{o}\}$, then $\psi(x) \mid h(x)$. If $h(x)$ is a monic of the same degree as $\psi(x)$, then $h(x) = \psi(x)$. Finally, $\psi(x)$ is also the least common multiple of the minimal polynomials of the vectors in any generating set of $\mathbf{V}'$.

Proof: Let us use the notation introduced above. For each i there is a factorization of $\psi(x)$ in the form $\psi(x) = \phi_i'(x)\phi_i(x)$. Hence, for $\mathbf{v}$ in $\mathbf{V}'$,

$$\psi(\boldsymbol{a})\mathbf{v} = \psi(\boldsymbol{a})\sum c_i\mathbf{u}_i = \sum c_i\psi(\boldsymbol{a})\mathbf{u}_i = \sum c_i\phi_i'(\boldsymbol{a})\phi_i(\boldsymbol{a})\mathbf{u}_i = \mathbf{o},$$

so $\psi(\boldsymbol{a})\mathbf{V}' = \{\mathbf{o}\}$. If $h(\boldsymbol{a})\mathbf{V}' = \{\mathbf{o}\}$, then, in particular, $h(\boldsymbol{a})\mathbf{u}_i = \mathbf{o}$ for each i. Therefore $\phi_i(x) \mid h(x)$ for each i, which implies $\psi(x) \mid h(x)$. Since this argument, so far, does not depend on $\{\mathbf{u}_1, \ldots, \mathbf{u}_{n'}\}$ being linearly independent, it holds for any finite generating set. Furthermore, if $\psi'(x)$ denotes the least common multiple of the minimal polynomials of a different finite generating set, then we have $\psi'(x) \mid \psi(x)$, as well as $\psi(x) \mid \psi'(x)$, which implies $\psi(x) = \psi'(x)$. Finally, if $\mathbf{V}' = [\mathrm{M}]$ for any generating set M, then (as in Section 4.6, proof of Theorem 2) we can cut M down to a finite subset M_0 such that $\mathbf{V}' = [\mathrm{M}_0]$. Since the minimal polynomial of any vector in $\mathbf{V}'$ must divide $\psi(x)$, then, in particular, the minimal polynomials of the vectors in M divide $\psi(x)$; furthermore, $\psi(x)$ must divide any polynomial divisible by all these minimal polynomials. q.e.d.

In particular, we may take $\mathbf{V}$ as the invariant subspace $\mathbf{V}'$ of Theorem 8. Then, the minimal polynomial $\psi(x)$ of $\mathbf{V}$ is also called *the **minimal polynomial** of $\boldsymbol{a}$*, and if A is any matrix which represents $\boldsymbol{a}$, then $\psi(x)$ is called *the **minimal polynomial** of A*.

Corollary 1. When $\mathbf{V}' = \mathbf{V}$ in Theorem 8, then $\psi(\boldsymbol{a}) = \boldsymbol{o}$ and $\psi(x)$ is the unique monic of minimal degree with scalar coefficients which has this property. If $h(x)$ is any polynomial with scalar coefficients such that $h(\boldsymbol{a}) = \boldsymbol{o}$, then $\psi(x) \mid h(x)$. In particular, $\psi(x)$ is a factor of the characteristic polynomial of $\boldsymbol{a}$. If $\boldsymbol{a} \leftrightarrow A$ and $h(x)$ is any polynomial with scalar coefficients such that $h(A) = O$, then $\psi(x) \mid h(x)$. When $\mathbf{V}' \neq \mathbf{V}$, the same facts are true if $\boldsymbol{a}$ is replaced by $\boldsymbol{a} \mid \mathbf{V}'$, and A by a representation of $\boldsymbol{a} \mid \mathbf{V}'$.

Proof: To prove the first three statements, we note that by definition $\psi(\boldsymbol{a})\mathbf{V} = \{\mathbf{o}\}$ if and only if $\psi(\boldsymbol{a}) = \boldsymbol{o}$, and that the coefficients of the characteristic polynomial always lie in the scalar field (see Problem 1 below). To prove the next statements, we note that, for any polynomial $p(x)$ with scalar coefficients, $p(A) = O \leftrightarrow p(\boldsymbol{a}) = \boldsymbol{o}$, and that $\psi(\boldsymbol{a}) \mid \mathbf{V}' = \psi(\boldsymbol{a} \mid \mathbf{V}')$ is a linear transformation of $\mathbf{V}'$ because $\mathbf{V}'$ is invariant (see Section 7.2, Problem 5). q.e.d

EXAMPLE 1. The degree of the minimal polynomial of a linear transformation can be as small as 1 or as large as n, where $n = \dim \mathbf{V}$. Thus, a similitude of magnitude k has minimal polynomial $x - k$, while any $\boldsymbol{a}$ with n distinct characteristic numbers $s_1, \ldots, s_n$ has minimal polynomial

$$\prod_1^n (x - s_k).$$

EXAMPLE 2. If we start with an arbitrary square matrix A, we can consider A as the representation of a linear transformation of a column vector space with any convenient field of scalars containing the entries of A, computed with respect to the coordinate basis of unit column vectors. The minimal polynomial, say $\eta(x)$, thus associated with A is actually the same as that derived from any other interpretation of A as a representation of a linear transformation, a fact we now show.

Corollary 2. Suppose $A = (a_{ij})$ is an arbitrary square matrix, considered with respect to some reference field containing all the entries of A. Let $\mathbf{V}$ and $\mathbf{V}'$ be vector spaces whose scalar fields may be different, but assume both scalar fields contain the reference field of A. If we regard A as a representation of two linear transformations, $\boldsymbol{a}$ of $\mathbf{V}$ and $\boldsymbol{a}'$ of $\mathbf{V}'$, that is, $\boldsymbol{a} \leftrightarrow A \leftrightarrow \boldsymbol{a}'$, then the minimal polynomials of $\boldsymbol{a}$ and $\boldsymbol{a}'$ are equal.

Proof: (See also the remarks below.) There is a pair of minimal polynomials, $\psi(x)$ of $\boldsymbol{a}$ and $\psi'(x)$ of $\boldsymbol{a}'$, and for these we have $\psi(A) = \psi'(A) = O$. The intersection of the scalar fields of $\mathbf{V}$ and $\mathbf{V}'$ is again a field containing the entries of A. Among all polynomials with coefficients in the latter field, there is, by Theorem 8, a unique monic $\eta(x)$ of minimal degree such that $\eta(A) = O$ (Example 2). Consider the powers of A as vectors (n^2-tuples), and $\eta(A) = O$ and $\psi(A) = O$ as linear dependences. Now, a linearly independent set of such powers remains linearly independent in any enlargement of the field over which they are treated as vectors (Section 6.6). Hence, over the scalar field of $\mathbf{V}$, we must have $\deg \eta(x) \leq \deg \psi(x)$; and by Corollary 1 above, $\deg \eta(x) \geq \deg \psi(x)$. Therefore, by the uniqueness property, Theorem 8, $\eta(x) = \psi(x)$. Similarly, we can show that $\eta(x) = \psi'(x)$. q.e.d.

Thus the minimal polynomial of A is independent of which linear transformation it is taken to represent, and, in particular, of the field over which A is being studied, as long as the scalar fields contain the reference field of A. (It is possible to consider $\boldsymbol{a}$ and $\boldsymbol{a}'$ (in Corollary 2) as linear transformations of a common vector space whose scalar field contains those of $\mathbf{V}$ and $\mathbf{V}'$. *Assuming this*, then $\boldsymbol{a} \leftrightarrow A \leftrightarrow \boldsymbol{a}'$ means that $\boldsymbol{a}$ and $\boldsymbol{a}'$ are similar linear transformations (Section 3.1), hence have same minimal polynomial.)

EXAMPLE 3. We can find the minimal polynomial of some matrices by inspection (see Problem 1 below). If $A = \text{diag}(A_1, A_2)$, where $A_1 = \begin{pmatrix} 1 & 1 \\ 0 & 1 \end{pmatrix}$ and $A_2 = (1)$, then the minimal polynomial of A is $(x - 1)^2$. If $A = \text{diag}(A_1, A_2, A_3)$ where $A_1 = A_2 = \begin{pmatrix} 0 & -1 \\ 1 & 0 \end{pmatrix}$ and $A_3 = (1)$, then the minimal polynomial of A is $(x^2 + 1)(x - 1)$.

PROBLEMS

1. If $\boldsymbol{a} \leftrightarrow A$, show that the minimal polynomial of $\boldsymbol{a}$ divides $|xI - A|$.
2. Find the minimal polynomials of the linear transformations represented by:
   (a) $\text{diag}(1, 2, 2, 0)$, (b) I, (c) O, (d) a $k \times k$ Jordan Block $sI + N$.
3. Suppose $A = \text{diag}(J_1, J_1, J_2)$, where J_1 is a 2×2 Jordan Block with characteristic number s_1, and J_2 is a 3×3 Jordan Block with characteristic number s_2. Find the minimal polynomial of A if: (a) $s_1 \neq s_2$, and (b) $s_1 = s_2$.

4. If two fields contain a field in common, show that the intersection of the two fields is itself a field.

5. Verify the statement in the proof of Corollary 1 to the effect that if $\mathbf{V}'$ is an invariant subspace of $\mathbf{V}$ with respect to a linear transformation $\boldsymbol{a}$, then $\psi(\boldsymbol{a}) \mid \mathbf{V}' = \psi(\boldsymbol{a} \mid \mathbf{V}')$ is zero on $\mathbf{V}'$.

6. Suppose the matrix $A = \begin{pmatrix} 1 & 1 \\ 1 & 1 \end{pmatrix}$ is considered first with respect to the field of rational numbers and then with respect to the field of integers modulo 2. Find the respective minimal polynomials.

7. Show that linear transformations (of the same vector space) with the same minimal polynomial need not be similar.

8. If $A = \operatorname{diag}(J_1, \ldots, J_t)$, where the J_i's are Jordan Blocks with distinct characteristic numbers, show that the minimal polynomial of A equals $|xI - A|$.

9. With respect to the field of complex numbers, show how to construct a matrix with a prescribed minimal polynomial.

7.8 VECTORS BELONGING TO THE MINIMAL POLYNOMIAL OF V

If $\boldsymbol{a}$ is a linear transformation of $\mathbf{V}$ and $\psi(x)$ is the minimal polynomial of $\mathbf{V}$ (hence $\psi(x)$ is the minimal polynomial of $\boldsymbol{a}$), let

$$\psi(x) = \mu_1(x)^{e_1}\mu_2(x)^{e_2}\cdots$$

be a factorization of $\psi(x)$ into irreducible monic polynomials. The $\mu_i(x)$'s are the unique irreducible monic factors of $\psi(x)$, and the e_j's are their unique multiplicities. If $\{\mathbf{u}_1, \ldots, \mathbf{u}_n\}$ is a basis of $\mathbf{V}$, then for a suitable set of integers $\{\ldots, e_{ij}, \ldots\}$, where $0 \leq e_{ij} \leq e_j$, the minimal polynomial of $\mathbf{u}_i$ is given by

$$\mu_1(x)^{e_{i1}}\mu_2(x)^{e_{i2}}, \ldots \quad (i = 1, \ldots, n),$$

and

$$e_j = \max_i e_{ij},$$

because $\psi(x)$ equals the least common multiple of the minimal polynomials of any generating set. Now, suppose that the i'-th basis vector is the one for which $e_1 = e_{i'1}$. Then the vector

$$\mathbf{v}_1 = \prod_{j \neq 1} \mu_j(\boldsymbol{a})^{e_{i'j}}\mathbf{u}_{i'}$$

has the polynomial $\nu_1(x) = \mu_1(x)^{e_1}$ as its minimal polynomial. Similarly, with $e_2 = e_{i''2}$, we take

$$\mathbf{v}_2 = \prod_{j \neq 2} \mu_j(x)^{e_{i''j}}\mathbf{u}_{i''},$$

which has $\nu_2(x) = \mu_2(x)^{e_2}$ as its minimal polynomial. Continuing in this way,

$\mathbf{v}_j$ will have
$$\nu_j(x) = \mu_j(x)^{e_j}$$
as its minimal polynomial.

Theorem 9. The vector $\mathbf{v} = \mathbf{v}_1 + \mathbf{v}_2 + \cdots$ has the minimal polynomial $\psi(x)$ of $\mathbf{V}$ as its minimal polynomial.

Proof: Let $\psi'(x)$ be the minimal polynomial of $\mathbf{v}$. Then $\psi'(x) \mid \psi(x)$. Now,
$$\mathbf{o} = \psi'(\boldsymbol{a}) \prod_{i \neq 1} \nu_i(\boldsymbol{a})\mathbf{v} = \Big(\psi'(\boldsymbol{a}) \prod_{i \neq 1} \nu_i(\boldsymbol{a})\Big)\mathbf{v}_1.$$
Since, for $i \neq 1$, the $\nu_i(x)$'s are relatively prime to $\nu_1(x)$, we must have $\nu_1(x) \mid \psi'(x)$. Similarly, $\nu_i(x) \mid \psi'(x)$ for $i \geq 2$. Hence $\psi(x) \mid \psi'(x)$, so $\psi'(x) = \psi(x)$. q.e.d.

EXAMPLE 1. If $\psi(x)$ is the minimal polynomial of $\mathbf{V}$ and if $\deg \psi(x) = n = \dim \mathbf{V}$, then by Theorem 9, there is some vector $\mathbf{v}$ in $\mathbf{V}$ for which $\mathbf{V} = [\mathbf{v}; \boldsymbol{a}]$, so $\mathbf{V}$ is cyclic. If we choose a coordinate basis in the form $\{\mathbf{v}, \boldsymbol{a}\mathbf{v}, \ldots, \boldsymbol{a}^{n-1}\mathbf{v}\}$, then $\boldsymbol{a}$ is represented by what is called the ***companion matrix*** *of the minimal polynomial*
$$\psi(x) = x^n + \sum c_i x^{n-i},$$
namely,
$$A = \begin{pmatrix} 0 & & & & -c_n \\ 1 & 0 & & & \cdot \\ & 1 & & & \cdot \\ & & \cdot & & \cdot \\ & & & \cdot & \cdot \\ & & & \cdot\ 0 & -c_2 \\ & & & 1 & -c_1 \end{pmatrix}. \tag{19}$$
(Any matrix created in this way from a given monic polynomial, is called the *companion matrix of the monic.*)

Note that $\psi(x) = |xI - A|$, and since $\boldsymbol{a} \leftrightarrow A$, the minimal polynomial of A is $\psi(x)$. In Section 7.6, Example 3, the companion matrix of the minimal polynomial of $\boldsymbol{a} \mid [\mathbf{w}; \boldsymbol{a}]$ has a similar appearance, but, in general, does not represent $\boldsymbol{a}$ on all of $\mathbf{V}$ because $p = \dim[\mathbf{w}; \boldsymbol{a}] \leq \dim \mathbf{V}$.

EXAMPLE 2. Suppose $\mathbf{V} = [\mathbf{u}; \boldsymbol{a}]$ for some non-zero vector $\mathbf{u}$, and let $\dim \mathbf{V} = n$. Then the minimal polynomial of $\mathbf{u}$ has degree n, hence this polynomial is the minimal polynomial $\psi(x)$ of $\mathbf{V}$. Combining this with Example 1, we see that *a non-zero vector space* $\mathbf{V}$ *is cyclic if and only if the degree of its minimal polynomial equals* $\dim \mathbf{V}$, that is, if and only if the minimal polynomial equals the characteristic polynomial of $\boldsymbol{a}$. Since the minimal polynomial is uniquely determined by $\boldsymbol{a}$, *there exists only one matrix representation of* $\boldsymbol{a}$ *by a companion matrix* (19) *when* $\mathbf{V}$ *is cyclic.*

PROBLEMS

1. If a linear transformation of an n-dimensional $\mathbf{V}$ is represented by a $n \times n$ Jordan Block J, find the coordinate column of a vector belonging to the minimal polynomial of J. Do the same if the matrix representation is $\operatorname{diag}(J_1, \ldots, J_t)$, where the J_i's have different characteristic numbers.
2. Find the companion matrix of the minimal polynomial of an $n \times n$ Jordan Block $sI + N$.
3. If a matrix A has the form of Equation (19), and if $E_1 = (1, 0, \ldots, 0)^t$ is $n \times 1$, show that
$$[E_1, \ldots, E_n] = [E_1, AE_1, \ldots, A^{n-1}E_1],$$
no matter what the constants $c_1, \ldots, c_n$.
4. If $\eta(x) = \sum c_i x^{n-i}$ is a monic polynomial with coefficients in a given field, construct an $n \times n$ matrix (with entries in the same field) whose minimal polynomial is $\eta(x)$.
5. Show that if $\mathbf{V}'$ is an invariant subspace of $\mathbf{V}$, then $\mathbf{V}'$ contains a vector whose minimal polynomial equals the minimal polynomial of $\boldsymbol{a} \mid \mathbf{V}'$.
6. If $\mathbf{V}'$ is an invariant subspace of $\mathbf{V}$, show that the minimal polynomial of $\boldsymbol{a} \mid \mathbf{V}'$ divides the minimal polynomial of $\boldsymbol{a}$.

7.9 MINIMAL POLYNOMIAL OF A FACTOR SPACE

For some linear transformation $\boldsymbol{a}$ of $\mathbf{V}$, let $\mathbf{V}'$ be a proper non-zero (that is, $\{\mathbf{o}\} \neq \mathbf{V}' \neq \mathbf{V}$) invariant subspace of $\mathbf{V}$. Denote the minimal polynomial of $\mathbf{V}/\mathbf{V}'$ (which is therefore the minimal polynomial of the factor linear transformation $\bar{\boldsymbol{a}}$) by $\psi_2(x)$. Hence $\psi_2(x)$ is the smallest-degree monic with the property $\psi_2(\bar{\boldsymbol{a}})\bar{\mathbf{u}} = \bar{\mathbf{o}}$ for every $\bar{\mathbf{u}}$ in $\mathbf{V}/\mathbf{V}'$ (which means that $\psi_2(\boldsymbol{a})\mathbf{u}$ *is in* $\mathbf{V}'$ *for every* $\mathbf{u}$ *in* $\mathbf{V}$). If $\psi_1(x)$ is the minimal polynomial of $\mathbf{V}$, then $\psi_1(\boldsymbol{a}) = \boldsymbol{o}$, therefore certainly $\psi_1(\bar{\boldsymbol{a}})\bar{\mathbf{u}} = \bar{\mathbf{o}}$. Hence $\psi_2(x) \mid \psi_1(x)$, or equivalently, the *minimal polynomial of* $\mathbf{V}/\mathbf{V}'$ *divides the minimal polynomial of* $\mathbf{V}$. We have already seen that the minimal polynomial of $\mathbf{V}'$ divides that of $\mathbf{V}$ (Section 7.8, Problem 6).

Theorem 10. Let $\boldsymbol{a}$ be a linear transformation of $\mathbf{V}$. Then
$$\mathbf{V} = \mathbf{U}_1 \dotplus \cdots \dotplus \mathbf{U}_t,$$
where each $\mathbf{U}_i$ is a cyclic subspace with a minimal polynomial $\psi_i(x)$ such that $\psi_{i+1}(x) \mid \psi_i(x)$ for $i = 1, \ldots, t-1$, and $\psi_1(x)$ is the minimal polynomial of $\mathbf{V}$.

Proof: Let
$$\psi_1(x) = x^{m_1} + \sum c_i x^{m_1 - i}$$
be the minimal polynomial of $\mathbf{V}$, and let $\mathbf{u}$ be a vector for which $\psi_1(x)$ is the minimal polynomial. Then the invariant subspace
$$\mathbf{U}_1 = [\mathbf{u}, \boldsymbol{a}\mathbf{u}, \ldots, \boldsymbol{a}^{m_1-1}\mathbf{u}]$$

is a cyclic subspace for which $\psi_1(x)$ is the minimal polynomial. If $\mathbf{U}_1 \neq \mathbf{V}$, let $\psi_2(x)$ be the minimal polynomial of $\mathbf{V}/\mathbf{U}_1$. We know that for some polynomial $\phi(x)$,

$$\psi_1(x) = \psi_2(x)\phi(x)$$

and that there is a vector $\bar{\mathbf{u}}'$ in $\mathbf{V}/\mathbf{U}_1$ such that $\psi_2(x)$ is the minimal polynomial of $\bar{\mathbf{u}}'$. Since $\psi_2(\boldsymbol{a})\mathbf{u}'$ is in $\mathbf{U}_1$, and $\mathbf{U}_1$ is cyclic, there is a polynomial $q(x)$ such that

$$\psi_2(\boldsymbol{a})\mathbf{u}' = q(\boldsymbol{a})\mathbf{u}.$$

Then

$$\phi(\boldsymbol{a})\psi_2(\boldsymbol{a})\mathbf{u}' = \mathbf{o} = \phi(\boldsymbol{a})q(\boldsymbol{a})\mathbf{u}, \quad \text{hence} \quad \psi_1(x) \mid \phi(x)q(x).$$

Hence $\psi_2(x) \mid q(x)$. Now set

$$q'(x) = q(x)/\psi_2(x)$$

and

$$\mathbf{v} = \mathbf{u}' - q'(\boldsymbol{a})\mathbf{u},$$

so $\bar{\mathbf{v}} = \bar{\mathbf{u}}' \neq \bar{\mathbf{o}}$ and

$$\psi_2(\boldsymbol{a})\mathbf{v} = \mathbf{o}.$$

Hence $\psi_2(x)$ is the minimal polynomial of $\mathbf{v}$. Set

$$\mathbf{U}_2 = [\mathbf{v}, \boldsymbol{a}\mathbf{v}, \ldots, \boldsymbol{a}^{m_2-1}\mathbf{v}],$$

where $m_2 = \deg \psi_2(x)$. Then $\dim \mathbf{U}_2 = m_2$. Therefore $[\mathbf{U}_1, \mathbf{U}_2] = \mathbf{U}_1 \dotplus \mathbf{U}_2$, with $\psi_1(x)$ the minimal polynomial of $\mathbf{U}_1$, and $\psi_2(x)$ the minimal polynomial of $\mathbf{U}_2$. If $m_1 + m_2 \neq n = \dim \mathbf{V}$, then we can continue this process as follows. Suppose we have found k cyclic subspaces $\mathbf{U}_i = [\mathbf{u}_i;\ \boldsymbol{a}]$ $(i = 1, \ldots, k)$, such that

$$[\mathbf{U}_1, \ldots, \mathbf{U}_k] = \mathbf{U}_1 \dotplus \cdots \dotplus \mathbf{U}_k,$$

$\psi_i(x)$ is the minimal polynomial of $\mathbf{U}_i$, and $\psi_{i+1} \mid \psi_i$. If $\mathbf{V} \neq [\mathbf{U}_1, \ldots, \mathbf{U}_k]$, set $\overline{\mathbf{V}} = \mathbf{V}/[\mathbf{U}_1, \ldots, \mathbf{U}_k]$, let $\psi_{k+1}(x)$ be the minimal polynomial of $\overline{\mathbf{V}}$ and suppose a vector $\bar{\mathbf{u}}'$ in $\overline{\mathbf{V}}$ has $\psi_{k+1}(x)$ as its minimal polynomial. Then it is readily verified that there exist polynomials $\phi_1(x), \ldots, \phi_k(x), q_1(x), \ldots, q_k(x)$ such that

$$\psi_i(x) = \psi_{k+1}(x)\phi_i(x),$$

$$\psi_{k+1}(\boldsymbol{a})\mathbf{u}' = \sum_1^k q_j(\boldsymbol{a})\mathbf{u}_j, \quad q_j(\boldsymbol{a})\mathbf{u}_j \ \text{ in } \ \mathbf{U}_j,$$

$$\phi_i(\boldsymbol{a})\psi_{k+1}(\boldsymbol{a})\mathbf{u}' = \sum \phi_i(\boldsymbol{a})q_j(\boldsymbol{a})\mathbf{u}_j, \quad \text{hence}$$

$$\phi_i(\boldsymbol{a})q_i(\boldsymbol{a})\mathbf{u}_i = \mathbf{o} \quad \text{and} \quad \psi_{k+1}(x) \mid q_i(x) \quad (i = 1, \ldots, k).$$

If we set

$$\mathbf{u}_{k+1} = \mathbf{u}' - \sum q_i'(\boldsymbol{a})\mathbf{u}_i, \quad \text{where} \quad q_i'(x) = q_i(x)/\psi_{k+1}(x),$$

then $\psi_{k+1}(\boldsymbol{a})(\mathbf{u}_{k+1}) = \mathbf{o}$ and we can take $\mathbf{U}_{k+1} = [\mathbf{u}_{k+1};\ \boldsymbol{a}]$. Finally, since $\mathbf{V}$ is finite-dimensional, $\mathbf{V} = \mathbf{U}_1 \dotplus \cdots \dotplus \mathbf{U}_t$, where each $\mathbf{U}_i$ is cyclic with minimal polynomial $\psi_i(x)$ such that $\psi_{i+1}(x) \mid \psi_i(x)$, and $\psi_1(x)$ is the minimal polynomial of both $\mathbf{U}_1$ and $\mathbf{V}$. q.e.d.

Corollary. If we arrange the indicated bases of the $\mathbf{U}_i$'s in suitable order as a coordinate basis for $\mathbf{V}$, then $\boldsymbol{a}$ can be represented by $\operatorname{diag}(C_1, \ldots, C_t)$, where C_i is the companion matrix of

$$\psi_i(x) = x^{m_i} + \sum_{j=1}^{m_i} c_{ij}x^{m_i-j},$$

that is,

$$\boldsymbol{a} \leftrightarrow \operatorname{diag}(C_1, \ldots, C_t), \tag{20}$$

where

$$\boldsymbol{a} \mid \mathbf{U}_i \leftrightarrow C_i = \begin{pmatrix} 0 & & & & -c_{im_i} \\ 1 & 0 & & & \vdots \\ & 1 & \ddots & & \vdots \\ & & \ddots & 0 & -c_{i2} \\ & & & 1 & -c_{i1} \end{pmatrix}.$$

Proof: Each $\mathbf{U}_i$ is cyclic, with minimal polynomial $\psi_i(x)$, and

$$\mathbf{V} = \mathbf{U}_1 \dotplus \cdots \dotplus \mathbf{U}_t. \qquad \text{q.e.d.}$$

The subspace $\mathbf{U}_i$ is generally decomposable into invariant subspaces, as we shall see in the next section. The matrix representation (20) is uniquely determined by $\boldsymbol{a}$ because the C_i's are uniquely determined by the $\psi_i(x)$'s. Hence, this representation is called a canonical representation of $\boldsymbol{a}$, if the blocks are listed in the indicated order.

EXAMPLE 1. From the representation of $\boldsymbol{a}$ as given in the Corollary above, it follows that the characteristic polynomial of $\boldsymbol{a}$ has the factorization

$$|xI - A| = \psi_1(x) \cdots \psi_t(x).$$

From the fact that $\mathbf{U}_i$ and $\mathbf{U}_i \dotplus \cdots \dotplus \mathbf{U}_t$ each have $\psi_i(x)$ as minimal polynomial, we know that the restrictions of $\boldsymbol{a}$ to $\mathbf{U}_i$ and to $\mathbf{U}_i \dotplus \cdots \dotplus \mathbf{U}_t$ each have $\psi_i(x)$ as minimal polynomial. Therefore, $\psi_i(A_j) = O$ for each $j \geq i$, and $\psi_i(x)$ is the minimal polynomial of C_i and of $\operatorname{diag}(C_i, \ldots, C_t)$, for each i.

EXAMPLE 2. If $\psi_1(x)$ is the minimal polynomial of a linear transformation $\boldsymbol{a}$, and

$$\boldsymbol{a} \leftrightarrow A = \begin{pmatrix} C_1 & * \\ O & D \end{pmatrix},$$

where C_1 is the companion matrix of $\psi_1(x)$, then A is similar to $\operatorname{diag}(C_1, E)$ and E is similar to D. For, we know $\boldsymbol{a} \leftrightarrow \operatorname{diag}(C_1, \ldots, C_t)$, and we can apply a computation similar to that in Section 7.2, Example 2.

EXAMPLE 3. If $a \leftrightarrow A = \begin{pmatrix} 1 & 0 & 1 \\ 0 & 1 & 0 \\ 0 & 0 & 1 \end{pmatrix}$, then $|xI - A| = (x - 1)^3$ and it is easy to see that $\psi_1(x) = (x - 1)^2$ and $\psi_2(x) = x - 1$. Hence A is similar to the canonical matrix $\operatorname{diag}\left(\begin{pmatrix} 0 & -1 \\ 1 & 2 \end{pmatrix}, 1\right)$

PROBLEMS

1. If the characteristic polynomial of a linear transformation $\boldsymbol{a}$ has distinct zeros, show that $\boldsymbol{a}$ can be represented by the companion matrix of its minimal polynomial.
2. If the characteristic polynomial of a linear transformation $\boldsymbol{a}$ is irreducible in the given field, show that $|xI - A| = \psi_1(x)$.
3. In each case below, find a similar matrix in canonical form, Equation (20):

   (a) $\begin{pmatrix} 0 & 1 \\ 1 & 0 \end{pmatrix}$, (b) $\begin{pmatrix} 0 & 1 \\ -1 & 0 \end{pmatrix}$, (c) $\begin{pmatrix} \cos\theta & -\sin\theta \\ \sin\theta & \cos\theta \end{pmatrix}$,

   (d) $\begin{pmatrix} 2 & 1 & 0 \\ 0 & 1 & -1 \\ 0 & 0 & 3 \end{pmatrix}$, (e) $\begin{pmatrix} 2 & 7 & 2 \\ 1 & 4 & 1 \\ -1 & -22 & -5 \end{pmatrix}$.
4. Find all possible canonical representations of type (20) for linear transformations whose characteristic polynomials are:

   (a) $x^5 - 1$, (b) $(x^2 + 2)(x^2 + 1)^2$.
5. Suppose $\boldsymbol{a}$ is a linear transformation of a real 4-dimensional vector space. What are the possible $\psi_i(x)$'s if: (a) $\psi_1(x) = x^2 + 1$, (b) $\psi_1(x) = x^2 - 1$?

7.10 DECOMPOSITION OF CYCLIC SPACES

Now, suppose the minimal polynomial $\psi_1(x)$ of $\mathbf{V}$ (with respect to a given linear transformation $\boldsymbol{a}$, as usual) can be factored into two relatively prime non-constant monic factors, say $\psi_1(x) = \phi_1(x)\phi_2(x)$, so the greatest common divisor of the non-constant polynomials $\phi_1(x)$ and $\phi_2(x)$ equals 1. We can define two invariant subspaces $\mathbf{W}_1$ and $\mathbf{W}_2$ by

$$\mathbf{W}_i = \{\mathbf{u} \mid \mathbf{u} \text{ in } \mathbf{V},\ \phi_i(\boldsymbol{a})\mathbf{u} = \mathbf{o}\} \quad (i = 1, 2). \tag{21}$$

These subspaces yield the decomposition of $\mathbf{V}$ described in the following theorem. This decomposition depends on the scalar field of $\mathbf{V}$.

Theorem 11. Suppose the minimal polynomial $\psi_1(x)$ of $\mathbf{V}$ factors into two relatively prime non-constant monic factors $\phi_1(x)$ and $\phi_2(x)$, and let $\mathbf{W}_i$ be defined by Equation (21). Then $\mathbf{V} = \mathbf{W}_1 \dotplus \mathbf{W}_2$, and $\phi_i(x)$ is the minimal polynomial of $\mathbf{W}_i$ $(i = 1, 2)$.

Proof: Since $\phi_1(x)$ and $\phi_2(x)$ are relatively prime, there exist polynomials $q_1(x)$ and $q_2(x)$ such that

$$q_1(x)\phi_1(x) + q_2(x)\phi_2(x) = 1.$$

Every vector $\mathbf{u}$ in $\mathbf{V}$ can be written

$$\mathbf{u} = \mathbf{u}_1 + \mathbf{u}_2 \quad \text{where} \quad \mathbf{u}_1 = q_2(\boldsymbol{a})\phi_2(\boldsymbol{a})\mathbf{u} \quad \text{and} \quad \mathbf{u}_2 = q_1(\boldsymbol{a})\phi_1(\boldsymbol{a})\mathbf{u},$$

because

$$\mathbf{u} = \boldsymbol{i}\mathbf{u} \quad \text{and} \quad q_1(\boldsymbol{a})\phi_1(\boldsymbol{a}) + q_2(\boldsymbol{a})\phi_2(\boldsymbol{a}) = \boldsymbol{i}.$$

Now,

$$\phi_1(\boldsymbol{a})\mathbf{u}_1 = \phi_2(\boldsymbol{a})\mathbf{u}_2 = \mathbf{o}, \text{ so } \mathbf{u}_i \text{ is in } \mathbf{W}_i \quad (i = 1, 2),$$

and we have

$$\mathbf{V} = [\mathbf{W}_1, \mathbf{W}_2].$$

Suppose $\mathbf{v}$ is in $\mathbf{W}_1 \cap \mathbf{W}_2$. Then

$$\mathbf{v} = q_1(\boldsymbol{a})\phi_1(\boldsymbol{a})\mathbf{v} + q_2(\boldsymbol{a})\phi_2(\boldsymbol{a})\mathbf{v} = \mathbf{o} + \mathbf{o}, \quad \text{so} \quad \mathbf{W}_1 \cap \mathbf{W}_2 = \{\mathbf{o}\}.$$

Therefore $\mathbf{V} = \mathbf{W}_1 \dotplus \mathbf{W}_2$. Suppose that $h(x)$ is a polynomial such that $h(\boldsymbol{a})\mathbf{w}_1 = \mathbf{o}$ for every vector $\mathbf{w}_1$ in $\mathbf{W}_1$. If $\mathbf{u} = \mathbf{u}_1 + \mathbf{u}_2$ is any vector in $\mathbf{V}$, then

$$h(\boldsymbol{a})\phi_2(\boldsymbol{a})\mathbf{u} = \phi_2(\boldsymbol{a})h(\boldsymbol{a})\mathbf{u}_1 + h(\boldsymbol{a})\phi_2(\boldsymbol{a})\mathbf{u}_2 = \mathbf{o}.$$

Hence

$$\psi_1(x) \mid h(x)\phi_2(x), \quad \text{so} \quad \phi_1(x) \mid h(x).$$

Thus $\phi_1(x)$ is the minimal polynomial of $\mathbf{W}_1$; and similarly, $\phi_2(x)$ is the minimal polynomial of $\mathbf{W}_2$. q.e.d.

EXAMPLE 1. Suppose $\deg \psi_1(x) = \dim \mathbf{V}$, that is, suppose $\mathbf{V}$ is cyclic. Then, with $\mathbf{W}_1$, $\mathbf{W}_2$ as in Theorem 11, we see that $\deg \phi_i(x) = \dim \mathbf{W}_i$ $(i = 1, 2)$. Hence each $\mathbf{W}_i$ is cyclic with minimal polynomial $\phi_i(x)$.

EXAMPLE 2. By an induction argument, Theorem 11 can be extended to any finite number of pairwise relatively prime factors of $\psi_1(x)$. Assume this done. Now, suppose $\mathbf{V}$ is a *real* vector space and that the minimal polynomial $\psi_1(x)$ of $\mathbf{V}$ (that is, of $\boldsymbol{a}$) has distinct zeros. Then, in the decomposition $\mathbf{V} = \mathbf{U}_1 \dotplus \cdots \dotplus \mathbf{U}_t$ of Theorem 10, each of the respective minimal polynomials $\psi_1(x), \ldots, \psi_t(x)$ factors into irreducible linear and quadratic monics, *each factor with multiplicity* 1. Hence each $\mathbf{U}_i$, and therefore $\mathbf{V}$, is the direct sum of invariant 1- and 2-dimensional subspaces. Consequently, $\boldsymbol{a}$ can be represented by a diagonal-block matrix with 1×1 and 2×2 real blocks, where the latter can be taken in the form

$$\begin{pmatrix} a & b \\ -b & a \end{pmatrix} \quad \text{or} \quad \begin{pmatrix} 0 & d \\ 1 & c \end{pmatrix}.$$

EXAMPLE 3. The characteristic polynomial of a real symmetric matrix A factors completely over the reals and we already know that A is similar to a diagonal matrix. Therefore, the minimal polynomial of A equals $\Pi(x - s_i)$, where only the *distinct* characteristic numbers of A appear.

Suppose we factor each of the minimal polynomials $\psi_1(x), \ldots, \psi_t(x)$ of the cyclic spaces $\mathbf{U}_1, \ldots, \mathbf{U}_t$ in Theorem 10 into *irreducible factors*, say

$$\psi_i(x) = \phi_1(x)^{e_{i1}}\phi_2(x)^{e_{i2}} \cdots \phi_s(x)^{e_{is}} \quad (i = 1, \ldots, t), \tag{22}$$

where, of necessity $e_{ij} \geq e_{i+1,j}$, and the $\phi_i(x)$'s are irreducible non-constant monics. Then we can apply Theorem 11 (see Example 2) to the cyclic space $\mathbf{U}_i$, whose minimal polynomial is $\psi_i(x)$, to get the decomposition

$$\mathbf{U}_i = \mathbf{U}_{i1} \dotplus \mathbf{U}_{i2} \dotplus \cdots, \tag{23}$$

where $\mathbf{U}_{ij}$ is an invariant subspace whose minimal polynomial is $\phi_j(x)^{e_{ij}}$. *The latter polynomial is called an* **elementary divisor** *of the linear transformation* $\boldsymbol{a}$. Since $\dim \mathbf{U}_i = \deg \psi_i(x)$, we have

$$\dim \mathbf{U}_{ij} = \deg \phi_j(x)^{e_{ij}}.$$

Therefore, each $\mathbf{U}_{ij}$ *is cyclic.* Just as in the special case of Section 7.5, Example 3, we can show that $\mathbf{U}_{ij}$ *is indecomposable*; but this result also follows from the results of Example 4 below. *An elementary divisor of* $\boldsymbol{a}$ *is also called an elementary divisor of the characteristic matrix* $xI - A$, *where* A *is any representation of* $\boldsymbol{a}$, or more briefly, *an elementary divisor of* A.

EXAMPLE 4. *If a cyclic space is decomposed, then the summands must be cyclic too, and the minimal polynomials of these summands must be relatively prime polynomials.* For, suppose some cyclic space $\mathbf{W}$ is the direct sum $\mathbf{W} = \mathbf{W}_1 \dotplus \mathbf{W}_2$ of invariant subspaces with $\dim \mathbf{W} = n$, $\dim \mathbf{W}_i = n_i$. Let $\mu(x)$, $\mu_1(x)$, $\mu_2(x)$ be the minimal polynomials of $\mathbf{W}$, $\mathbf{W}_1$, $\mathbf{W}_2$, respectively, of degrees m, m_1, m_2. Then $m_i \leq n_i$ $(i = 1, 2)$. But $\mu(x)$ is the least common multiple of $\mu_1(x)$ and $\mu_2(x)$ because it is the least common multiple for any generating set of $\mathbf{W}$. Thus we have

$$m \leq m_1 + m_2 \leq n_1 + n_2 = n.$$

Since $\mathbf{W}$ is cyclic, we have $m = n$, which forces

$$m_1 + m_2 = n_1 + n_2.$$

This can hold only if $m_i = n_i$ $(i = 1, 2)$. Therefore, $\dim \mathbf{W}_i = \deg \mu_i(x)$ $(i = 1, 2)$, so each $\mathbf{W}_i$ is cyclic. Also $\mu(x) = \mu_1(x)\mu_2(x)$ because $n = n_1 + n_2$, hence $\mu_1(x)$ and $\mu_2(x)$ are relatively prime. If we apply this to $\mathbf{W} = \mathbf{U}_i$, we see again that each $\mathbf{U}_{ij}$ is cyclic. Furthermore, $\mathbf{U}_{ij}$ is indecomposable because its minimal polynomial is not a product of relatively prime factors.

Each $\mathbf{U}_{ij}$ in Equation (23) is cyclic with minimal polynomial $\phi_j(x)^{e_{ij}}$, where $\phi_j(x)$ is irreducible. Set $f_j = \deg \phi_j(x)$. Then there is a vector, say $\mathbf{u}$ in $\mathbf{U}_{ij}$, which has the same minimal polynomial as $\mathbf{U}_{ij}$. As a coordinate basis of $\mathbf{U}_{ij}$, choose the following set, where we temporarily abbreviate ϕ_j by ϕ, e_{ij} by e, and f_j by f:

$$\begin{aligned}&\{\phi(\boldsymbol{a})^{e-1}\mathbf{u}, \boldsymbol{a}\phi(\boldsymbol{a})^{e-1}\mathbf{u}, \ldots, \boldsymbol{a}^{f-1}\phi(\boldsymbol{a})^{e-1}\mathbf{u};\\ &\phi(\boldsymbol{a})^{e-2}\mathbf{u}, \boldsymbol{a}\phi(\boldsymbol{a})^{e-2}\mathbf{u}, \ldots, \boldsymbol{a}^{f-1}\phi(\boldsymbol{a})^{e-2}\mathbf{u}; \ldots; \mathbf{u}, \boldsymbol{a}\mathbf{u}, \ldots, \boldsymbol{a}^{f-1}\mathbf{u}\}.\end{aligned} \tag{24}$$

Note that if

$$\phi(x) = x^f + \sum b_i x^{f-i},$$

then the formula

$$\boldsymbol{a}^f = \phi(\boldsymbol{a}) - \sum b_i \boldsymbol{a}^{f-i},$$

helps us to compute $\boldsymbol{a}^f\phi(\boldsymbol{a})^k$.

When $\phi_j(x)$ is linear for each j, this coordinate basis (24) yields the Jordan Blocks of Section 7.4. In contrast to the canonical matrix in Section 7.9, Equation (20), our present representation depends on the scalar field.

EXAMPLE 5. If

$$\phi_j(x) = x^2 + x + 2 \quad \text{and} \quad e_{ij} = 3,$$

then $\boldsymbol{a} \mid \mathbf{U}_{ij}$ is represented by

$$\begin{pmatrix} 0 & -2 & 0 & 1 & & \\ 1 & -1 & 0 & 0 & & \\ & & 0 & -2 & 0 & 1 \\ & & 1 & -1 & 0 & 0 \\ & & & & 0 & -2 \\ & & & & 1 & -1 \end{pmatrix}.$$

We see that the typical diagonal block is the companion matrix of the polynomial $\phi_j(x)$.

EXAMPLE 6. Suppose a linear transformation of a 6-dimensional real vector space has characteristic polynomial $(x^2 + 1)^2(x - 1)^2$. To find the possibilities for such an incompletely specified mapping, we may consider the permissible minimal polynomials of $\mathbf{U}_1, \ldots, \mathbf{U}_t$:

(a) $\psi_1(x) = (x^2 + 1)^2(x - 1)^2$,

(b) $\psi_1(x) = (x^2 + 1)^2(x - 1), \psi_2(x) = x - 1$,

(c) $\psi_1(x) = (x^2 + 1)(x - 1)^2, \psi_2(x) = x^2 + 1$,

(d) $\psi_1(x) = (x^2 + 1)(x - 1) = \psi_2(x)$.

The corresponding matrices, with blocks grouped by the subspaces $\{\mathbf{U}_i\}$, are:

$$\text{(a)}\begin{pmatrix} 0 & -1 & 0 & 1 & & \\ 1 & 0 & 0 & 0 & & \\ & & 0 & -1 & & \\ & & 1 & 0 & & \\ & & & & 1 & 1 \\ & & & & & 1 \end{pmatrix}, \quad \text{(b)}\begin{pmatrix} 0 & -1 & 0 & 1 & & \\ 1 & 0 & 0 & 0 & & \\ & & 0 & -1 & & \\ & & 1 & 0 & & \\ & & & & 1 & \\ & & & & & 1 \end{pmatrix},$$

$$\text{(c)}\begin{pmatrix} 0 & -1 & & & & \\ 1 & 0 & & & & \\ & & 1 & 1 & & \\ & & & 1 & & \\ & & & & 0 & -1 \\ & & & & 1 & 0 \end{pmatrix}, \quad \text{(d)}\begin{pmatrix} 0 & -1 & & & & \\ 1 & 0 & & & & \\ & & 1 & & & \\ & & & 0 & -1 & \\ & & & 1 & 0 & \\ & & & & & 1 \end{pmatrix}.$$

PROBLEMS

1. In each case, find the elementary divisors and a corresponding representation:
   (a) $\boldsymbol{a}$ has $\psi_1(x) = (x^2 - 1)^3$ and $\psi_2(x) = x^2 - 1$, while $\dim \mathbf{V} = 8$.
   (b) $\boldsymbol{a}$ has characteristic polynomial x^5 and rank 3.
   (c) $\boldsymbol{a}^2 = \boldsymbol{a}$, rank $\boldsymbol{a} = 2$, and $\dim \mathbf{V} = 4$.
2. Let $A = \begin{pmatrix} 0 & 0 & 0 & -2 \\ 1 & 0 & 0 & 0 \\ 0 & 1 & 0 & 3 \\ 0 & 0 & 1 & 0 \end{pmatrix}$.
   (a) With respect to the rationals, find a similar matrix with three diagonal blocks.
   (b) With respect to the reals, find a similar diagonal matrix.
3. Show that if an invariant subspace $\mathbf{W}$ is a direct sum of two cyclic subspaces whose minimal polynomials are relatively prime, then $\mathbf{W}$ is cyclic. What is its minimal polynomial?
4. Show that a subspace $\mathbf{W}$ is indecomposable if and only if it is cyclic and its minimal polynomial is a power of an irreducible polynomial.

7.11 INVARIANT FACTORS

Suppose the linear transformation $\boldsymbol{a}$ of $\mathbf{V}$ is represented by some matrix A. We know that the characteristic polynomial $|xI - A|$, formed from the characteristic matrix $xI - A$ of A, does not change if A is replaced by any other representation of $\boldsymbol{a}$, or by any similar matrix $P^{-1}AP$ where P may have entries in a field containing the scalar field of $\mathbf{V}$. On the other hand, the fact that two matrices C and D with entries in the same field have the same characteristic polynomials,

$$|xI - C| = |xI - D|,$$

does not insure their similarity.

But associated with each linear transformation $\boldsymbol{a}$ of $\mathbf{V}$, there is a finite set of polynomials with coefficients in the scalar field of $\mathbf{V}$, namely, the set of minimal polynomials $\{\psi_1(x), \ldots, \psi_t(x)\}$ of Theorem 10, which characterizes the class of similar linear transformations containing $\boldsymbol{a}$, as well as the class of similar matrices which represent $\boldsymbol{a}$. This gives one way to show that the choice of the field in which the entries of the connecting matrix P in the relation $B = P^{-1}AP$ lie is irrelevant to the existence of a matrix similarity of A and B, just so long as the entries of P lie in a field containing the scalar field of $\mathbf{V}$. In particular, if P has some imaginary entries, while A and $B(= P^{-1}AP)$ are real, then there exists a real Q such that $B = Q^{-1}AQ$ (Problem 4 and Section 7.13, Example 2 below).

Let A be an $n \times n$ matrix and suppose $B = P^{-1}AP$, without any restriction on the common field from which the entries of A, B, P are drawn. Then

$$xI - B = P^{-1}(xI - A)P$$

and an application of Section 6.2, Example 3 shows that each i-rowed minor of $xI - B$ is a linear combination of the i-rowed minors of $xI - A$ with coefficients which are products of i-rowed minors of P^{-1} and P. Since

$$xI - A = P(xI - B)P^{-1},$$

each i-rowed minor of $xI - B$ is similarly expressible in terms of the i-rowed minors of $xI - A$.

Now, denote by $\delta_i(x)$ *the greatest common divisor of all the i-rowed minors of* $xI - A$, and denote by $\epsilon_i(x)$ *the greatest common divisor of all the i-rowed minors of* $xI - B$, with $\delta_0(x) = \epsilon_0(x) = 1$ by definition. Then

$$\delta_i(x) \mid \epsilon_i(x) \quad \text{and} \quad \epsilon_i(x) \mid \delta_i(x),$$

so

$$\delta_i(x) = \epsilon_i(x) \quad (i = 0, \ldots, n). \tag{25}$$

Each $\delta_i(x)$ is a monic and

$$\delta_{i-1}(x) \mid \delta_i(x) \quad (i = 1, \ldots, n),$$

because $\delta_i(x)$ can be expressed as a linear combination of $(i - 1)$-rowed minors. In particular,

$$\delta_n(x) = |xI - A|.$$

EXAMPLE 1. If an $n \times n$ matrix A is the companion matrix (see for instance Section 7.8, Equation (19)) of a polynomial $f(x)$, then for $xI - A$ we have $\delta_n(x) = f(x)$, but

$$\delta_{n-1}(x) = \cdots = \delta_0(x) = 1.$$

EXAMPLE 2. If $A = kI$, then $\delta_i(x) = (x - k)^i$, $i = 1, \ldots, n$.

The monic polynomials $\delta_0(x), \ldots, \delta_n(x)$ are equally well specified by the quotients

$$i_1(x) = \delta_n(x)/\delta_{n-1}(x), \ldots, i_n(x) = \delta_1(x)/\delta_0(x). \tag{26}$$

The monics $i_1(x), \ldots, i_n(x)$ *in Equations* (26) *are called the* ***invariant factors*** *of* $xI - A$, or more briefly, *of* A. Similar matrices have the same invariant factors (see Problem 3(b) below). We shall see that $i_k(x) = \psi_k(x)$, $k = 1, \ldots, t$.

EXAMPLE 3. In Example 1 above, the invariant factors are

$$i_1(x) = f(x) = |xI - A|, \quad i_2(x) = \cdots = i_n(x) = 1.$$

In Example 2, they are all equal to $x - k$.

PROBLEMS

1. Compute the set $\{\delta_i(x)\}$ and the invariant factors of $xI - A$ if

$$\text{(a) } A = \begin{pmatrix} 1 & 0 \\ 0 & -1 \end{pmatrix}, \qquad \text{(b) } A = \begin{pmatrix} 0 & 1 \\ 1 & 0 \end{pmatrix}, \qquad \text{(c) } A = \begin{pmatrix} 1 & 1 & 0 \\ 0 & 1 & 0 \\ 0 & 0 & 1 \end{pmatrix}.$$

2. For the invariant factors of $xI - A$ that are not equal to 1, show that

$$\sum_{k=1}^{t} \deg i_k(x) = \deg |xI - A| \quad (\deg = \text{degree of}).$$

3. (a) Prove that the invariant factors of $xI - A$ do not change if the field of reference is enlarged. (b) *Show that if A is similar to B, then* $xI - A$ *and* $xI - B$ *have the same invariant factors.*
4. In connection with Section 7.5, Problem 8, find a real matrix R such that

$$R^{-1}\begin{pmatrix} a & b \\ -b & a \end{pmatrix}R = \begin{pmatrix} 0 & -a^2 - b^2 \\ 1 & 2a \end{pmatrix}, \quad b \neq 0.$$

Does $R = PQ$ always work?
5. Suppose a linear transformation of a complex $2k$-dimensional vector space is represented by diag(J, J^c), where $J = sI + N$ and $J^c = \bar{s}I + N$ are Jordan Blocks and $s = a + ib$ (a and b real, $b \neq 0$). Express $\psi_1(x)$ over the complex numbers and over the rationals. Show that the linear transformation can be represented by an upper triangular-block matrix whose diagonal blocks have the form of either matrix in Problem 4. (See Section 7.10, Example 5, and compare with Section 7.5, Problem 10.)

7.12 DIAGONALIZATION OF $xI - A$

The characteristic matrix $xI - A$ has polynomials of first degree on its diagonal, but constants elsewhere. The following modified elementary row and column operations will be successively applied to $xI - A$:

Allow the elementary row and column operations, that we applied to "constant" matrices (in Section 6.7), to include the effect of *adding to a row (or column) any polynomial multiple of a different row (or column)*. This amounts to now allowing the off-diagonal, *formerly constant*, entry c in the elementary matrix $T_{ij}(c)$ to be any polynomial $p(x)$ with coefficients in the scalar field of $\mathbf{V}$.

By a suitable choice of elementary operations which include the type $T_{ij}(p(x))$, we can find invertible matrices R and S with polynomial entries (inversion of R and S is with respect to the field of fractions $p(x)/q(x)$, $q(x) \neq 0$ mentioned in Section 4.4), such that R^{-1} and S^{-1} also have polynomial entries *and*

$$R(xI - A)S = \operatorname{diag}(f_1(x), f_2(x), \ldots, f_t(x), 1, \ldots, 1),$$

where each $f_i(x)$ is a monic not equal to 1, and

$$f_i(x) \mid f_{i-1}(x) \quad (i = 2, \ldots, t).$$

EXAMPLE 1. Suppose

$$xI - A = \begin{pmatrix} x-2 & -1 & 0 \\ 0 & x & -1 \\ -1 & -1 & x \end{pmatrix}.$$

Then, by a sequence of the above elementary row and column operations we can change $xI - A$ to

$$\operatorname{diag}(x^3 - 2x^2 - x + 1, 1, 1).$$

Starting with an interchange of rows 1 and 3, and skipping some steps, we find that one possible sequence of events is

$$xI - A \rightarrow \begin{pmatrix} 1 & 1 & -x \\ 0 & x & -1 \\ x-2 & -1 & 0 \end{pmatrix} \rightarrow \begin{pmatrix} 1 & 0 & 0 \\ 0 & x & -1 \\ 0 & -x+1 & x^2-2x \end{pmatrix}$$

$$\rightarrow \begin{pmatrix} 1 & 0 & 0 \\ 0 & -1 & x \\ 0 & x^2-2x & -x+1 \end{pmatrix} \rightarrow \text{diagonal form.}$$

Before proving that this process always works, consider the class of matrices which can be derived from a given matrix by a sequence of such row and column operations. Because the elementary matrices which represent the (modified) elementary operations are invertible and have inverses that are also elementary, the relation between any two matrices in this class is symmetric. Any two matrices in this class are related by a sequence of elementary operations. The set of all $n \times n$ matrices with polynomial entries (coefficients in a given field) is thus partitioned into disjoint non-empty classes, and we want a particular "canonical" matrix from each class.

Theorem 12. Let F be a square matrix with entries which are polynomials in x that have coefficients in a given field. In the class of all matrices that can be obtained from F by elementary row and column operations which include the type represented by $T_{ij}(p(x))$, there is one whose entry in the 1,1-position is a monic that divides the entries in every matrix of the class, or else $F = O$. Hence a non-zero F can be converted by elementary operations to

$$\text{diag}(f_1(x), \ldots, f_s(x), 0, \ldots, 0)$$

where each $f_i(x)$ is a monic and

$$f_i(x) \mid f_{i-1}(x) \quad (i = 2, \ldots, s).$$

Proof: Assume $F \neq O$. Then, in the class containing F there may be a matrix $C = (c_{ij})$ with $c_{11} = 1$, failing which there is a matrix C with the degree of c_{11} not greater than the degree of any non-zero entry in any matrix of the class, and with c_{11} a monic. Now, we can show that $c_{11} \mid c_{ij}$ for every i, j. Suppose first that some c_{1i} or c_{j1} is not divisible by c_{11}. Then $c_{11} \neq 1$ and the division algorithm suggests elementary operations which can change C to another matrix C' of the class such that C' has $c'_{11} = 1$ which is a contradiction, or c'_{11} is of degree less than that of c_{11}, which also is a contradiction. Hence $c_{11} \mid c_{1i}$ and $c_{11} \mid c_{j1}$ for every i, j. This allows us to change C by elementary operations to a matrix diag(c_{11}, D). Suppose that for some d_{ij} in D we do *not* have $c_{11} \mid d_{ij}$. Then, add the i-th row of diag(c_{11}, D) to the first row. The resulting matrix C'' has $c''_{11} = c_{11}$, but c_{11} does not divide $c'_{1j}(= d_{ij})$. This leads to a contradiction in C'' just as it did in C. Hence $c_{11} \mid d_{ij}$ for every entry d_{ij} in D. Now, make the induction hypothesis that $(n - 1)$-rowed non-zero matrices like F can be changed by elementary operations to the form

$$\text{diag}(g_1(x), \ldots, g_{s-1}(x), 0, \ldots, 0),$$

where the monics $g_i(x)$ satisfy $g_i(x) \mid g_{i+1}(x)$. Since elementary operations on D are readily extended to C'' without changing the first row and column of C'', we can reduce C'' to

$$\text{diag}(c_{11}, g_1(x), \ldots, g_{s-1}(x), 0, \ldots, 0).$$

Furthermore, elementary operations on D do not affect the divisibility of the entries by c_{11}. So, finally, we can reverse the order of the non-zero diagonal entries, and set

$$f_1(x) = g_{s-1}(x), \ldots, f_s(x) = c_{11}. \qquad \text{q.e.d.}$$

In applying this to the characteristic matrix $xI - A$ of a *constant* $n \times n$ matrix A, we note that $s = n$ because

$$|R|\,|xI - A|\,|S| \neq 0.$$

Corollary. There exists a diagonalization of $xI - A$, by elementary row and column operations which include $T_{ij}(p(x))$, to diagonal form:

$$C = \operatorname{diag}(f_1(x), \ldots, f_t(x), 1, \ldots, 1), \quad f_i(x) \mid f_{i-1}(x) \quad (i = 2, \ldots, t), \tag{27}$$

where each $f_i(x)$ is a monic not equal to 1. *For any such diagonalization, we always have:*

$$f_k(x) = i_k(x) \quad (k = 1, \ldots, t), \quad i_{t+1}(x) = \cdots = i_n(x) = 1.$$

Proof: Suppose $f_{t+1}(x) = 1$, but $f_t(x) \neq 1$. If for each i we compute the greatest common divisor of the i-th ordered minors of C and denote it by $\epsilon_i(x)$, then we find by inspection of C that

$$\epsilon_n(x) = f_1(x)f_2(x)\cdots f_t(x), \quad \epsilon_{n-1}(x) = f_2(x)\cdots f_t(x),$$
$$\ldots, \epsilon_{n-t+1}(x) = f_t(x), \quad \epsilon_{n-t}(x) = 1, \ldots, \epsilon_0(x) = 1.$$

By Section 6.2, Example 3, we know that $\epsilon_i(x) = \delta_i(x)$ $(i = 0, 1, \ldots, n)$. Hence the invariant factors of $xI - A$ which are not equal to 1 are:

$$i_1(x) = f_1(x), \ldots, i_t(x) = f_t(x).$$ q.e.d.

EXAMPLE 2. In Example 1, our result means that the 3×3 characteristic matrix $xI - A$ given there has invariant factors

$$i_1(x) = x^3 - 2x^2 - x + 1, \quad i_2(x) = i_3(x) = 1.$$

EXAMPLE 3. If $J = sI + N$ is an $n \times n$ Jordan Block, then

$$\delta_n(x) = |xI - J| = (x - s)^n, \quad \delta_{n-1}(x) = \cdots = \delta_0(x) = 1.$$

Hence

$$i_1(x) = (x - s)^n, \quad i_2(x) = \cdots = i_n(x) = 1.$$

EXAMPLE 4. If $A = \operatorname{diag}\left(\begin{pmatrix} 1 & 1 \\ 0 & 1 \end{pmatrix}, 1\right)$, then $xI - A$ is easily reduced (that is, diagonalized by elementary operations) to $\operatorname{diag}((x - 1)^2, 1, x - 1)$. Hence

$$i_1(x) = (x - 1)^2, \quad i_2(x) = x - 1, \quad i_3(x) = 1.$$

EXAMPLE 5. Suppose $xI - A$ is reduced to

$$\operatorname{diag}(g_1(x), \ldots, g_n(x)),$$

not necessarily in any divisibility relation, such as Equation (27). Then it is possible to determine the invariant factors as follows. Let $\phi(x)$ be an irreducible monic factor of $|xI - A|$, and set

$$g_i(x) = \phi(x)^{e_i} g_i'(x), \quad \phi(x) \text{ and } g_i'(x) \quad \text{relatively prime.}$$

Let $\{e'_1, \ldots, e'_n\}$ be a relabeling of $\{e_1, \ldots, e_n\}$ such that

$$e'_1 \leq e'_2 \leq \cdots \leq e'_n.$$

Then the $(e'_1 + \cdots + e'_j)$-th power of $\phi(x)$ divides $\delta_j(x)$, and since

$$i_{n-j+1}(x) = \delta_j(x)/\delta_{j-1}(x),$$

we have that the e'_j-th power of $\phi(x)$ is the highest that divides $i_{n-j+1}(x)$. This applies to each irreducible factor of $|xI - A|$.

PROBLEMS

1. Show that $i_1(x) = x^3 - x$, $i_2(x) = x$, $i_3(x) = i_4(x) = 1$ if

$$A = \begin{pmatrix} 0 & 1 & 0 & 0 \\ 0 & 0 & 1 & 0 \\ 0 & 1 & 0 & 0 \\ 0 & 0 & 1 & 0 \end{pmatrix}.$$

2. Suppose A is a 6×6 matrix and that $xI - A$ can be reduced to

$$\text{diag}((x - 1)x,\ (x + 1)x^2,\ x, 1, 1, 1).$$

Find the invariant factors.

3. Suppose you are given an $n \times n$ diagonal matrix

$$C = \text{diag}(g_1(x), \ldots, g_n(x))$$

such that $\sum \deg g_i(x) = n$. Does there exist a constant matrix A for which C is the diagonalization of $xI - A$ by elementary operations?

4. Find the invariant factors of $xI - A$ in each case:
   (a) A is the companion matrix of $x^n + \sum c_i x^{n-i}$.
   (b) $A = \text{diag}(J_1, J_2)$, $J_i = s_i I_i + N_i$ is an $n_i \times n_i$ Jordan Block ($i = 1, 2$) and J_1 is not similar to J_2. (Note that s_1 may be equal to s_2 if $n_1 \neq n_2$.)

5. Use the analogy between factorization among integers and factorization of polynomials (in x as usual here), to prove an analogue to Theorem 12 for integral matrices.

7.13 UNIQUENESS OF CANONICAL FORMS

We have seen in Section 7.9, Equation (20), that when an $n \times n$ matrix A is considered in any given field containing its entries, it is similar to a canonical form

$$C = \text{diag}(C_1, \ldots, C_t), \tag{28}$$

where C_i is the companion matrix of the minimal polynomial $\psi_i(x)$ of a cyclic direct summand $\mathbf{U}_i$ of a suitable n-dimensional vector space $\mathbf{V}$, with $\psi_1(x)$ the minimal polynomial of A and $\psi_{i+1}(x) \mid \psi_i(x)$. If we apply the elementary operations of Section 7.12 to the characteristic matrix

$$xI - \operatorname{diag}(C_1, \ldots, C_t),$$

we first find (see Section 7.11, Example 1) that it can be reduced block by block to

$$\operatorname{diag}(\psi_1(x), 1, \ldots, 1; \psi_2(x), 1, \ldots, 1; \ldots; \psi_t(x), 1, \ldots, 1).$$

After a sequence of like permutations of the rows and columns, this becomes

$$\operatorname{diag}(\psi_1(x), \ldots, \psi_t(x), 1, \ldots, 1).$$

Hence, by Section 7.12, Corollary of Theorem 12,

$$\psi_k(x) = i_k(x) \quad (k = 1, \ldots, t), \tag{29}$$

and *the other invariant factors equal* 1. Therefore *C_i is the companion matrix of the i*-th *invariant factor of $xI - C$ (and $xI - A$).*

Theorem 13. Let

$$C = \operatorname{diag}(C_1, \ldots, C_t) \quad \text{and} \quad C' = \operatorname{diag}(C'_1, \ldots, C'_{t'}.)$$

be $n \times n$ matrices in the canonical form of Equation (28), with entries in a common field. Then C is similar to C' if and only if $C = C'$. Also, $xI - C$ and $xI - C'$ have the same invariant factors if and only if $C = C'$.

Proof: Suppose C is similar to C'. Then as is true for any two similar matrices (see Section 7.11, Problem 3(b)), $xI - C$ and $xI - C'$ have *the same invariant factors.* By Equation (29), each block in C and C' is the companion matrix of a distinct non-constant invariant factor, and each factor occurs once. Thus the blocks in C and C' must be the same. Since the order of the blocks is uniquely determined, we conclude that $C = C'$. q.e.d.

Corollary. Two $n \times n$ matrices A and A' are similar if and only if $xI - A$ and $xI - A'$ have the same invariant factors. Let A and A' have canonical forms C and C', respectively; then A is similar to A' if and only if $C = C'$.

Proof: Let A be similar to a canonical matrix C, and let A' be similar to a canonical matrix C', where C and C' are of the type in Equation (28). Then $xI - A$ and $xI - A'$ have the same invariant factors if and only if $xI - C$ and $xI - C'$ have the same invariant factors. By Theorem 13, the latter condition means that C is equal to C', which in turn means that A is similar to A'. q.e.d.

EXAMPLE 1. If we reduce $xI - A$ to

$$\operatorname{diag}\big(g_1(x), \ldots, g_n(x)\big),$$

then the distinct maximal powers of the irreducible monic factors in each $g_i(x)$ are the elementary divisors of $xI - A$. This can be seen from Section 7.12, Example 5 and the definition of elementary divisor. In particular, if $A = \text{diag}(B, C)$, then the set of elementary divisors of $xI - A$ is the join of those of $xI - B$ and $xI - C$. This can simplify the construction of the $\psi_i(x)$'s.

EXAMPLE 2. Suppose A and A' are $n \times n$ matrices with entries in a given field. Let P be any invertible matrix, whose entries are in a field that contains the given field, such that $A' = P^{-1}AP$. By the Corollary to Theorem 13, A and A' are similar to the same canonical form of the type in Equation (28). There exist connecting matrices that have entries in the given field, because C and C' result from changes of coordinate bases. Hence A and A' are similar to each other by a connecting matrix with entries in the given field.

PROBLEMS

1. Working over the complex numbers, find the invariant factors and elementary divisors of $xI - A$ when

$$\text{(a) } A = \begin{pmatrix} 1 & 1 & 1 \\ 0 & 1 & 1 \\ 0 & 0 & 1 \end{pmatrix}, \quad \text{(b) } A = \begin{pmatrix} -3 & -1 & 3 \\ 22 & 9 & -27 \\ 5 & 2 & -6 \end{pmatrix}, \quad \text{(c) } A = \begin{pmatrix} 2 & 0 & 0 \\ 0 & 1 & -1 \\ 0 & 1 & 3 \end{pmatrix},$$

$$\text{(d) } A = \text{diag}\left(\begin{pmatrix} 0 & 2 \\ 2 & 0 \end{pmatrix}, \begin{pmatrix} 1 & 1 \\ 1 & 1 \end{pmatrix}\right), \quad \text{(e) } A = \begin{pmatrix} 0 & 0 & -1 \\ 0 & 1 & 0 \\ 1 & 0 & -1 \end{pmatrix}.$$

2. Show that a linear transformation of a complex vector space has a diagonal representation if and only if its elementary divisors are of first degree, that is, if and only if the minimal polynomial $\psi_1(x)$ of $\boldsymbol{a}$ has distinct zeros.

3. Show that if the minimal polynomial $\psi_1(x)$ of a linear transformation $\boldsymbol{a}$ of a vector space $\mathbf{V}$ has distinct zeros and if $\mathbf{V}_0$ is a non-zero invariant subspace, then the minimal polynomials of $\boldsymbol{a} \mid \mathbf{V}_0$ and $\bar{\boldsymbol{a}}$ also have distinct zeros.

4. If $\boldsymbol{a} \leftrightarrow A$ is a representation of a linear transformation of a complex vector space, and $\psi_1(x)$ is the minimal polynomial of $\boldsymbol{a}$, show that $\psi_1(x) = |xI - A|$ if and only if $\boldsymbol{a} \leftrightarrow \text{diag}(J_1, \ldots, J_t)$ where the J_i's are Jordan Blocks with distinct characteristic numbers.

5. Let A be an $n \times n$ matrix with t distinct characteristic numbers $s_1, \ldots, s_t$ of multiplicities $n_1, \ldots, n_t$, respectively. Show that:

$$A = \sum_{1}^{t} s_i E_i, \quad \text{where} \quad E_i E_j = O \quad \text{if} \quad i \neq j, \quad E_i^2 = E_i, \quad \text{and rank } E_i = n_i.$$

6. Let $\boldsymbol{a} \leftrightarrow A$ and suppose $\psi_1(x) = |xI - A|$. Show that $BA = AB$ if and only if B is a polynomial in A.

7. Show that A and A^t are similar with a connecting matrix whose entries are in any given field containing the entries of A.

BIBLIOGRAPHY

ELEMENTARY

Johnson, R. E., *Vector Algebra*, Prindle, Weber & Schmidt, Inc. 1966

Kelley, J. L., *Algebra, A Modern Introduction*, D. Van Nostrand Co., Inc. 1965

Schwartz, J. T., *Introduction to Matrices and Vectors*, McGraw-Hill Book Co., Inc. 1961

Yefimov, N. Y., *Quadratic Forms and Matrices*, Academic Press, Inc. 1964

INTERMEDIATE

Dieudonné, J., *Algèbre Lineáre et Géométrie Élementaire*, Hermann, 1964

Gantmacher, F. R., *The Theory of Matrices*, Chelsea Publishing Co. 1960

Halmos, P. R., *Finite-dimensional Vector Spaces*, D. Van Nostrand Co. 1958

Herstein, I. N., *Topics in Algebra*, Blaisdell Publishing Co. 1964

Malcev, A. I., *Foundations of Linear Algebra*, W. H. Freeman and Co. 1963

Thrall, R. M. and Tornheim, L., *Vector Spaces and Matrices*, John Wiley & Sons, Inc. 1957

ADVANCED

Artin, E., *Geometric Algebra*, Interscience Publishers, Inc. 1957

Baer, R., *Linear Algebra and Projective Geometry*, Academic Press, Inc. 1952

Jacobson, N., *Lectures in Abstract Algebra, Vol.* II, D. Van Nostrand Co. 1953

MacLane, S. and Birkhoff, G., *Algebra*, The Macmillan Co. 1967

APPLICATIONS AND SURVEYS

Bellman, R., *Introduction to Matrix Analysis*, McGraw-Hill Book Co., Inc. 1960

Faddeeva, V. N., *Computational Methods of Linear Algebra*, Dover Publications, Inc. 1959

Gantmacher, F. R., *Applications of the Theory of Matrices*, Interscience Publishers, Inc. 1959

Marcus, M. and Minc, H., *A Survey of Matrix Theory and Matrix Inequalities*, Allyn and Bacon, Inc. 1964

Smirnov, V. I., *Linear Algebra and Group Theory*, McGraw-Hill Book Co., Inc. 1961

SUGGESTIONS AND ANSWERS FOR SELECTED PROBLEMS

SUGGESTIONS AND ANSWERS FOR SELECTED PROBLEMS

SECTION 1.1, Page 2

2. $x^2 + 4y^2 + \sqrt{2}\,xy = 1$.

3. The oblique frame is the one in Problem 2, where y is in terms of twice the standard unit. The unit point on the y-axis is at $(\sqrt{2}, \sqrt{2})$. The line $y' = x'$ coincides with the y-axis.

4. $(k^2x^2 + l^2y^2 + 2klxy \cos \theta)^{1/2}$.

5. Draw oblique x, y axes through $\boldsymbol{O}$ and compare similar triangles determined by two points.

7. $a^2 + b^2 = 1$, $c^2 + d^2 = 1$, and $ac + bd = 0$.

SECTION 1.2, Page 5

1. Let (x', y') denote the image of (x, y). (a) $x' = x$, $y' = 0$. (b) $x' = 0$, $y' = 0$.

2. In the first case, each point (x, y) is reflected across the line $y = x$ in a direction parallel to the line $x + y = 1$. In the second case, lines parallel to the y-axis map onto central ellipses, while lines parallel to the x-axis map onto lines through $\boldsymbol{O}$.

3. (a) A square (interior plus perimeter); $x = 0$, $y \sim 7$ at fixed point. (b) Whole plane; nothing is fixed unless $c = d = 0$. (c) Upper half-plane (including x-axis); $(0, 0)$ and $(1, 1)$ are fixed.

4. (a) Images of $x^2 + y^2 = 1$ are: $x^2 + y^2 = k$ under similitude; $x^2 + y^2 = 1$ under reflection through $\boldsymbol{O}$; $-1 \leq y \leq 1$ under projection onto y-axis. (b) Images of $x + y = 1$ are: $x + y = k$, $x + y = -1$; y-axis.

5. By Problem 5, Section 1.1, $x = (dx' - cy')/(ad - bc)$ and $y = (ay' - bx')/(ad - bc)$. Hence the image of a line $Ax + By + C = 0$ has the form $A'x + B'y + C' = 0$.

6. The image of $x^2 + y^2 = 1$ is $2x^2 - 4xy + 3y^2 = 2$; $x = 1$ is the counterimage of $x + y\sqrt{2} = 1$.

SECTION 1.3, Page 7

1. The resultant of the position vector to (x, y) and the position vector to (a, b) is $(x + a, y + b)$; hence $x' = x + a$ and $y' = y + b$.

2. Let $\mathbf{u}$, $\mathbf{v}$, $\mathbf{w}$ be the vectors. Draw the resultant $\mathbf{w}'$ of $\mathbf{u}$ and $\mathbf{v}$, then the resultant of $\mathbf{w}'$ and $\mathbf{w}$.

3. Draw a parallelepiped with one vertex at $\boldsymbol{O}$ and with the vectors $\mathbf{u}$, $\mathbf{v}$, $\mathbf{w}$ at $\boldsymbol{O}$ along the edges. The diagonal from $\boldsymbol{O}$ is the resultant.

4. The range consists of all points (x, y) such that $x \geq 0$, $y \geq 1$; there are no fixed points. In particular: image of $x^2 + y^2 = 1$ is $x^2 + (y - 1)^2 = 1$, and image of $y = x$ is $y = x + 1$ $(x \geq 0)$.

SECTION 1.4, Page 9

2. This distributive law is a special case of the parallelogram law.

3. Use another mixed distributive law, namely, $c(\mathbf{u} + \mathbf{v}) = c\mathbf{u} + c\mathbf{v}$.

4. $t'(\mathbf{i} + 2\mathbf{j}) = \mathbf{i} + t(2\mathbf{j} - \mathbf{i})$, $t = t' = \frac{1}{2}$, $\mathbf{u} = \mathbf{i}/2 + \mathbf{j}$.
$t'(\mathbf{i} + 2\mathbf{j}) = \mathbf{j} + t\mathbf{i}$, $t = t' = \frac{1}{2}$, $\mathbf{u} = \mathbf{i}/2 + \mathbf{j}$.
$t'(\mathbf{i} + 2\mathbf{j}) = \mathbf{j} + t(2\mathbf{i} - \mathbf{j})$, $t = \frac{1}{5}$, $t' = \frac{2}{5}$, $\mathbf{u} = 2\mathbf{i}/5 + 4\mathbf{j}/5$.

SECTION 1.5, Page 12

2. Using coordinate rows of position vectors to given points, we get: (a) Equation of a line through (a, b, c) and (d, e, f) is $(x, y, z) = (a, b, c) + t(d - a, e - b, f - c)$. (b) Equation of a plane through (a, b, c), (d, e, f), and (g, h, i) is $(x, y, z) = (a, b, c) + t(d - a, e - b, f - c) + t'(g - a, h - b, i - c)$, where t and t' are independent.

4. Since the indicated correspondence is meant to hold for every choice of c and c', we can first set $c = c' = 1$ and then $c = 1$, $c' = 0$, thus giving the isomorphism of Equation (3). Conversely, note that the isomorphism of Equation (3) implies $c\mathbf{u} \leftrightarrow c(x, y)$ and $c'\mathbf{u}' \leftrightarrow c'(\mathbf{x}, \mathbf{y})$.

5. We may substitute coordinate rows, using the isomorphism $\mathbf{u} \leftrightarrow (x, y)$, so $(x, y) \leftrightarrow (-x, -y)$. $-[(x, y) + (x', y')] = (-x, -y) + (-x', -y')$, and $-[c(x, y)] = c(-x, -y)$. The projection onto the y-axis satisfies conditions (a) and (b) in the definition of an isomorphism, but is not a one-to-one correspondence.

6. With a 2-tuple (a, b) associate a function f defined by: $f(1) = a, f(2) = b$. Denote this correspondence by $(a, b) \leftrightarrow f$.

SECTION 1.6, Page 14

1. With respect to $\{(1, 0), (0, 1)\}$, a 2-tuple vector (x, y) has coordinate row (x, y). With respect to $\{\mathbf{i}, \mathbf{j}\}$, a vector $x\mathbf{i} + y\mathbf{j}$ at $\boldsymbol{O}$ has coordinate row (x, y). A change in the order of the basis vectors causes a permutation of the coordinates.

2. To get $1 \cdot \mathbf{u} = \mathbf{u}$ from IV′ show that $1 \cdot \mathbf{o} = \mathbf{o}$, then multiply $\mathbf{u} + (-1)\mathbf{u} = \mathbf{o}$ by 1 and add $\mathbf{u}$ to both sides. Then, to get $0\mathbf{u} = \mathbf{o}$ for every $\mathbf{u}$, note that $\mathbf{u} + 0\mathbf{u} = 1\mathbf{u} + 0\mathbf{u} = 1\mathbf{u} = \mathbf{u} = \mathbf{u} + \mathbf{o}$ for every $\mathbf{u}$ and add $(-1)\mathbf{u}$ to both sides. Conversely, note that $\mathbf{u} + \mathbf{o} = 1\mathbf{u} + 0\mathbf{u}$ and $\mathbf{u} + (-1)\mathbf{u} = 1\mathbf{u} + (-1)\mathbf{u}$.

3. $\mathbf{w} = (a/bc)\mathbf{u} + (-1/c)\mathbf{v}$.

SECTION 1.7, Page 16

1. (a) $(a, b) = a'(1, 1) + b'(1, -1)$ has a unique solution for the pair a', b', namely $a' = (a + b)/2$ and $b' = (a - b)/2$. (b) $(a, b, c) = a'(1, 0, 1) + b'(1, 1, 0) + c'(0, 1, 1)$ has the unique solution $a' = (a - b + c)/2$, $b' = (a + b - c)/2$, $c' = (-a + b + c)/2$. (c) (a', b') and (a', b', c'), respectively.

3. $ad - bc = 0$ implies $ed - bf = af - ec = 0$, so the latter condition is certainly necessary for a solution to exist. Suppose $ed - bf = af - ec = 0$. If $(e, f) = (0, 0)$, we find the equations are proportional. If $(e, f) \neq (0, 0)$, then either $(a, b) = (e/f)(c, d)$ or $(c, d) = (f/e)(a, b)$, and the equations are again proportional.

4. If (a, b) were a basis, then $(1, 0) = x(a, b)$ and $(0, 1) = y(a, b)$, which imply $x(1, 0) = y(0, 1)$.

6. $(1, 1) = a(1, i) + b(1, -i)$ where $a = (1 - i)/2$ and $b = (1 + i)/2$. It is a basis for same reason as in the real case.

7. Consider real n-tuples.

SECTION 1.8, Page 18

1. Note that $\mathbf{o} = 0\mathbf{u}_1 + \cdots + 0\mathbf{u}_t$.

2. If the polynomial is a non-zero constant, then it is of course never zero. If it has degree n, then it equals zero for at most n distinct real numbers (the factor theorem of elementary algebra). To justify the definition of equality of real polynomials given in Example 1, call two polynomials equal if and only if they define the same function.

3. (a) Write any complex number in the form $a1 + bi$ where a and b are real. Take the real numbers as scalars. Then $\{1, i\}$ is a basis. (b) Take the real numbers as scalars and $\{(1, 0), (i, 0), (0, 1), (0, i)\}$ as a basis.

4. Consider the correspondence $(x, y, 0) \leftrightarrow (x, y)$.

5. Take each given basis, in the order indicated, as a coordinate basis. A different ordering will lead to a permuted form of the coordinate rows. Then $\sum a_i x^i \leftrightarrow (a_0, a_1, \ldots, a_{k-1})$, $a + bi \leftrightarrow (a, b)$, $(a + bi, c + di) \leftrightarrow (a, b, c, d)$.

6. Consider the 2-dimensional case. Let $\{\mathbf{u}, \mathbf{v}\}$ be a coordinate basis of one of the vector spaces and $\{\mathbf{u}', \mathbf{v}'\}$ a coordinate basis of the other. The correspondence $x\mathbf{u} + y\mathbf{v} \leftrightarrow x\mathbf{u}' + y\mathbf{v}'$ for all real number x, y is a one-to-one correspondence between the two vector spaces, and we already know that $x\mathbf{u} + y\mathbf{v} \leftrightarrow (x, y)$ and $x\mathbf{u}' + y\mathbf{v}' \leftrightarrow (x, y)$ are isomorphisms with 2-tuple vector space.

7. If $m = -\infty$, use the convention $-\infty + n = -\infty$.

SECTION 1.9, Page 19

1. Any vector has the form $e\mathbf{u} + f\mathbf{v}$. Hence the two linear combinations constitute a basis if and only if for any (e, f) there is a unique (x, y) such that $e\mathbf{u} + f\mathbf{v} = x(a\mathbf{u} + e\mathbf{v}) + y(b\mathbf{u} + d\mathbf{v})$. Now apply Section 1.7, Example 2 to the equations $e = ax + by$, $f = ex + dy$.

2. The latter condition is equivalent to neither vector being a multiple of the other. This in turn is equivalent to $\{\mathbf{u}, \mathbf{v}\}$ being a basis when we are dealing with the vectors at $\boldsymbol{O}$ (Section 1.7). If we do not wish to assume our vector space is the vector space at $\boldsymbol{O}$, then we may use the isomorphism of Section 1.8, Problem 6, or use the method of Problem 3 below.

3. For any $\mathbf{w}$, $a\mathbf{u} + b\mathbf{v} + c\mathbf{w} = \mathbf{o}$ non-trivially. If $c = 0$ then a or b would be non-zero. Hence $\mathbf{w} = k\mathbf{u} + l\mathbf{v}$. If $\mathbf{w} = k'\mathbf{u} + l'\mathbf{v}$, then $(k - k')\mathbf{u} + (l - l')\mathbf{v} = \mathbf{o}$, which forces $k = k'$ and $l = l'$. Hence $\{\mathbf{u}, \mathbf{v}\}$ is a basis by Rule V.

4. We need show uniqueness only. Use the fact that $\mathbf{o}$ has a unique expression as a linear combination of $\mathbf{u}$, $\mathbf{v}$, $\mathbf{w}$.

SECTION 2.1, Page 25

2. $x + ky = c$.

4. $x' = ax + by$, $y' = kax + kby$ (a or b non-zero).

5. Suppose one-to-one. Obviously (0, 0) is a solution; hence it is the only solution. Suppose, on the other hand, that (0, 0) is the only solution; then (a, c) and (b, d) are not proportional, so $ad - bc \neq 0$, which implies that each (e, f) has a unique counterimage. Finally, (a, c), (b, d) are proportional if and only if $ad - bc = 0$.

6. Each (e, f) is in the range if and only if $ad - bc \neq 0$ (see Example 6), and if and only if the mapping is one-to-one (see Problem 5).

7. Substituting into Equation 3 we find $(1, 1) = (a, c)$ and $(1, 2) = (b, d)$, so $a = b = c = 1$ and $d = 2$. The systems: $x_1' = x_1a + y_1b$, $x_2' = x_2a + y_2b$; $y_1' = x_1c + y_1d$, $y_2' = x_2c + y_2d$ have unique solutions for (a, b), (c, d) respectively. The determinant condition qualifies (x_1, y_1), (x_2, y_2) as unit points.

SECTION 2.2, Page 26

2. Every polynomial is a linear combination of $1, 2^{1/3}, 2^{2/3}$. Show that $a + b2^{1/3} + c2^{2/3} = 0$ for rational a, b, c if and only if $a = b = c = 0$.

3. When the determinant is not zero, Cramer's rule applies and uses only field operations. When the determinant is zero, we can substitute a field element for one of the unknowns and solve for the other.

4. p^n.

5. $l = qp + r$ with $0 \leq r < p$, so $\bar{l} = \bar{r}$. Hence, each integer belongs to exactly one of the p classes. Verify that $\overline{m + n}$ and $\overline{mn}$ are uniquely determined by $\bar{m}$ and $\bar{n}$. Then check the field properties.

SECTION 2.3, Page 30

1. Set $\mathbf{w}_0 = e\mathbf{u} + f\mathbf{v}$, so $\mathbf{w} = f\mathbf{v} + (t + e)\mathbf{u}$. Compute $\boldsymbol{a}\mathbf{w}$.

2. $\mathbf{w} = \mathbf{w}_0 + t\mathbf{u}$, $\boldsymbol{a}\mathbf{w} = \boldsymbol{a}\mathbf{w}_0 + t\boldsymbol{a}\mathbf{u}$. We write a parallel line as $\mathbf{w} = \mathbf{w}_0' + t'\mathbf{u}$, so $\boldsymbol{a}\mathbf{w} = \boldsymbol{a}\mathbf{w}_0' + t'\boldsymbol{a}\mathbf{u}$. If $\mathbf{w}_0' + c'\mathbf{u} = \mathbf{w}_0 + c\mathbf{u}$ for particular scalars c', c, then also $\boldsymbol{a}\mathbf{w}_0' + c'\boldsymbol{a}\mathbf{u}' = \boldsymbol{a}\mathbf{w}_0 + c\boldsymbol{a}\mathbf{u}$.

3. $\boldsymbol{O}$ is fixed; let $\boldsymbol{P}, \boldsymbol{Q}, \boldsymbol{R}$ be the three fixed points. Among these, some triple including $\boldsymbol{O}$, say $\boldsymbol{O}, \boldsymbol{P}, \boldsymbol{Q}$, is not collinear. Consider the position vectors to $\boldsymbol{P}$ and $\boldsymbol{Q}$.

4. See Figure 20 and include the degenerate case.

5. $\boldsymbol{a}(x\mathbf{u} + y\mathbf{v}) = y\mathbf{u} + x\mathbf{v}$, $(y\mathbf{u} + x\mathbf{v}) - (x\mathbf{u} + y\mathbf{v}) = -(x - y)\mathbf{u} + (x - y)\mathbf{v} = (x - y)(\mathbf{v} - \mathbf{u})$.

6. Choose $\mathbf{w} = y\mathbf{u}$ for the y-axis, and $\mathbf{w} = x\mathbf{v}$ for the x-axis.

SECTION 2.4, Page 35

1. (1) $1, -1, k, 1$; (2) $0, 1$; (4) $aei + bfg + cdh - ceg - bdi - ahf, 1$; (5) 1; (6) kl.

2. Note that $x = (x' \cos \phi + y' \sin \phi)/k$, $y = (-x' \sin \phi + y' \cos \phi)/l$. Hence, $(lm \cos \phi + k \sin \phi)x + (lm \sin \phi - k \cos \phi)y = 0$, and $y = x$ is invariant if and only if $k/l = \tan (\phi + \pi/4)$.

3. (a) $x' = 2x - y$, $y' = 2y$. (b) $x' = 2x$, $y' = -x + 2y$. (c) $x' = x + z$, $y' = y + z$, $z' = x + y$. (d) $x' = kx$, $y' = ly$, $z' = mx$.

SECTION 2.5, Page 38

2. x arbitrary, $y = 0$, $z = 2$ if $x \neq 0$ and z arbitrary if $x = 0$. Consider the 2×2 matrix as the representation of a linear transformation. Then every vector to a point on the x-axis is mapped onto twice itself. Hence, the x-axis is the only line through $\boldsymbol{O}$ that is invariant.

3. $BA = I$, $U = \begin{pmatrix} 1 \\ 0 \end{pmatrix}$.

4. $\begin{pmatrix} 0 & 0 & 1 \\ 1 & 0 & 0 \\ 0 & 1 & 0 \end{pmatrix}$.

5. Add by adding corresponding entries. For scalar multiple, multiply each entry by the scalar.

6. By Section 2.1, Example 6, Part (c), we know that $A \neq O$ if and only if $\begin{pmatrix} e \\ f \end{pmatrix}$ is a unique linear combination of the columns of A for every $\begin{pmatrix} e \\ f \end{pmatrix}$.

SECTION 2.6, Page 43

1. From $\boldsymbol{a}\begin{pmatrix} 1 \\ 1 \end{pmatrix} = \frac{1}{2}\begin{pmatrix} 1 \\ 1 \end{pmatrix} + \frac{1}{2}\begin{pmatrix} 1 \\ -1 \end{pmatrix}$, $\boldsymbol{a}\begin{pmatrix} 1 \\ -1 \end{pmatrix} = \frac{1}{2}\begin{pmatrix} 1 \\ 1 \end{pmatrix} - \frac{1}{2}\begin{pmatrix} 1 \\ -1 \end{pmatrix}$ we have $\boldsymbol{a} \leftrightarrow \frac{1}{2}\begin{pmatrix} 1 & 1 \\ 1 & -1 \end{pmatrix}$. If we solve $\boldsymbol{a}E_1 + \boldsymbol{a}E_2 = E_1$, $\boldsymbol{a}E_1 - \boldsymbol{a}E_2 = E_2$ for $\boldsymbol{a}E_1$ and $\boldsymbol{a}E_2$, we get the same representation of $\boldsymbol{a}$. See Section 3.2, Example 3.

2. $\begin{pmatrix} a & b \\ c & d \end{pmatrix}$.

3. $\sqrt{2} \cdot 1 = 0 \cdot 1 + 1 \cdot \sqrt{2}$, $\sqrt{2} \cdot \sqrt{2} = 2 \cdot 1 + 0 \cdot \sqrt{2}$

4. $ae^{i\phi}z = a'e^{i\phi'}z$ for all z if and only if $a = a'$, $\phi = \phi' + 2\pi k$.

6. Set $\mathbf{i} = \mathbf{u}$, $\mathbf{j} = -\mathbf{u} + \sqrt{2}\,\mathbf{v}$.

SECTION 2.7, Page 47

2. (a) $a = \frac{1}{2}$, $b = \frac{1}{3}$, $c = 3$. (b) $a = 2$, $b = 0$, $c = 0$, $d = 3$. (c) $a = b = \frac{1}{2}$, $c = 0$, $d = -1$. (d) $b = d = e = f = 1$, $c = 0$. (e) See Section 1.1, Problem 7.

3. $\begin{pmatrix} a & b \\ 0 & a \end{pmatrix}$. If $\sin\phi \neq 0$, then $b = -c$, $a = d$, so $\begin{pmatrix} a & b \\ -b & a \end{pmatrix} \leftrightarrow \pm\sqrt{a^2 + b^2}\, e^{i\phi}$, $\cos\phi = a/\sqrt{a^2 + b^2}$, $\sin\phi = b/\sqrt{a^2 + b^2}$. Given matrix commutes only with rotations and similitudes (including negative ones).

4. $AB = \begin{pmatrix} A_1B \\ A_2B \end{pmatrix}$, $(AB)C = (ABC_1, ABC_2)$.

5. Reduce all possibilities to $\boldsymbol{a}(\boldsymbol{b}(\boldsymbol{c}(\boldsymbol{d}\mathbf{u})$.

SECTION 2.8, Page 51

2. $(s(\boldsymbol{ab}))\mathbf{u} = s(\boldsymbol{a}(\boldsymbol{b}\mathbf{u})) = (s\boldsymbol{a})(\boldsymbol{b}\mathbf{u}) = \boldsymbol{a}(s(\boldsymbol{b}\mathbf{u})) = (\boldsymbol{a}(s\boldsymbol{b}))\mathbf{u}$.

3. Use Example 7 and Problem 2.

4. 0.

5. 0.

6. It is one-to-one, sums correspond to sums, products to products.

SECTION 2.9, Page 54

1. O.

3. In the 2×2 case, can always solve $\begin{pmatrix} s & 0 \\ 0 & t \end{pmatrix} = pI + qA$ for p and q.

SECTION 2.10, Page 56

1. Notice that the zero vector in any subspace is the same as the zero vector of the given vector space.

3. Solve $x - y + 2z = 0$, $x + y + z = 0$ simultaneously to get $(3, -1, -2)$.

5. $\mathbf{u} = \mathbf{v} = \mathbf{o}$: point. $\mathbf{u}$ and $\mathbf{v}$ proportional and not both zero : line.

6. Let $\mathbf{u}$, $\mathbf{u}'$ be in the set. Then for any scalars s, s', $s\mathbf{u} + s'\mathbf{u}' = s\boldsymbol{a}\mathbf{v} + s'\boldsymbol{a}\mathbf{v}' = \boldsymbol{a}(s\mathbf{v} + s'\mathbf{v}')$.

SECTION 2.11, Page 58

1. $\ker \boldsymbol{a} = \{(x, y) \mid y = 0\}$, $\operatorname{im} \boldsymbol{a} = \{(x, y) \mid fx = ey\}$.

2. $\boldsymbol{a}\mathbf{u} = \mathbf{o}$, $\boldsymbol{a}\mathbf{v} = \mathbf{u}$, where $\{\mathbf{u}, \mathbf{v}\}$ is a basis.

3. The conditions imply $\operatorname{im} \boldsymbol{a} = [\mathbf{u}]$, $\mathbf{u} \neq \mathbf{o}$, $\ker \boldsymbol{a} = [\mathbf{v}]$, $\mathbf{v} \neq \mathbf{o}$. Either $\ker \boldsymbol{a} = \operatorname{im} \boldsymbol{a}$, so take a basis $\{\mathbf{u}, \mathbf{u}'\}$ to get $\boldsymbol{a} \leftrightarrow \begin{pmatrix} 0 & k \\ 0 & 0 \end{pmatrix}$; or $\ker \boldsymbol{a} \neq \operatorname{im} \boldsymbol{a}$, so take $\{\mathbf{u}, \mathbf{v}\}$ as a basis to get $\boldsymbol{a} \leftrightarrow \begin{pmatrix} k & 0 \\ 0 & 0 \end{pmatrix}$.

5. Suppose $\mathbf{u}$, $\mathbf{v}$, $\mathbf{w}$ along these lines. Then $\{\mathbf{u}, \mathbf{v}\}$ is a basis and $\mathbf{w} = e\mathbf{u} + f\mathbf{v}$ with $ef \neq 0$. Also $\boldsymbol{a}\mathbf{u} = r\mathbf{u}$, $\boldsymbol{a}\mathbf{v} = s\mathbf{v}$, $\boldsymbol{a}\mathbf{w} = t\mathbf{w}$. Consider $\boldsymbol{a}\mathbf{w}$.

SECTION 2.12, Page 61

2. $\text{cof-}\begin{pmatrix} a & b \\ c & d \end{pmatrix} = \begin{pmatrix} d & -c \\ -b & a \end{pmatrix}$.

$$\text{cof-}\begin{pmatrix} a & b & c \\ d & e & f \\ g & h & i \end{pmatrix} = \begin{pmatrix} ei\text{-}fh & fg\text{-}di & dh\text{-}eg \\ ch\text{-}bi & ai\text{-}cg & bg\text{-}ah \\ bf\text{-}ce & cd\text{-}af & ae\text{-}bd \end{pmatrix}.$$

3. $(1/adf)\begin{pmatrix} pdf - qbf + rbe - rcd \\ qaf - rae \\ rad \end{pmatrix}$.

5. Note that $\omega^2 + \omega + 1 = 0$.

SECTION 2.13, Page 65

1. $AA^t = I$.

3. $(\boldsymbol{ab})(\boldsymbol{b}^{-1}\boldsymbol{a}^{-1}) = \boldsymbol{a}(\boldsymbol{bb}^{-1})\boldsymbol{a}^{-1} = \boldsymbol{aa}^{-1} = \boldsymbol{i}$.

4. $|A^t| = |A|$ and $\text{cof-}A^t = (\text{cof-}A)^t$. Apply this to Equation 43. If you start with $(AB)^t = B^tA^t$ (Section 3.2, Problem 3), then it follows from $AA^{-1} = I = A^{-1}A$ and the uniqueness of the inverse.

5. a^{-1} is defined by $a^{-1}\mathbf{u}' = \mathbf{u}$, $a^{-1}\mathbf{v}' = \mathbf{v}$. Substituting for $\mathbf{u}'$ and $\mathbf{v}'$ and solving for $a^{-1}\mathbf{u}$ and $a^{-1}\mathbf{v}$, we find $a^{-1} \leftrightarrow A^{-1}$ with respect to $\{\mathbf{u}, \mathbf{v}\}$.

6. In Section 6.5, Problem 6, we saw that $|A| = O$ if and only if the column vectors form a basis (same for rows). But now we know that $|A| \neq O$ if and only if A^{-1} exists.

7. $(\text{adj-}A)A = |A|I$. If $|\text{adj-}A| \neq 0$, then $(\text{adj-}A)^{-1}(\text{adj-}A)A = A = O$; and of course $|\text{adj-}O| = 0$.

SECTION 2.14, Page 66

1. Show that the three vectors constitute a basis.

3. For the converse (yes): Assume a 3-dimensional vector space must have three vectors in each basis, and apply Section 1.9, Problem 4.

4. (a) For example, [(1, 0, 0, 0), (0, 1, 0, 0)]. (b) For example, [1].

SECTION 2.15, Page 68

1. Let $\mathbf{w} = x\mathbf{u} + y\mathbf{v} + z\mathbf{w}$. Now such a reflection is determined by $a(x\mathbf{u} + y\mathbf{v} + z\mathbf{w}) = x\mathbf{u} + y\mathbf{v} - z\mathbf{w}$; hence $a\mathbf{w} = xa\mathbf{u} + ya\mathbf{v} + za\mathbf{w}$.

2. In Example 3: $x' = x$, $y' = y$, $z' = -z$. In Example 2: If we assume $\mathbf{v}$, $\mathbf{w}$ are already mutually perpendicular unit vectors, then $x' = x$, $y' = y\cos\phi - z\sin\phi$, $z' = y\sin\phi + z\cos\phi$.

3. $x' = z$, $y' = w$, $z' = x$, $w' = y$ are linear coordinate equations. A possible representation is by $\begin{pmatrix} 0 & 1 & 0 & 0 \\ 1 & 0 & 0 & 0 \\ 0 & 0 & 0 & 1 \\ 0 & 0 & 1 & 0 \end{pmatrix}$.

4. (a) $a(s_1\mathbf{v}_1 + s_2\mathbf{v}_2) = s_1\mathbf{v}_1 = s_1a\mathbf{v}_1 + s_2a\mathbf{v}_2$; $[\mathbf{v}_1]$.
(b) $a(s_1\mathbf{v}_1 + s_2\mathbf{v}_2) = s_1\mathbf{v}_1 - s_2\mathbf{v}_2 = s_1a\mathbf{v}_1 + s_2a\mathbf{v}_2$; $[\mathbf{v}_1]$.

SECTION 2.16, Page 70

1. Rotation through 45° in real 2-dimensional vector space:

$$a \leftrightarrow (\sqrt{2}/2)\begin{pmatrix} 1 & -1 \\ 1 & 1 \end{pmatrix}$$

with respect to a Cartesian coordinate system. No.

2. If $a\mathbf{u} = t\mathbf{u}$, $\mathbf{u} \neq \mathbf{o}$, then the characteristic numbers are t^{-1}, st, t^2 respectively.

3. $(si - a)\mathbf{u} = \mathbf{o}$ for $\mathbf{u} \neq \mathbf{o}$ implies $a\mathbf{u} = s\mathbf{u}$ for $\mathbf{u} \neq \mathbf{o}$.

4. Suppose $\mathbf{u}_2 = k\mathbf{u}_1$ $(k \neq 0)$. Then $a\mathbf{u}_2 = ka\mathbf{u}_1$, so $s_2\mathbf{u}_2 = s_2k\mathbf{u}_1 = ks_1\mathbf{u}_1$ implies $s_2\mathbf{u}_1 = s_1\mathbf{u}_1$ and $\mathbf{u}_1 = \mathbf{o}$.

5. By second part of Problem 1, there exists at least one characteristic vector, say $\mathbf{u}$, $a\mathbf{u} = s\mathbf{u}$. Use $\{\mathbf{u}, \mathbf{v}, \mathbf{w}\}$ as a basis.

SECTION 2.17, Page 73

1. $\{0, 2\}$, $\left\{\begin{pmatrix} 1 \\ -1 \end{pmatrix}, \begin{pmatrix} 1 \\ 1 \end{pmatrix}\right\}$. No.

2. Same characteristic numbers because $|xI - A^t| = |xI - A|$. Generally different vectors, although if one has none, then neither does the other. Note that $\begin{pmatrix}1\\2\end{pmatrix}$ is a characteristic vector of $\begin{pmatrix}0 & 1\\4 & 0\end{pmatrix}$ but not of $\begin{pmatrix}0 & 4\\1 & 0\end{pmatrix}$.

3. $\{0, \pm\sqrt{3}\}$, $\left\{\begin{pmatrix}1\\1\\-1\end{pmatrix}, \begin{pmatrix}\sqrt{3}+1\\1\\\sqrt{3}+2\end{pmatrix}, \begin{pmatrix}\sqrt{3}-1\\1\\-\sqrt{3}+2\end{pmatrix}\right\}$.

4. Roots of $x^2 + b^2 = 0$ are $\pm ib$. So $\boldsymbol{a}$ has no characteristic numbers and therefore no characteristic vectors. For A, we get $\begin{pmatrix}1\\i\end{pmatrix}$ and $\begin{pmatrix}-1\\i\end{pmatrix}$ corresponding to ib and $-ib$ respectively.

5. $\{0, \pm i\sqrt{b^2 + c^2 + f^2}\}$.

SECTION 2.18, Page 75

2. $\boldsymbol{a}(\mathbf{u} + (f - s)\mathbf{v}') = s\mathbf{u} + (f - s)(\mathbf{u} + f\mathbf{v}') = f(\mathbf{u} + (f - s)\mathbf{v}')$, not a multiple of $\mathbf{u}$.

3. $z \cdot 1 = 0 + z$ and $z \cdot z = -z\bar{z} + 2xz$.

SECTION 3.1, Page 79

1. (a) $\boldsymbol{a} = k\boldsymbol{i}$, $\boldsymbol{p}(k\boldsymbol{i}) = k(\boldsymbol{pi}) = k(\boldsymbol{ip}) = (k\boldsymbol{i})\boldsymbol{p}$, even if $k < 0$.
(b) $k \neq 0$. $k\boldsymbol{a} = k\boldsymbol{b}$ if and only if $\boldsymbol{a} = \boldsymbol{b}$.

2. (a) $\boldsymbol{b} \leftrightarrow A$ with respect to $\{\mathbf{u}_1, \mathbf{u}_2\}$.
(b) $\boldsymbol{b} \leftrightarrow \begin{pmatrix}0 & 3\\-\frac{1}{3} & 0\end{pmatrix}$ with respect to $\{\mathbf{u}_1, \mathbf{u}_2\}$.

3. (c) Let $\boldsymbol{a} \leftrightarrow I$ and $\boldsymbol{b} \leftrightarrow \begin{pmatrix}0 & 1\\1 & 0\end{pmatrix}$ with respect to the same coordinate basis.

4. $\boldsymbol{bp}\mathbf{u} = \boldsymbol{pa}\mathbf{u} = s\boldsymbol{p}\mathbf{u}$, $\boldsymbol{p}\mathbf{u} \neq \mathbf{o}$ because $\boldsymbol{p}$ is invertible.

5. Note that if $\boldsymbol{a}$ and $\boldsymbol{b}$ are both similar to $\boldsymbol{c}$, then $\boldsymbol{a}$ is similar to $\boldsymbol{b}$.

7. Eliminate algebraically to show that $\boldsymbol{c}\mathbf{u} = (\frac{4}{3})\mathbf{u} - (\frac{2}{3})\mathbf{v}$, $\boldsymbol{c}\mathbf{v} = (-\frac{1}{3})\mathbf{u} + (\frac{5}{3})\mathbf{v}$. It is immediate to get $P = \begin{pmatrix}1 & 1\\1 & -2\end{pmatrix}$.

SECTION 3.2, Page 82

1. Matrices resulting from all six permutations of the columns of the 3×3 I; premultiply the coordinate columns.

2. Six matrices like $\begin{pmatrix}1 & k & 0\\0 & 1 & 0\\0 & 0 & 1\end{pmatrix}$.

3. The i, j entry in $(AB)^t$ is $\sum_k a_{jk}b_{ki}$. The i, j entry in B^tA^t is $\sum_k b_{ki}\, a_{jk}$.

SECTION 3.3, Page 88

1. (b) If $B = P^{-1}AP$ and $P^{-1} = (p'_{ij})$, then $\sum p'_{ik}a_{kl}p_{li} = \sum a_{kl}\sum p_{li}p'_{ik} = \sum a_{kk}$. The latter sum is called the *trace* of A.

2. (a) Consider $P\,\mathrm{diag}(t_1, t_2) = \mathrm{diag}(s_1, s_2)P$; or apply Problem 1. (b) Like (a).

3. If $P^{-1}AP = \mathrm{diag}(s, t)$, apply Problem 1 to show that $s^2 + s + 1 = 0$.

4. $P = \begin{pmatrix} 0 & 0 & 1 \\ 0 & 1 & 0 \\ 1 & 0 & 0 \end{pmatrix}$; $\{\mathbf{v}, \mathbf{u}, \mathbf{w}\}$.

5. $P = \begin{pmatrix} 1 & \omega^2 & \omega \\ 1 & \omega & \omega^2 \\ 1 & 1 & 1 \end{pmatrix}$, $P^{-1}AP = \mathrm{diag}(1, \omega, \omega^2)$.

6. Take $\{\mathbf{i} + \mathbf{j} + \mathbf{k}, \mathbf{i} - \mathbf{j}, \mathbf{i} - \mathbf{k}\}$ as *first* coordinate basis. Hence, with respect to the first, it is obvious that $\boldsymbol{a} \leftrightarrow A = \mathrm{diag}(1, -1, -1)$. Also we see that

$$P^{-1} = \begin{pmatrix} 1 & 1 & 1 \\ 1 & -1 & 0 \\ 1 & 0 & -1 \end{pmatrix} \text{ and } P^{-1}A = \begin{pmatrix} 1 & -1 & -1 \\ 1 & 1 & 0 \\ 1 & 0 & 1 \end{pmatrix}.$$

Now compute P, so with respect to the second basis $\boldsymbol{a} \leftrightarrow P^{-1}AP = (\frac{1}{3})\begin{pmatrix} -1 & 2 & 2 \\ 2 & -1 & 2 \\ 2 & 2 & -1 \end{pmatrix}$.

SECTION 3.4, Page 94

1 Premultiply $aU + bV + cW = O$ by U^t, V^t, and W^t in turn.

2. (a) Characteristic numbers $\{0, 0\}$; characteristic vectors are the non-zero multiples $(i, 1)^t$. (b) $\{0, 2\}$; non-zero multiples of $(-1, i)^t$, $(i, 1)^t$.

3. $P = \begin{pmatrix} 1 & 1 \\ 1 & -1 \end{pmatrix}$; $\{0, 2\}$; $(1, 1)^t$, $(1, -1)^t$.

4. (a) $X(A - B)Y = O$, $E_i^t(A - B)E_j = a_{ij} - b_{ij} = 0$.
(b) $E_i^tAE_i = a_{ii} = 0$, $(E_i + E_j)^tA(E_i + E_j) = 2a_{ij} = 0$.

5. Consider the discriminant of $|xI - A|$.

6. Consider a linear dependence which involves a minimal number of the U_i's. Premultiply by A and by one of the characteristic numbers in turn.

SECTION 3.5, Page 96

1. $\begin{pmatrix} 7 & -2 & 0 \\ -2 & 6 & -2 \\ 0 & -2 & 5 \end{pmatrix}$, $x^3 - 18x^2 + 99x - 162$.

$\begin{pmatrix} 1 & 2 & -4 \\ 2 & -2 & -2 \\ -4 & -2 & 1 \end{pmatrix}$, $x^3 - 27x - 54$. $\begin{pmatrix} 2 & 2 & 1 \\ 2 & 2 & 1 \\ 1 & 1 & 3 \end{pmatrix}$, $x^3 - 7x^2 + 10x$.

2. $\begin{pmatrix} 2 & -1 & -1 \\ -1 & 2 & -1 \\ -1 & -1 & 2 \end{pmatrix}$, $\{0, 3, 3\}$. $\begin{pmatrix} 1 & 1 & 1 \\ 1 & 1 & 1 \\ 1 & 1 & 1 \end{pmatrix}$, $\{3, 0\ 0\}$.

$(\frac{1}{2})\begin{pmatrix} 0 & 1 & 1 \\ 1 & 0 & 1 \\ 1 & 1 & 0 \end{pmatrix}$, $\{1, -\frac{1}{2}, -\frac{1}{2}\}$.

3. $X^tB^tBX = (XB)^tXB = \sum y_i^2$. **5.** See Section 3.4, Problem 4.

SECTION 3.6, Page 98

1. In Problem 1, $X = (1, 1)^t \to X' = E$, $Y = (1, -1)^t \to Y' = E_2$; so $(X', Y') = I$. Parts (a) and (c) therefore have the same answer, namely $(X, Y)^{-1} = (\frac{1}{2})\begin{pmatrix} 1 & 1 \\ 1 & -1 \end{pmatrix}$. This can be done directly by solving for X and Y in terms of E_1 and E_2. In Problem 2, $X = E_1 \to X' = (a, c)^t$, $Y = E_2 \to (b, d)^t$; so $(X', Y') = \begin{pmatrix} a & b \\ c & d \end{pmatrix}$; hence by Part (c), $\boldsymbol{a} \leftrightarrow \begin{pmatrix} a & b \\ c & d \end{pmatrix}$, as is obvious anyhow because X' and Y' are easy linear combinations of X and Y.

2. (a) $\begin{pmatrix} 2 & 1 \\ 1 & 2 \end{pmatrix}^{-1} \begin{pmatrix} 1 & 0 \\ 2 & 0 \end{pmatrix} = \begin{pmatrix} 0 & 0 \\ 1 & 0 \end{pmatrix}$. (c) $\begin{pmatrix} 1 & 0 \\ 2 & 0 \end{pmatrix} (\frac{1}{3}) \begin{pmatrix} 2 & -1 \\ -1 & 2 \end{pmatrix} = (\frac{1}{3}) \begin{pmatrix} 2 & -1 \\ 4 & -2 \end{pmatrix}$

3. For Problem 2: $2\boldsymbol{a}E_1 + \boldsymbol{a}E_2 = E_1 + 2E_2, \boldsymbol{a}E_1 + 2\boldsymbol{a}E_2 = 0E_1 + 0E_2$; eliminate and get $\boldsymbol{a} \leftrightarrow (\frac{1}{3}) \begin{pmatrix} 2 & -1 \\ 4 & -2 \end{pmatrix}$.

4. See Section 3.3, remarks preceding Example 1.

SECTION 3.7, Page 104

1. $\mathbf{v} = \mathbf{u} + c\mathbf{u}_0$, $\mathbf{v}' = \mathbf{u}' + c'\mathbf{u}_0$ so $\mathbf{v}'' = \mathbf{u} + \mathbf{u}' + c''\mathbf{u}_0 = \mathbf{u}'' + c''\mathbf{u}_0$.

2. A, $\{s, s\}$, $(k, 0)^t$, $k \neq 0$; C, $\{1, 1\}$, $(k, 0)^t$, $k \neq 0$; B, $\{s, s\}$, any non-zero vector.

3. (a) 1. $(1, 0)^t + [(0, 1)^t]$,
2. $(1, 1)^t + [(1, -1)^t]$,
3. $(-1, -1)^t + [(3, 2)^t]$.

(b) 1. $(1, 0, 0)^t + [(0, 1, 0)^t, (0, 0, 1)^t]$,
2. $(1, 0, 0)^t + [(1, -1, 0)^t, (1, 0, -1)^t]$,
3. $(0, 0, 1)^t + [(1, 1, 1)^t]$.

4. For any column vector U, $U = xX + yY + zZ$. Hence (a) $\overline{U} = y\overline{Y}$, (b) $\overline{U} = x\overline{X} + z\overline{Z}$.

5. It is meant that $\boldsymbol{a}$ is a linear transformation. (a) $\bar{\boldsymbol{a}}\overline{Y} = \overline{O}$, so $\bar{\boldsymbol{a}} \leftrightarrow (0)$ with respect to $\{\overline{Y}\}$, or indeed any other basis. (b) $\bar{\boldsymbol{a}}\overline{X} = \overline{Z}$, $\bar{\boldsymbol{a}}\overline{Z} = \overline{X}$, so $\bar{\boldsymbol{a}} \leftrightarrow \begin{pmatrix} 0 & 1 \\ 1 & 0 \end{pmatrix}$ with respect to $\{\overline{X}, \overline{Z}\}$.

6. For $\mathbf{V}_0 = [\mathbf{o}]$, use $\mathbf{V}$. For $\mathbf{V}_0 = \mathbf{V}$, use $[\mathbf{o}]$. Otherwise, extend a basis of $\mathbf{V}_0$ to one of $\mathbf{V}$.

7. $\boldsymbol{n}\mathbf{u}_0 = \mathbf{o}$, $\boldsymbol{n}\mathbf{v}_0 = \mathbf{u}_0$, $\boldsymbol{a}(x\mathbf{u}_0 + y\mathbf{v}_0) = s(x\mathbf{u}_0 + y\mathbf{v}_0) + y\mathbf{u}_0$, or by matrix multiplication.

8. $\bar{\boldsymbol{a}} \leftrightarrow (0)$, $(\boldsymbol{b} = \boldsymbol{o}, \boldsymbol{c} = \boldsymbol{n})$; $\bar{\boldsymbol{a}} \leftrightarrow \begin{pmatrix} 0 & 1 \\ 0 & 0 \end{pmatrix}$, etc.

9. $\boldsymbol{a}\mathbf{u}_0 = s\mathbf{u}_0$, $\boldsymbol{a}\mathbf{v}_0 = \mathbf{u}_0 + s\mathbf{v}_0$ (by definition of $\boldsymbol{a}$), $\boldsymbol{a}\mathbf{w}_0 = \mathbf{v}_0 + s\mathbf{w}_0$.

10. See Section 3.3, Example 3.

11. $y\bar{\mathbf{v}}_0 = y'\bar{\mathbf{v}}_0$ if and only if $y = y'$.

SECTION 4.1, Page 106

1. None.

2. $A = (a_{ij})$, $U = (x_1, \ldots, x_q)^t$, $AU = (\sum a_{1j}x_j, \ldots, \sum a_{pj}x_j)^t$; $A^t = B = (b_{ij})$, $U^tB = (\sum x_jb_{j1}, \ldots, \sum x_jb_{jp})$; $(j = 1, \ldots q)$.

SECTION 4.2, Page 108

1. (a) $(3, 1)\begin{pmatrix} x \\ y \end{pmatrix} = (1)$; $(x, y)^t = (0, 1)^t + t(1, -3)^t$.

(b) $\begin{pmatrix} 2 & 4 & -3 \\ 1 & 4 & -1 \end{pmatrix}\begin{pmatrix} x \\ y \\ z \end{pmatrix} = \begin{pmatrix} 8 \\ 3 \end{pmatrix}$; $(1, 0, -2)^t + t(8, -1, 4)^t$.

(c) $\begin{pmatrix} 2 & -2 & -2 & 0 \\ 1 & -1 & -3 & -2 \end{pmatrix}\begin{pmatrix} x \\ y \\ z \\ w \end{pmatrix} = \begin{pmatrix} 3 \\ 1 \end{pmatrix}$;

$(x, y, z)^t = (\frac{7}{4}, 0, \frac{1}{4}, 0)^t + t_1(1, 1, 0, 0)^t + t_2(1, 0, 1, -1)^t$.

2. (a) $(0, 0)^t$. (b) $t(7, -3, 1)$. (c) $\begin{pmatrix} 1 & 2 & -1 \\ 0 & 1 & 3 \\ 0 & 3 & 9 \end{pmatrix}\begin{pmatrix} x \\ y \\ z \end{pmatrix} = \begin{pmatrix} 0 \\ 0 \\ 0 \end{pmatrix}$, $t(7, -3, 1)^t$.

(d) $\begin{pmatrix} 6 & -1 \\ -1 & 10 \end{pmatrix}\begin{pmatrix} x \\ y \end{pmatrix} = \begin{pmatrix} 0 \\ 0 \end{pmatrix}$, $(0, 0)^t$.

3. (a) $(AX, DY) = (E, F)$ or $\begin{pmatrix} A & O \\ O & D \end{pmatrix}\begin{pmatrix} X \\ Y \end{pmatrix} = \begin{pmatrix} E \\ F \end{pmatrix}$. (b) $\begin{pmatrix} A \\ C \end{pmatrix} X = \begin{pmatrix} E \\ F \end{pmatrix}$.

(c) $\begin{pmatrix} A & B \\ C & D \end{pmatrix}\begin{pmatrix} X \\ Y \end{pmatrix} = \begin{pmatrix} E \\ F \end{pmatrix}$.

SECTION 4.3, Page 110

1. (a) $(0, 0, 0)^t + [(1, -1, 1)^t]$. (b) $(1, 1, 1)^t + [(1, 0, -1)^t]$.
(c) $(0, 0, 0)^t + [(1, 1, 1)^t, (1, -1, 0)^t]$. (d) $(1, 0, 0)^t + [(-1, 1, 0)^t, (0, 0, 1)^t]$.

2. (a) $(x, y, z)^t = t(1, -1, 1)^t$; $x = -y = -z$.
(b) $(x, y, z)^t = (1, 1, 1)^t + t(1, 0, -1)$; $x + z = 2$, $y = 1$.
(c) $(x, y, z)^t = t_1(1, 1, 1)^t + t_2(1, -1, 0)$, $x + y - 2z = 0$.
(d) $(x, y, z)^t = t_1(-1, 1, 0)^t + t_2(0, 0, 1)$, $x + y = 0$.

4. Yes.

SECTION 4.4, Page 112

2. (a) $(a_{j1}, \dots, a_{jp}) = i$-th row of $E_{ij}A$, other rows are zero.
(b) $(a_{1k}, \dots, a_{pk})^t = l$-th column of AE_{kl}, others are zero.
(c) a_{jk} in the i, l-position, zeros elsewhere.
(d) $(a_{1i}, \dots, a_{pi})^t(a_{j1}, \dots, a_{jp})$.

3. Test $AE_{ij} = E_{ij}A$ for all i, j.

4. $\{E_{ij}, iE_{ij}\}$, $i, j = 1, \dots, 4$.

5. There are $p^2 - 1$ non-zero rows, so $(p^2 - 1) - (p - 1) = p(p - 1)$ are not multiples of a fixed row. Hence $p(p - 1)(p^2 - 1)$ invertible matrices.

SECTION 4.5, Page 115

2. (a) $3(1, 3, 2) - (3, 7, 4) - 2(0, 1, 1) = (0, 0, 0)$.
(b) $1(2, 1, 4)^t + 1(-2, -1, -4)^t = (0, 0, 0)^t$.
(c) $2(2 + x) - 11x^2 - 5(1 - 2x^2) + (1 - x)^2$.

(d) 1, 1, -2, -2, 2 are the coefficients.
(e) $-abI + (b + a)A - A^2 = O$ if $a = b$; $I - A = O$ if $a = b$.

3. (1, 0, 0, 0), (0, 1, 0, 0), (0, 0, 1, 0), (1, 1, 1, 0).

SECTION 4.6, Page 116

1. (a) Delete any one. (b) Keep I and A.

2. (a) Any 2. (b) Columns 1 and 3, or 1 and 4, or 2 and 3, or 2 and 4, or 3 and 4. (c) Any 3. (d) Any 4. (e) Any two unequal ones, if $a \neq b$.

3. List it in first place in a generating set and see proof of Theorem 2.

4. (a) Consider a proper subset of a finite generating set. (b) Yes. If it were infinitely generated, use our assumption that there is a basis in every vector space, and delete a vector.

SECTION 4.7, Page 118

1. (a) Add (0, 0, 1). (b) Add $\begin{pmatrix} 0 & 0 & 1 \\ 0 & 0 & 0 \end{pmatrix}$, $\begin{pmatrix} 1 & 0 & 0 \\ 0 & 0 & 0 \end{pmatrix}$, $\begin{pmatrix} 0 & 1 & 0 \\ 0 & 0 & 0 \end{pmatrix}$.
(c) Add $(0, 0, 1, 0)^t$, $(0, 0, 0, 1)^t$.

2. A basis of n-dimensional column vector space consists of n vectors. Hence there must be a linear dependence. The given equation is of course itself a single matrix equation, but another is $(U_1, \ldots, U_m)(a_1, \ldots, a_m)^t = (0, \ldots, 0)^t$.

4. Use the vectors in a basis. There exist $p^3 - 1$ non-zero vectors. Each 1-dimensional subspace has $p - 1$ non-zero vectors; hence there are $(p^3 - 1)/(p - 1) = p^2 + p + 1$ such subspaces. But better (see Section 4.9), from a given vector (a, b, c) we can generate the type $(1, *, *)$ or $(0, 1, *)$ or $(0, 0, 1)$. For every fixed choice of $*$'s we get different subspaces. From every two basis vectors (a, b, c), (a', b', c'), we get from $\begin{pmatrix} a & b & c \\ a' & b' & c' \end{pmatrix}$ to $\begin{pmatrix} 1 & 0 & * \\ 0 & 1 & * \end{pmatrix}$ or $\begin{pmatrix} 0 & 1 & 0 \\ 0 & 0 & 1 \end{pmatrix}$ or $\begin{pmatrix} 1 & * & 0 \\ 0 & 0 & 1 \end{pmatrix}$, hence $p^2 + p + 1$ subspaces of dimension 2.

5. Let $\mathbf{V}_1$, $\mathbf{V}_2$ be the subspaces. If statement is false, select $\mathbf{v}_1$ not in $\mathbf{V}_2$ and $\mathbf{v}_2$ not in $\mathbf{V}_1$. Consider $\mathbf{v}_1 + \mathbf{v}_2$.

6. Yes.

SECTION 4.8, Page 121

2. Use Example 2 to see that 3, 2, 1, 0 are the possibilities.

3. Apply Example 2 to $\mathbf{V}_2$, $\mathbf{V}_2'$.

4. $\mathbf{v}_2 \leftrightarrow \bar{\mathbf{v}}_2 = \bar{\mathbf{v}}_2'$ implies $\mathbf{v}_2 - \mathbf{v}_2'$ in $\mathbf{V}_1$.

SECTION 4.9, Page 125

1. $\begin{pmatrix} 2 & 1 & 1 & 3 \\ -2 & 1 & 0 & -2 \\ 0 & 1 & 1 & 1 \\ 4 & 1 & 0 & 4 \\ 4 & 1 & 1 & 5 \end{pmatrix} \to \begin{pmatrix} 2 & 1 & 1 & 3 \\ 0 & 1 & 1 & 1 \\ 0 & 0 & 1 & 1 \\ 0 & 0 & 0 & 0 \\ 0 & 0 & 0 & 0 \end{pmatrix}$, $\{(2, 0, 0, 2)^t, (0, 1, 0, 0)^t, (0, 0, 1, 1)^t\}$
is a basis and there are two linear dependences with coefficients -2, 0, 1, 0, 1 and -3, -1, 3, 1, 0 respectively, obtained by keeping track of the row operations on I.

2. They are reversible.

4. $(a_0, a_1, \ldots, a_n, 0, \ldots)$, $(a_1, 2a_2, \ldots, na_n, 0, \ldots)$, $\ldots$, $(n!a_n, 0, \ldots)$.

SECTION 5.1, Page 128

2. There is a C such that $CAB = I$; hence $(CA)B = I$, $(CA)^{-1} = B^{-1}$. Also consider $A = I$, $B = O$; hence $A + B = I$.

4. (a) $st(s - t) \neq 0$. (b) $s \neq 0$. (c) $st(s - 1)(t - 1)(t - s) \neq 0$.

5. (a) $\operatorname{diag}(s^{-1}, t^{-1}, (s - t)^{-1})$. (b) $(1/s)\begin{pmatrix} 0 & 0 & 1 \\ s & 0 & 0 \\ 0 & s & 0 \end{pmatrix}$.

(c) $\begin{pmatrix} st/(s-1)(t-1) & -(t+s)/(s-1)(t-1) & 1/(s-1)(t-1) \\ -t/s(s-1)(t-s) & t(t+1)/s(s-1)(t-s) & -1/s(s-1)(t-s) \\ s/t(t-1)(t-s) & -(s+1)/t(t-1)(t-s) & 1/t(t-1)(t-s) \end{pmatrix}$.

6. $X_i = (1/|A|)[(\text{cof} - a_{1i})E_1 + (\text{cof} - a_{2i})E_2 + (\text{cof} - a_{3i})E_3]$, $i = 1, 2, 3$.

7. $\begin{pmatrix} A^{-1} & -A^{-1}CB^{-1} \\ O & B^{-1} \end{pmatrix}$.

8. U_i's constitute a basis, so each column of B is a linear combination of the U_i's. In particular, set $B = I$ and consider rows of an inverse matrix.

9. Real orthogonal matrices which arise from permuting columns of I.

SECTION 5.2, Page 133

1. $AY = O$ has only the zero solution if and only if A^{-1} exists if and only if $XA = O$ has only the zero solution.

2. $P = (\frac{1}{9})\begin{pmatrix} 3 & 1 & -1 \\ -3 & 8 & 1 \\ 0 & -3 & 3 \end{pmatrix}$, $A = (\frac{1}{9})\begin{pmatrix} 0 & 7 & 0 \\ 9 & 2 & 0 \\ 0 & -3 & 0 \end{pmatrix}$.

3. Let $U_i = (u_{ij})$, $V_i = (v_{ij})$, so $\boldsymbol{a}U_i = \sum u_{ij}\boldsymbol{a}E_j = \sum v_{ij}E_j$; hence $(\boldsymbol{a}E_1, \ldots, \boldsymbol{a}E_n) \times (U_1, \ldots, U_n) = (V_1, \ldots, V_n)$.

4. (b) $\{(2, 0, 0)^t, (0, 2, 4)^t, (-1, 1, 1)^t\}$. (c) The given A is the matrix C of the Corollary; hence we need $\begin{pmatrix} 1 & 1 & 0 \\ 1 & 2 & 0 \\ 0 & 3 & 1 \end{pmatrix}^{-1}\begin{pmatrix} 2 & 0 & -1 \\ 0 & 2 & 1 \\ 0 & 4 & 1 \end{pmatrix}$; hence $\begin{pmatrix} 4 & -2 & -3 \\ -2 & 2 & 2 \\ 6 & -2 & -5 \end{pmatrix}$.

(d) Same as (c). (e) $U_1 \to U_2$, $U_2 \to U_3$, $U_3 \to U_2$, so $P = \begin{pmatrix} 0 & 1 & 0 \\ 0 & 0 & 1 \\ 1 & 0 & 0 \end{pmatrix} = (U_1, U_2, U_3)^{-1}(U_1', U_2', U_3')$ as in Corollary, Part (b), but is more easily computed from the given information. Use P to transform the matrix in (c) to get $\begin{pmatrix} 2 & 2 & -2 \\ -2 & -5 & 6 \\ -2 & -3 & 4 \end{pmatrix}$.

SECTION 5.3, Page 135

1. (a) $(x - s_1) \cdots (x - s_n)$; substitute into factored form. (b) $x^3 + (l^2 + m^2 + n^2)x$. (c) $\psi_1(x) \cdots \psi_t(x)$. (d) $|xI - A|\,|xI - B| = x^3(x - 2)(x - 5)$.

2. (a) $-A = (-I)A$. (b) $B_0 = \text{adj} - (-A)$. (c) Is this true when $|A| = 0$?

3. (a) $(\frac{1}{2})A$. (b) A^2. (c) $A^3 = 3A^2 + 3A$.

4. $xI - A^{-1} = -xA^{-1}((1/x)I - A)$.

SECTION 5.4, Page 139

1. (c) Note that $Y^*X + (Y^*X)^t$.

3. $\begin{pmatrix} E^* & G^* \\ F^* & H^* \end{pmatrix}$.

4. (b) $F = \text{diag}(d_1^{1/2}, \ldots, d_p^{1/2})$.

5. $\{(\frac{1}{2})(1, 1, 0)^t, (1/\sqrt{6})(1, -1, 2)^t, (1/\sqrt{3})(-1, 1, 1)^t\}$.

SECTION 6.1, Page 144

2. $\boldsymbol{a}(AB) = \boldsymbol{a}(BA)$.

3. Embed the polynomials in A in a vector space of square matrices.

6. Take two column vector spaces with a common scalar field containing the entries of A.

7. If $(\mathbf{v}_1 + \mathbf{v}_2) + \mathbf{V}_2 = (\mathbf{v}_1' + \mathbf{v}_2') + \mathbf{V}_2$, then $\mathbf{v}_1 - \mathbf{v}_1'$ is in $\mathbf{V}_1 \cap \mathbf{V}_2$. Hence a mapping is defined by the suggested correspondence.

SECTION 6.2, Page 148

1. (a) $\begin{pmatrix} 1 & 0 \\ 0 & 1 \end{pmatrix}$.

2. (a) $s(ax + by + cz) + t(dx + ey + fz)$. (b) $(ae + bf + cg)(x, y, z)^t$.

7. Apply the expansion in Example 2 to the equation

$$\begin{pmatrix} X^tX & X^tY \\ Y^tX & Y^tY \end{pmatrix} = \begin{pmatrix} X^t \\ Y^t \end{pmatrix} (X, Y).$$

SECTION 6.3, Page 151

1. (a) a set of linearly independent column vectors. (b) $p \times p$ I.

2. With respect to bases $\{E_{11}, E_{12}, E_{21}, E_{22}\}$ and $\{(1)\}$, $\boldsymbol{a}$ is represented by a 1×16 matrix $(E_1^t, E_2^t, E_3^t, E_4^t)$, where the E_i's are unit column vectors.

3. (a) $\begin{pmatrix} 0 & 0 \\ 1 & 0 \\ 1 & 0 \\ 0 & 1 \end{pmatrix}$. (b) $\begin{pmatrix} 1 & 1 & 1 \\ 0 & 0 & 0 \end{pmatrix} \begin{pmatrix} 1 & 1 & 1 \\ 1 & 0 & 1 \\ 0 & -1 & 1 \end{pmatrix} = \begin{pmatrix} 1 & 0 & 0 \\ 0 & 0 & 0 \end{pmatrix}$.

4. (a) With respect to im $\boldsymbol{a} = [E_{11}, E_{12}, E_{13}]$, $\boldsymbol{a} \leftrightarrow \text{diag}(I, O)$, where I is 3×3 and O is 3×3. (b) With respect to im $\boldsymbol{a} = [E_{11} - E_{21}, E_{21} - E_{22}, E_{31} - E_{23}]$, $\boldsymbol{a} \leftrightarrow \text{diag}(I, I)$, I is 3×3.

5. With respect to im $\boldsymbol{a} = [E_{11}]$, $\boldsymbol{a} \leftrightarrow \text{diag}(1, O)$, where O is 3×3.

6. Extend a basis of $\mathbf{V}'$ to one of $\mathbf{V}$ and define a suitable linear transformation on this basis.

SECTION 6.4, Page 155

1. (a) $\begin{pmatrix} 1 & 0 & 1 \\ 1 & 1 & 0 \end{pmatrix}$. (b) $\begin{pmatrix} 1 & 0 & \frac{2}{3} \\ 0 & 1 & -\frac{2}{3} \end{pmatrix}$.

2. $\begin{pmatrix} 1 & -\frac{1}{2} \\ 0 & \frac{1}{2} \\ 1 & 0 \end{pmatrix}$.

3. Use (8) to find B. (a) $\begin{pmatrix} -1 & -1 & -1 \\ 1 & 0 & 2 \end{pmatrix}$. (b) $\begin{pmatrix} \frac{1}{2} & \frac{1}{4} \\ 1 & 1 \\ 0 & \frac{1}{2} \end{pmatrix}$.

SECTION 6.5, Page 157

1. No. No.

6. Apply Theorem 2 to $\boldsymbol{a} \mid \mathbf{V}'$ and use the fact that ker $\boldsymbol{a}$ contains $\ker(\boldsymbol{a} \mid \mathbf{V}')$.

SECTION 6.6, Page 162

1. $Q_0 = I, P_0 = \begin{pmatrix} 1 & -1 \\ 0 & 1 \end{pmatrix}$.

2. rank $\boldsymbol{a}$ = rank $\boldsymbol{b}$ = 1; $x' = z, y' = z$; $x' = z, y' = -z$.

5. If ker $\boldsymbol{a}$ = im $\boldsymbol{a}$, then $\boldsymbol{a} \leftrightarrow \begin{pmatrix} O & C \\ O & O \end{pmatrix}$ for a suitable basis.

6. Apply Theorem 6, (2).

7. (a) Theorems 6 and 7. (b) See proof of Theorem 6.

8. In Problem 7(b), substitute $\boldsymbol{bc}$ for $\boldsymbol{b}$ and use $\text{null}(\boldsymbol{a} \mid \text{im } \boldsymbol{bc}) \leq \text{null}(\boldsymbol{a} \mid \text{im } \boldsymbol{b})$.

SECTION 6.7, Page 170

4. r.

5. $R = (1/\sqrt{13}) \begin{pmatrix} 13 & -3 \\ 0 & 4\sqrt{10} \end{pmatrix}$.

7. $A = nI - E$, where $E = (e_{ij})$, $e_{ij} = 1$; $b_1 = \ldots = b_{n-1} = 1$, $b_n = 0$.

9. Yes.

12. Note that $T_{12} = T_{12}(-1)T_{21}(1)T_{12}(-1)T_2(-1)$.

13. Use the matrices $\begin{pmatrix} I & 0 \\ -B & I \end{pmatrix}, \begin{pmatrix} I & -A \\ 0 & I \end{pmatrix}$.

SECTION 6.8, Page 176

1. $[(2, 1, 0, 0, 0)^t, (0, 1, 1, -1, 0)^t, (0, 0, 1, 0, -1)^t]$, $[(0, 0)^t]$.

2. rank A = rank$(A, C) < n$.

4. Columns of M_0^t give basis of solution space of $AX = O$. Columns of B_r^t give basis of column space of A.

5. $A = \begin{pmatrix} -1 & 1 & 0 & \ldots & 0 \\ -1 & 0 & 1 & \ldots & 0 \\ \vdots & & & & \\ -1 & 0 & 0 & \ldots & 1 \end{pmatrix}$.

6. (b) $\begin{pmatrix} 1 & 1 & -1 & -3 & 0 \\ 0 & 1 & -2 & -2 & 1 \end{pmatrix} X = O.$

7. $\begin{pmatrix} -1 & 0 & 1 & 0 \\ -3 & -1 & 0 & 1 \end{pmatrix} X = (0, 1)^t.$ **9.** $\{(8, 3, 13)\}$.

10. C^t is in row space of A^t. Keep track of changes in A^t.

$$\begin{pmatrix} A^t \\ C^t \end{pmatrix} \to \begin{pmatrix} 1 & 0 & 2 \\ 0 & 1 & -1 \\ 0 & 0 & 0 \\ 2 & -3 & 7 \end{pmatrix} \begin{matrix} \\ \to (1, 1, 1) - (1, 0, 2) \\ \\ \to 2(1, 0, 2) - 3(0, 1, -1) = 5(1, 0, 2) - 3(1, 1, 1), \end{matrix}$$

$X = (5, -3, 0)^t$.

SECTION 7.1, Page 181

2. g.c.d. $= g(x)^m$, l.c.m. $= f(x)^h g(x)^k h(x)^n$.

3. $(x - 2^{1/3})(x - i)$; $(x - 2^{1/3})(x^2 + 1)$; $(x^3 - 2)(x^2 + 1)$.

5. $xI - P^{-1}AP = P^{-1}(xI - A)P$; AB and BA have the same sums of principal minors (see Section 6.2, Example 2).

6. All minors of order greater than r (that is, all $(r + t)$-rowed minors, $t > 0$) equal zero. $\begin{pmatrix} 0 & 1 \\ 0 & 0 \end{pmatrix}$ has rank 1 and characteristic polynomial x^2.

7. $q_1(x) = (\frac{1}{6})(x - 1)$, $q_2(x) = (-\frac{1}{6})(x^2 - x - 2)$.

9. Note that $q_1(\boldsymbol{a})f_1(\boldsymbol{a}) + q_2(\boldsymbol{a})f_2(\boldsymbol{a}) = \boldsymbol{i}$, and use Cayley-Hamilton Theorem.

10. Let $\boldsymbol{a} \leftrightarrow A$. Then $\dim \ker(s\boldsymbol{i} - \boldsymbol{a}) = \text{nullity}(s\boldsymbol{i} - \boldsymbol{a}) = n - \text{rank}(s\boldsymbol{i} - \boldsymbol{a})$.

11. Suppose $(sI - A)^{n+1}U = O$, $U \neq O$, but $(sI - A)^n U \neq O$. This implies $\{U, (sI - A)U, \ldots, (sI - A)^n U\}$ is a linearly independent set, which is impossible.

SECTION 7.2, Page 189

1. (b) $|H| = s_1 s_2 \cdots$. (d) $X^*HX^* = \sum s_i |y_i|^2$.

2. Let $P^*P = I$ and $PU = sU$. Then $(PU)^*PU = |s|^2 U^*U$, $|s|^2 = 1$. Note that $|P^*| = \overline{|P|}$.

3. (a) Inverse of a triangular matrix is triangular.

4. Extend them with zeros. Multiply by P on opposite sides.

5. $(\boldsymbol{a} \mid \mathbf{V}_0)^i \mathbf{v}_0 = \boldsymbol{a}^i \mathbf{v}_0 = (\boldsymbol{a}^i \mid \mathbf{V}_0)\mathbf{v}_0$, for every $\mathbf{v}_0$ in $\mathbf{V}_0$.

6. $\boldsymbol{a} \mid \mathbf{V}_0 \leftrightarrow A_1$.

7. Replace A by its Schur canonical form (actually not "canonical" since it is not uniquely determined!)

8. $P^*HP = D^2$, where D is diagonal.

9. $xI - SP = Q^{-1}(xI - QSQ)Q$, $Q = Q^t$.

10. Use $(P^tAP)^t P^t AP = (P^t MP)^2 = D^2$. Complete the orthogonal columns to a basis.

11. By Problem 7, $P^*AP = \text{diag}(s_1, \ldots, s_n)$, P^* unitary. So, starring both sides, $-P^*AP = \text{diag}(\bar{s}_1, \ldots, \bar{s}_n)$. $s_i = -\bar{s}_i$, $|xI - A|$ has real coefficients, so for odd degree there exists a real root.

12. (a) Characteristic polynomials differ by a power of x (see Section 7.1, Problem 6). (b) If A is $p \times q$, then rank AA^t = rank A^tA = rank A, the non-zero roots are real and same for both, AA^t has p − rank A zero characteristic numbers and A^tA has q − rank A zero characteristic numbers.

13. $X^tAX = \sum s_i y_i^2$, $s_i > 0$; apply Section 7.1, Equation (1) and Descartes' Rule of Signs.

14. (a) $P^*AP = \text{diag}(s_1, \ldots, s_n)$, $P^*A^*AP = \text{diag}(|s_1|^2, \ldots, |s_n|^2)$. (b) For any normalized vector X, there is a vector Y (related to X by a unitary matrix) such that $X^*A^*AX = \sum t_i |y_i|^2$.

15. Write $AX = sX$ out coordinatewise when X is a characteristic vector, and take absolute values.

16. Show that only diagonal entries count.

SECTION 7.3, Page 194

1. Note that $\boldsymbol{a} \leftrightarrow \begin{pmatrix} 1 & 2 & 0 \\ 0 & 1 & 0 \\ 0 & -1 & 2 \end{pmatrix}$ and set $s_1 = 1$, $s_2 = 2$ and $\mathbf{R}_1 = [\mathbf{u}, \mathbf{v} + \mathbf{w}]$, $\mathbf{R}_2 = [\mathbf{w}]$, so $\text{diag}\left(\begin{pmatrix} 1 & 2 \\ 0 & 1 \end{pmatrix}, 2\right)$.

2. (a) By Equation (10), a representation of $\boldsymbol{b}$ has rank at least $k - 1$.

3. $\text{im}\, \boldsymbol{a}^{t+1} = \text{im}\, \boldsymbol{a}^t$, $\text{im}\, \boldsymbol{a}^{t+1} = \boldsymbol{a}\, \text{im}\, \boldsymbol{a}^t$, $\text{im}\, \boldsymbol{a}^{t+2} = \boldsymbol{a}\, \text{im}\, \boldsymbol{a}^{t+1} = \boldsymbol{a}\, \text{im}\, \boldsymbol{a}^t, \cdots$. (Compare Section 7.1, Problem 10.)

4. Can use Equation (8), if we immerse the problem in a suitable field of scalars.

5. $\mathbf{V}_0$ is invariant under $\boldsymbol{a}'$ too, and $\boldsymbol{a}' \mid \mathbf{R}_i$ is invertible.

SECTION 7.4, Page 200

3. $\begin{pmatrix} 0 & 1 \\ 0 & 0 \end{pmatrix}^2 = \begin{pmatrix} 0 & 0 \\ 0 & 0 \end{pmatrix}$.

4. Consider the A_i's in Section 7.3.

5. 2×2: $\begin{pmatrix} s & 0 \\ 0 & s \end{pmatrix}, \begin{pmatrix} s & 1 \\ 0 & s \end{pmatrix}, \begin{pmatrix} s & 0 \\ 0 & t \end{pmatrix}$.

3×3: $\begin{pmatrix} s & 0 & 0 \\ 0 & s & 0 \\ 0 & 0 & s \end{pmatrix}, \begin{pmatrix} s & 1 & 0 \\ 0 & s & 0 \\ 0 & 0 & s \end{pmatrix}, \begin{pmatrix} s & 1 & 0 \\ 0 & s & 1 \\ 0 & 0 & s \end{pmatrix}, \begin{pmatrix} s & 0 & 0 \\ 0 & s & 0 \\ 0 & 0 & t \end{pmatrix}, \begin{pmatrix} s & 1 & 0 \\ 0 & s & 0 \\ 0 & 0 & t \end{pmatrix}, \begin{pmatrix} s & 0 & 0 \\ 0 & t & 0 \\ 0 & 0 & u \end{pmatrix}$.

SECTION 7.5, Page 201

1. $P = \begin{pmatrix} c & 0 \\ 0 & 1 \end{pmatrix}, Q = \begin{pmatrix} 0 & 1 \\ 1 & 0 \end{pmatrix}$.

2. (a) $(sI + cN)P = P(sI + N)$. Use $P = \text{diag}(c^{n-1}, c^{n-2}, \ldots, 1)$. (c) Indecomposable.

3. Expand $(sI + N)^n$. **4.** Apply Problem 3.

5. (b) $B = \begin{pmatrix} a & b & c \\ 0 & a & b \\ 0 & 0 & a \end{pmatrix}$ in the 3×3 case.

6. Use Problem 5. $P = (P_{ij})$ such that for each j there is exactly one i for which $P_{ij} \neq O$. The non-zero blocks are invertible.

7. $A = A^c$; $\operatorname{rank}(sI - A)^t = \operatorname{rank}(\bar{s}I - A)^t$ for every t.

8. $P = \begin{pmatrix} 1 & 1 \\ i & -i \end{pmatrix}$, $Q = \begin{pmatrix} 1 & s \\ 1 & \bar{s} \end{pmatrix}$.

9. Replace A by $P \operatorname{diag}(s, \bar{s})P^{-1}$ from Problem 8 and form $\operatorname{diag}(P, P)T_{23}$.

10. Replace A as in Problem 9 and use T_{23}, T_{67}, $T_{10,\,11}, \ldots$; then interchange blocks.

SECTION 7.6, Page 204

1. (a) $x^2 - 2x + 1$. (b) x for E_1, x^3 for E_3.

2. If $\mathbf{u} \neq \mathbf{o}$, $\mathbf{u}$ in $\mathbf{W}$, note that $\mathbf{u} = g(\boldsymbol{a})\mathbf{w}$ for some non-constant $g(x)$ and apply division algorithm.

3. Let $\phi(x)$ be minimal polynomial of $\mathbf{w}$ and $\xi(x)$ the minimal polynomial of $h(\boldsymbol{a})\mathbf{w}$. Show that $\xi(x)$ and $h(x)$ divide $\phi(x)$, and $\phi(x) = \xi(x)h(x)$ if $h(x)$ is chosen monic.

SECTION 7.7, Page 207

1. If $h(x) = |xI - A|$, then $h(\boldsymbol{a}) = \boldsymbol{o}$. Hence $\psi(x) \mid h(x)$ by Corollary 1.

2. (a) $x(x - 1)(x - 2)$. (b) $x - 1$. (c) x. (d) $(x - s)^k$.

3. (a) $(x - s_1)^2(x - s_2)^3$. (b) $(x - s_1)^3$.

4. Check that $a - b$ and $ab^{-1} (b \neq 0)$ are in the intersection when a and b are.

5. See Section 7.2, Problem 5. Here, $\psi(x)$ is the minimal polynomial of $\mathbf{V}'$.

6. (a) $x^2 - 2x = x(x - 2)$. (b) x^2.

7. $\begin{pmatrix} 0 & 1 & 0 & 0 \\ 0 & 0 & 0 & 0 \\ 0 & 0 & 0 & 1 \\ 0 & 0 & 0 & 0 \end{pmatrix}, \begin{pmatrix} 0 & 1 & 0 & 0 \\ 0 & 0 & 0 & 0 \\ 0 & 0 & 0 & 0 \\ 0 & 0 & 0 & 0 \end{pmatrix}$; $\dim \mathbf{V} = 4$ is smallest possible.

9. Factor and write the given polynomial as $\Pi(x - s_i)^{k_i}$ and apply Problem 8.

SECTION 7.8, Page 210

1. E_n. If J_i is $n_i \times n_i$, then take $E_{n_1} + E_{n_1+n_2} + \cdots + E_n$.

4. The companion matrix.

6. If $\psi(x)$ is the minimal polynomial of $\boldsymbol{a}$, then $\psi(\boldsymbol{a} \mid \mathbf{V}')\mathbf{V}' = \{\mathbf{o}\}$, so the minimal polynomial of $\boldsymbol{a} \mid \mathbf{V}'$ divides $\psi(x)$.

SECTION 7.9, Page 213

1. $\psi_2(x) \mid \psi_1(x)$, so $\psi_1(x) = |xI - A|$.

2. Note that $|xI - A| = \psi_1(x)\psi_2(x) \cdots$.

3. (a) $\begin{pmatrix} 0 & 1 \\ 1 & 0 \end{pmatrix}$. (b) $\begin{pmatrix} 0 & -1 \\ 1 & 0 \end{pmatrix}$. (c) $\begin{pmatrix} 1 & 1 \\ 1 & 2\cos\theta \end{pmatrix}$. (d) $\begin{pmatrix} 0 & 0 & -6 \\ 1 & 0 & -11 \\ 0 & 1 & -6 \end{pmatrix}$.

(e) $\begin{pmatrix} 0 & 0 & -4 \\ 1 & 0 & 5 \\ 0 & 1 & 1 \end{pmatrix}$, $x^3 - x^2 - 5x + 4 = 0$ has 3 distinct real roots.

4. (a) Only the companion matrix. (b) Two possibilities.

5. (a) $\psi_1(x) = \psi_2(x)$. (b) $\psi_1(x) = x^2 - 1$, with $\psi_2(x) = x^2 - 1$, or $\psi_2(x) = \psi_3(x) = x - 1$, or $\psi_2(x) = \psi_3(x) = x + 1$.

SECTION 7.10, Page 217

1. (a) $(x + 1)^3$, $(x - 1)^3$, $(x + 1)$, $(x - 1)$,

$$\operatorname{diag}\left(\begin{pmatrix} 1 & 1 & 0 \\ 0 & 1 & 1 \\ 0 & 0 & 1 \end{pmatrix}, \begin{pmatrix} -1 & 1 & 0 \\ 0 & -1 & 1 \\ 0 & 0 & -1 \end{pmatrix}, -1\ 1\right).$$

(b) x^3, x^2,

$$\operatorname{diag}\left(\begin{pmatrix} 0 & 1 & 0 \\ 0 & 0 & 1 \\ 0 & 0 & 0 \end{pmatrix}, \begin{pmatrix} 0 & 1 \\ 0 & 0 \end{pmatrix}\right), \text{ or } x^4, x, \operatorname{diag}\left[\begin{bmatrix} 0 & 1 & 0 & 0 \\ 0 & 0 & 1 & 0 \\ 0 & 0 & 0 & 1 \\ 0 & 0 & 0 & 0 \end{bmatrix}, 0\right].$$

(c) $(x - 1)$, $(x - 1)$, x, diag(1, 0, 1, 0).

2. $x^4 - 3x^2 + 2 = (x^2 - 2)(x^2 - 1)$.

(a) $\operatorname{diag}\left(\begin{pmatrix} 0 & 2 \\ 1 & 0 \end{pmatrix}, 1, -1\right)$; (b) $\operatorname{diag}(\sqrt{2}, -\sqrt{2}, 1, -1)$.

3. $\mathbf{W} = \mathbf{W}_1 \dotplus \mathbf{W}_2 = [\mathbf{w}_1; \boldsymbol{a}] \dotplus [\mathbf{w}_2; \boldsymbol{a}]$. Let $\phi_i(x)$ be the minimal polynomial of $\mathbf{W}_i$. Note that the minimal polynomial of $\mathbf{W}$ is the l.c.m. of $\phi_1(x)$ and $\phi_2(x)$; hence $\phi_1(x)\phi_2(x)$, and $\deg \phi_i(x) = \dim \mathbf{W}_i$; hence $\dim \mathbf{W} = \deg \phi_1(x)\phi_2(x)$.

4. If $\mathbf{W}$ is cyclic with minimal polynomial $\mu(x)^e$ (irreducible $\mu(x)$), then $\mathbf{W}$ must be indecomposable (Example 4). If $\mathbf{W}$ is indecomposable, its minimal polynomial must be $\mu(x)^e$ for an irreducible $\mu(x)$ (Theorem 11); if it were not cyclic, then $\psi_2(x) \neq 0$, so $\mathbf{W}$ would be decomposable (Theorem 10).

SECTION 7.11, Page 219

1. (a) and (b) $\delta_1 = 1$, $\delta_2 = x^2 - 1$, $i_1 = x^2 - 1$, $i_2 = 1$.
(c) $\delta_1 = 1$, $\delta_2 = x - 1$, $\delta_3 = (x - 1)^3$, $i_1 = (x - 1)^2$, $i_2 = x - 1$, $i_3 = 1$.

3. (a) Show that no δ_i changes because it is a linear combination of the minors it divides (see Section 7.1, Problem 7). (b) They have the same δ_i's.

5. $\psi_1(x) = (x - s)^k(x - \bar{s})^k = (x^2 - 2ax + a^2 + b^2)^k$, so get an upper triangular-block matrix of the form (k diagonal blocks)

$$\begin{pmatrix} 0 & -a^2 - b^2 & 0 & 1 & & & \\ 1 & 2a & 0 & 0 & \cdot & & \\ & & 0 & -a^2 - b^2 & 0 & 1 & \\ & & 1 & 2a & 0 & 0 & \\ & & & & & \ddots & \end{pmatrix}$$

SECTION 7.12, Page 223

2. The elementary divisors may be determined (see Example 5) by taking highest powers of irreducible monic factors of the diagonal entries. They are therefore $\{x, x, x^2, x + 1, x - 1\}$. Hence $i_1 = x^2(x - 1)$, $i_2 = i_3 = x$.

3. Yes. Form the i_k's as in Example 5.

4. (a) $\psi_i = 1$ for $i > 1$, $\psi_1 =$ given polynomial.
(b) If $s_1 \neq s_2$: $i_1 = (x - s_1)^{n_1}(x - s_2)^{n_2}$. If $s_1 = s_2$ and $n_1 > n_2$: $i_1 = (x - s_1)^{n_1}$, $i_2 = (x - s_2)^{n_2}$, rest equal 1.

SECTION 7.13, Page 225

1. (a) $i_1 = (x - 1)^3$, $i_2 = i_3 = 1$, $(x - 1)^3$ is only elementary divisor. (b) $i_1 = x^3 - 2x$, others equal 1; elementary divisors are $x, x - \sqrt{2}, x + \sqrt{2}$. (c) $i_1 = (x - 2)^2$, $i_2 = (x - 2)$, and these are also the elementary divisors. (d) $i_1 = x(x^2 - 4)$, $i_2 = x - 2$; the elementary divisors are $x, x - 2, x - 2, x + 2$. (e) $i_1 = x^3 - 1$, $i_2 = i_3 = 1$; over the real numbers, the elementary divisors are $x - 1$ and $x^2 + x + 1$.

INDEX

NOTATION

c	scalar
$\mathbf{u}$	vector
$\mathbf{o}$	zero vector
$\boldsymbol{a}$	linear transformation
$\boldsymbol{o}$	zero linear transformation
$\boldsymbol{i}$	identity linear transformation
$\mathbf{V}$	vector space
A	matrix
O	zero matrix
I	identity matrix
A^t	transpose
A^*	conjugate transpose
(A_{ij})	partitioned matrix
$\|A\|$	determinant
[M]	subspace generated by M
$[\mathbf{u}; \boldsymbol{a}]$	cyclic subspace generated by a vector
$\mathbf{u} + \mathbf{V}_0$	coset of $\mathbf{V}_0$
$\bar{\mathbf{u}}$	coset with representative $\mathbf{u}$
$\mathbf{V}/\mathbf{V}_0$	factor space
$\boldsymbol{a} \mid \mathbf{V}_0$	restriction to $\mathbf{V}_0$; induced mapping
$\bar{\boldsymbol{a}}$	factor linear transformation; induced mapping
$f(x) \mid g(x)$	divides
diag	diagonal
ker	kernel
im	image
dim	dimension
$\rightarrow$	mapping
$\leftrightarrow$	one-to-one correspondence; representation
$\subset$	contained in
$\supset$	contains
$\cap$	intersection
$\cup$	union
$\dot{+}$	direct sum

1234567890